Mar
the

From professional colleagues...to bride and groom!

*Look out for these brand-new books
by three bestselling authors*

A PAPER MARRIAGE
by emotionally compelling author
Jessica Steele
On sale September 2003, in
Tender Romance™!

MISTRESS BY AGREEMENT
by international bestselling author
Helen Brooks
On sale September 2003, in
Modern Romance™!

CONSULTANT IN CRISIS
by Australian medical author
Alison Roberts
On sale December 2003, in
Medical Romance™!

Marrying the Boss

A NINE-TO-FIVE AFFAIR
by
Jessica Steele

THE MISTRESS CONTRACT
by
Helen Brooks

A CHANGE OF HEART
by
Alison Roberts

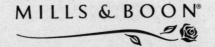

MILLS & BOON®

DID YOU PURCHASE THIS BOOK WITHOUT A COVER?
If you did, you should be aware it is **stolen property** as it was
reported *unsold and destroyed* by a retailer. Neither the author nor
the publisher has received any payment for this book.

*All the characters in this book have no existence outside the imagination
of the author, and have no relation whatsoever to anyone bearing the
same name or names. They are not even distantly inspired by any
individual known or unknown to the author, and all the incidents are
pure invention.*

*All Rights Reserved including the right of reproduction in whole or in part
in any form. This edition is published by arrangement with Harlequin
Enterprises II B.V. The text of this publication or any part thereof may not
be reproduced or transmitted in any form or by any means, electronic or
mechanical, including photocopying, recording, storage in an
information retrieval system, or otherwise, without the written
permission of the publisher.*

*This book is sold subject to the condition that it shall not, by way of trade
or otherwise, be lent, resold, hired out or otherwise circulated without the
prior consent of the publisher in any form of binding or cover other than
that in which it is published and without a similar condition including this
condition being imposed on the subsequent purchaser.*

*MILLS & BOON and MILLS & BOON with the Rose Device
are registered trademarks of the publisher.
Harlequin Mills & Boon Limited,
Eton House, 18-24 Paradise Road, Richmond, Surrey, TW9 1SR*

MARRYING THE BOSS © by Harlequin Enterprises II B.V., 2003

A Nine-to-Five Affair, The Mistress Contract and *A Change of Heart*
were first published in Great Britain by Harlequin Mills & Boon Limited
in separate, single volumes.

A Nine-to-Five Affair © Jessica Steele 1999
The Mistress Contract © Helen Brooks 2000
A Change of Heart © Alison Roberts 1999

ISBN 0 263 83594 4

05-0903

*Printed and bound in Spain
by Litografia Rosés S.A., Barcelona*

Jessica Steele lives in a friendly Worcestershire village with her super husband, Peter. They are owned by a gorgeous Staffordshire bull terrier called Florence, who is boisterous and manic, but also adorable. It was Peter who first prompted Jessica to try writing, and, after the first rejection, encouraged her to keep on trying. Luckily, with the exception of Uruguay, she has so far managed to research inside all the countries in which she has set her books, travelling to places as far apart as Siberia and Egypt. Her thanks go to Peter for his help and encouragement.

A NINE-TO-FIVE AFFAIR
by
Jessica Steele

CHAPTER ONE

SO MANY thoughts and emotions went through Emmie's mind as she drove to the job interview that winter's afternoon, chiefly how desperately she needed this position, and the tremendous hope that she would be successful in getting it. It didn't matter that it was only temporary—probably a maximum of nine months—it paid extremely well and would afford her some financial breathing space.

The work involved as assistant PA, and then acting PA while Mr Barden Cunningham's PA took maternity leave, would be very demanding, which accounted for the high salary. But, though Emmie had endured a blip in her career during this last year—well, several blips in actual fact—she knew, previous to that, her work record was exemplary.

Her secretarial training had been first class, and she had thought that, after three years with Usher Trading, she was really going places, and that she was due to be promoted as PA to one of the directors—only to go into work one Tuesday morning to learn, with utter astonishment, that the firm had folded. Usher Trading had, with a mile-long list of creditors, ceased trading.

It had not been her only shock that month. She had still been getting over her astonishment that, overnight, or so it seemed, Usher Trading had gone under, when her stepfather had suffered a heart attack and had died. The fact that she'd been without a job or financial security had been neither here nor there to her then. She had loved Alec Whitford as a daughter, and now he was gone.

Emmie clearly remembered her own father. He had been a scientist dedicated to his work, and for a lot of the time had seemed to be in a world of his own. He had also died,

in some experiment that had gone wrong, when she had
been ten years old.

Her life had been different then, Emmie recalled. Her
family had lived in an elegant house in Berkshire and had
been very comfortably off—sufficiently so for her mother
to be able to indulge her love of antiques.

They'd had a whole houseful of beautiful furniture when,
two years after her husband's death, her mother had married
Alec Whitford. Alec had been a total contrast with Emmie's
father. Alec had loved to laugh, and had been full of life,
but—he hadn't liked work.

Though it hadn't been until after her mother's death three
years later, in one of those freak garden machinery acci-
dents that were never supposed to happen, that Emmie had
begun to have any inkling that she and Alec were not financially sound.

She had been fifteen then. 'Shall I get a job, Alec?' she'd
asked him, her thoughts on evening and weekend work.

'I wouldn't dream of it, sweetheart,' he'd said. 'We'll
sell something.'

By the time she was eighteen, and had completed a most
meticulous business training, there hadn't been much left
to sell. By then Emmie had grown up fast to value security
above all else. She'd loved her stepfather, and wouldn't
have had him be any different, but he had seemed to make
an art out of spending. She'd rather thought then—and later
knew—that he was having a one-sided affair with his bookmaker—Alec doing the giving, his bookmaker taking.

Emmie's mother had died intestate, so the house had
passed to Alec. By that time Alec's mother, a formidable
if slightly unconventional woman, had been living with
them. Hannah Whitford had turned eighty, but was as sharp
as a tack—and didn't suffer fools gladly. Emmie had calculated that she must be some kind of step-grandmother to
her, but when out of respect she'd addressed her as Mrs
Whitford, the thin, straight, white-haired woman had ad-

vised her that, since she drew the line at being called 'Granny', Emmie could call her Aunt Hannah.

So Aunt Hannah she had become. She had her own private pension—but, having already 'lent' her son her savings, had declined to let him see any of her pension. 'If you're that hard up,' she'd told him forthrightly when he'd come on the scrounge, 'sell the house!'

So he had. And they'd moved to a three-bedroomed rented apartment in a very nice area of London. And Emmie had started work at Usher Trading. All in all, given that Emmie had learned to more and more value her security, she had come to love Aunt Hannah too, and the next three years had passed very pleasantly.

And then Emmie had been made redundant and dear Alec had died. About that time, when Emmie had been trying to get a grip on things, she'd become startled to realise that Aunt Hannah was occasionally losing her grip a little!

At first Emmie had put it down to the fact that, for all Alec's mother had used to tear him off a strip from time to time, she had dearly loved him—and had lost him. Perhaps, when she had come to terms with her grief, she would be her old self again.

In the meantime, Emmie had found herself a new job with a firm of insurance brokers—and managed to hold it down for six weeks! Then her womanising boss, not content with the extra-marital affair he was having—the phone calls she'd overheard had spoken volumes—had had the utter nerve, after many ignored hints, to one day openly proposition *her*! That was when Emmie had discovered she was quite good in the tearing-off-a-strip department herself. Because, though it had been entirely unplanned, she'd been goaded beyond all possibility of suffering her new employer's lecherous advances any longer, she'd let fly with her tongue—and found herself out of a job.

She'd consoled herself that she didn't want to work there

anyway. And found herself another job. It had taken her ten weeks to lose it—this time for bad time-keeping. And it was true, her time-keeping *had* become appalling. But Aunt Hannah hadn't seemed to want to get out of bed in the morning any more and, while it had been no problem to take her breakfast in bed, Emmie had found she didn't love her work well enough to leave the apartment until she was sure Aunt Hannah was up and about.

Her third job after being made redundant from Usher Trading had lasted four months. It hadn't paid as well, but it had been nearer to her home, which had meant she hadn't had to leave for work so early. All had seemed to be well, until her employer's son had come home from abroad and, obviously believing himself to be irresistible, alternated between being overbearingly officious with her or, despite the fact he had a lovely wife and children, making suggestive, sickening remarks about how good he could be to her if she'd let him.

Emmie hadn't known how much more she could take, but supposed that working for fatherly Mr Denby at Usher Trading had rather sheltered her from the womanising types lurking out there. She'd recognised she was a novice at knowing how to handle them, and had been near to exploding again one day, when a call had come through from the local police station. Apparently they had a Mrs Hannah Whitford there, who seemed a little confused.

'I'm on my way!' Emmie exclaimed, holding down panic, grabbing up her bag, car keys at the ready.

'Where are you going?' Kenneth Junior demanded.

'Can't stop!'

'Your job?' he warned threateningly.

'It's yours—with my compliments,' she told him absently. The fact that she'd just walked out was the least of her worries just then. She made it to the police station in record time. 'Mrs Whitford?' she enquired of the man at the front desk.

'She's having a cup of tea with one of the WPCs,' he replied, and explained how the elderly lady had been found wandering the streets in her bedroom slippers and seemed distressed because she couldn't remember where she lived.

'Oh, the poor love!' Emmie cried.

'She's all right now,' the police officer soothed. 'Fortunately she had her handbag with her, and we were able to find your office telephone number in her spectacle case.'

'Oh, thank goodness I thought to jot it down!' Emmie's exclamation was heartfelt. She'd only put it in Aunt Hannah's spectacle case because she'd known the dear soul would look first for her glasses before she thought to look for her phone number.

'Has Mrs Whitford been—er—forgetful for very long?' the policeman asked in a kindly fashion. Emmie explained how, if Aunt Hannah had, it was only recently, and only since she had lost her son earlier in the year. Whereupon, on learning that Emmie was away from the apartment for most of the day, the officer tentatively suggested that it might be an idea to consider establishing Mrs Whitford in a residential home.

'Oh, I couldn't possibly!' was Emmie's initial shocked reaction. 'She would hate it!' And, getting over her shock a little, she asked, 'Was she very upset when you found her?'

'Upset—confused, distressed—and,' he added with a small smile, 'just a little aggressive.'

'Oh, dear,' Emmie mumbled feebly. But, fully aware that Aunt Hannah had a tart tongue when the mood took her, was in no mind to have Alec's mother 'established' in a residential home. Even if, while waiting for Aunt Hannah, the kindly policeman did suggest to her not to dismiss the notion out of hand, that residential homes weren't jails, and that if those in charge knew where residents were, they were quite at liberty to come and go as they pleased. For unintentional but added weight, he mentioned that while indoors someone was there all the time to keep an eye on residents, and see to it that they had their lunch.

Hannah Whitford suddenly appeared from nowhere. 'All this fuss!' she snapped shortly, quite back to normal, but Emmie, who knew her well, knew that she was more embarrassed than cross. 'Have you got your car outside?'

Emmie was not about to give the police officer's 'residential home' suggestion another thought. But Aunt Hannah, either having had a similar conversation with the woman police constable who'd looked after her, or having done some serious thinking of her own, brought the subject up herself. It was around lunchtime the following day that, having been deep in thought, Aunt Hannah suddenly seemed to realise that Emmie was not at work.

'What are you doing home?' she demanded in her forth-right way.

'I thought I'd look for another job,' Emmie replied, aware that, with yesterday's confusion behind her, Aunt Hannah was getting back to being as sharp as she had ever been.

'Because of me.'

It was a statement, and despite Emmie telling her that she would have walked out of her job anyway, without receiving the phone call from the police station, Aunt Hannah would not have it.

Nor would she countenance—despite Emmie's protestation—that she should become a burden to her step-granddaughter. But it was only when Emmie saw that she was growing extremely agitated that she agreed—more in the hope of calming her down than anything—to investigate the possibility of her step-grandmother moving to a residential home.

Aunt Hannah, as Emmie later realised—and might have known—was not prepared to stop at mere investigation. So they set off doing the rounds of residential homes. The first one they looked at, Keswick House, was in actual fact a very pleasant surprise. Light and airy, with its residents seemingly busy with their own pursuits, and a general cheerful atmosphere about the place. All residents were encouraged to bring their own furniture. There was, however, one very big drawback—it was expensive. To stay there was going to take all of Mrs Whitford's income and more.

With Aunt Hannah not ready to give up the idea, they began to look at other establishments. By then Emmie was starting to realise that, if she herself was out all day—as she would be when she found herself a new job—perhaps as a legacy of when Aunt Hannah had forgotten where she lived that day, the old lady would be frightened and nervous of being on her own. Aunt Hannah, Emmie all at once knew, needed to feel safe.

But, in adjusting to the fact that the dear soul was determined to move out, Emmie was not prepared to let her go and live just anywhere. The trouble was, though, that while one or two of the places they looked at were adequate, there were others that Emmie would not dream of allowing her step-grandmother to move to.

Emmie couldn't bear the thought that Aunt Hannah might feel frightened and unsafe in their apartment. She blamed herself that, when clearly Aunt Hannah needed company, she had left her on her own for so many hours during the day. But—Emmie had to work.

It wasn't until the following day, when Aunt Hannah had another spell of confusion—and came out of it looking very bewildered—that Emmie knew for sure what had to be done. How, for goodness' sake, would Aunt Hannah have coped if she'd been out at work? Aunt Hannah had to feel safe! Emmie rang Lisa Browne, the owner of Keswick House.

A week later, on the day before Emmie started her new job, Mrs Whitford moved into Keswick House. Fortunately, what with packing her personal treasures and looking forward to the move, she had entirely forgotten the stated fee required, and was happy to sign anything Emmie gave her and to leave all the paperwork to her step-granddaughter. Two weeks after that Emmie moved out of the well-maintained three-bedroomed apartment that had been the family home, to a two-bedroomed flat in a much less salubrious area.

Emmie ignored the peeling paint and the rotting woodwork of the front door, and strove to think positively. The house was old; what did she expect? Anyhow, because of its age, it would set off her few remaining pieces of antique furniture a treat. Well, it would when she'd stripped the walls and redecorated. And also, don't forget, it was a ground-floor flat—ideal for when Aunt Hannah, who wasn't so good with stairs, came to stay. As an extra bonus, it was only half the rent of the former apartment, so, providing she hung on to her new job at Smythe and Wood International, she could just about scrape up the shortfall required to keep Aunt Hannah at Keswick House.

A month later, however, and Emmie was having a hard time in staying optimistic. Her new flat was looking super. Newly decorated, with carpets and curtains as well as her mother's good quality furniture, which had transformed it. Emmie had become friends with Adrian Payne, the man who had the upstairs flat. Non-licentious Adrian, who was true to his ex-live-in-girlfriend Tina, had in part restored her faith in men.

Not completely, however. For her new boss, Clive Norris, turned out to be the womanising type she had just about had enough of. Her job at Smythe and Wood, it had to be said, was just not working out. While the tasks were no problem—she had a quick brain and absorbed instruction easily—she couldn't help wondering what was wrong with some of these men that they had to touch her, to hint—more than hint in some cases—that they'd quite care to be more than boss-PA-friendly.

Or, was it her? She didn't think so. She was sure she

didn't go around giving off come hither signals. She knew she hadn't been at the back of the queue when looks had been handed out. Alec had once declared she was utterly beautiful, but he had been in one of his happy moods. Though she *had* taken herself off to the mirror to check. Slender, five feet eight in bare feet, she had studied her flawless complexion, her straight, shoulder-length black hair, and looked into her liquid brown eyes. And then grinned, revealing perfect white teeth, and concluded that her stepfather had been just a little bit biased in her favour.

All this came back to her now, as she pulled into the car park of Progress Engineering for her interview. She was early. Emmie sat in her car, reflecting how disastrous everything had been just lately.

Needing the money she had doggedly stuck it out at Smythe and Wood, but she hadn't liked working for Clive Norris. Nor, to start with, had Aunt Hannah settled at Keswick House very easily. She disliked rules, and either by accident or design forgot to note in the 'Out' book where she was going when she went for a morning's short walk.

She invariably returned before anyone started to get anxious, but Emmie had received several phone calls to say Mrs Whitford had disappeared without saying where she was going, and had been absent some hours now, and they were starting to be concerned that she hadn't returned. Emmie had given Aunt Hannah a key to the new flat, and on that first occasion Emmie had to leave her office and hare back to the flat—Aunt Hannah hadn't been there. Thinking that perhaps Aunt Hannah might have returned to their old apartment, Emmie had rushed there, and with overwhelming relief had found her there, chatting, as nice as you please, to one of their former neighbours.

Emmie had Aunt Hannah to stay with her at the weekends, yet, despite her becoming familiar with the new area, whenever her step-grandmother did her disappearing act from Keswick House it was never to Emmie's new flat in the run-down area that she made for, but always their previous apartment.

But now, two and a half months after moving into Keswick House, Aunt Hannah seemed to have settled down. In fact, Emmie hadn't had to have any unexpected time off in the last two weeks. Until yesterday. She'd had Aunt Hannah with her for an extended weekend, and the plan had been to return her to Keswick House, five miles away, on Monday morning. But Emmie had overlooked the fact that her step-grandmother was never in any hurry to start her day, the result being that Emmie had been an hour late in getting to work yesterday.

She always worked late to make up for any time she had off. But yesterday, unfortunately, so too had Clive Norris.

'We could be doing better things than this,' he hinted, coming over and causing her to have to move away from the filing cabinet by which she was standing. 'Come and have a drink with me,' he went on, managing to make it sound more suggestive than a suggestion as he backed her into a corner.

'No, thanks,' Emmie replied, coolly but politely—and she saw Clive's expression change.

He didn't like it. 'You're too stuck-up by half,' he said nastily. 'You want taking down a peg!' he went on resentfully. And while she stood there feeling uncomfortable, wishing he'd go home and leave her in peace, to her absolute amazement the next thing she knew was that he made a grab for her and tried to kiss her.

His wet, lascivious lips made her heave. She wasn't thinking by then, but reacting—and her reaction was swift and immediate. She hit him with full force, and compounded that by giving him a furious push away from her. He ended up on the floor—looking ridiculous. He didn't like that either.

She stepped over him, grabbing up her coat and her bag. 'Goodnight!' she exploded, already on her way.

'Don't come back!' he screamed after her. He should be so lucky!

An hour later she calmed down, knowing that while she couldn't regret what she had done at the same time she simply couldn't afford to have done it. Not that she was going to ask for her job back. The thought of working for Clive Norris again made her shudder.

There had been just one letter in the post on Tuesday morning. She'd opened it and very nearly weakened in her resolve not to ask for her job back. Her letter was from Keswick House. One of the larger rooms had become available and Mrs Whitford had asked to transfer—would that be in order? Emmie had read on down, taking in the increased charge of the room. Oh, heavens, she couldn't afford it; she really couldn't. Well, not unless she managed to find a much better-paid job than the one she'd just walked out of. Clearly Aunt Hannah just hadn't taken into consideration when deciding that she'd like to move to a larger room that it would be more expensive.

Emmie went out and bought a paper and scanned the Situations Vacant column. One job had stood out from all the rest—assistant and then acting PA. The salary alone suggested it would be to someone very high up. She could do it, she knew that she could, and the salary named was beyond her wildest imaginings. The only snag was that the post was to cover maternity leave, and as such was only temporary. Emmie put the paper aside—then picked it up again as it dawned on her that so far over these last twelve months the longest she'd stayed anywhere had been four months. To work somewhere while covering maternity absence was starting to sound more like permanence to her. Besides which, if she had this sort of a salary coming in Aunt Hannah could move into the larger room and would perhaps be even more settled.

And, anyhow, Progress Engineering was no twopenny-halfpenny firm. The company were well-known in the mechanical and electronic engineering field. Surely, if she proved herself as good as Mr Denby had always said she was, might they find a niche for her within the organisation when the PA returned from maternity leave?

First, though, get the job. Hoping against hope that anyone better qualified would be more career-minded than to want to apply for a temporary job, Emmie picked up the phone and dialled. 'You're available straight away?' the head of Human Resources to whom she spoke had enquired efficiently.

'That's correct,' she'd answered, having not yet worked out what reason she was going to give for leaving her previous employer.

'Can you come and see me this afternoon?'

My word—they didn't hang about at Progress Engineering! 'Yes, of course,' she'd replied.

And now she discovered, as she sat before Mr Garratt, that the post she was applying for was not only as assistant and acting PA, but to Mr Barden Cunningham, the head of the whole conglomerate no less! The reason they weren't hanging about getting someone in was because Dawn Obrey, who was in around the fifth month of her pregnancy, was starting to have a few complications which, together with her antenatal appointments, meant she was out of the office quite a lot—sometimes very unexpectedly.

'Which, as you can appreciate—' Mr Garratt smiled '—is not always so convenient in the running of an extremely busy office. We've been able to switch people from other departments, of course, but Mr Cunningham prefers his own team.'

'That's quite understandable, from a continuity standpoint,' Emmie put in, having stretched the truth a mile by saying she had taken temporary jobs this past year to gain experience in many branches of industry. She had felt that her interview was going well, but owned to feeling a little let down when, the interview over, Mr Garratt stood up and, shaking her hand, advised her that he had two other candidates to see, but would be in touch very quickly.

Emmie drove home from her interview feeling very despondent. She hadn't known that the job was as PA to the head of the whole outfit. Barden Cunningham would want someone older; she was sure of it. Which was unfair, because she was good at her job; she knew she was.

By the time she reached her flat Emmie was convinced that she hadn't a hope of being taken on by Barden Cunningham. And though she knew that she should straight away ring Keswick House, and give some kind of reason why Aunt Hannah should not move into a larger room, somehow she could not.

Mr Garratt had said he would be in touch very quickly, but Emmie saw little point in holding her breath or looking forward to opening tomorrow's post. She knew how it would read: 'Thank you very much for attending for interview, but…'

A few hours later Emmie was again scanning the Situations column when the phone rang. Aunt Hannah had a phone in her room, but it wouldn't be her because as far as she knew Emmie was out at work. Emmie picked up the phone, 'Hello?' she answered pleasantly, trying not to panic that it might be Lisa Browne or one of the care assistants ringing to say Mrs Whitford had gone missing.

There was a small silence, then, 'Emily Lawson?' queried a rather nice all-male voice.

'Speaking,' she answered carefully.

'Barden Cunningham,' he introduced himself—and Emmie only just managed to hold back a gasp of shock.

'Oh, hello,' she said, and cringed—she'd already said hello once!

He came straight to the point. 'I should like to see you Friday afternoon. Are you free?'

'Yes, of course,' she answered promptly, her heartbeat

starting to pick up with excitement. 'What time would suit you?'

'Four-thirty,' he replied. 'Until then,' he added, and rang off—and Emmie's face broke out into one huge grin. She had an interview with no less a person than the top man himself!

She was still grinning ten minutes later. Mr Garratt had said he would be in touch very quickly—indirectly, he had been. He must have reported back to his employer the moment he had concluded all interviews. And, not waiting for mail to reach her, Barden Cunningham had phoned her within a very short space of time.

Which told her two things. One, that despite there being other candidates she was still in there with a chance. The other, that Progress Engineering were anxious to fill the temporary vacancy with all speed. Though from what Mr Garratt had said she thought she knew that already. Oh, roll on Friday; the suspense was unbearable.

Adrian Payne asked her to go out with him for a bite to eat on Thursday evening, but Emmie put him off. She wanted to be bright-eyed and bushy-tailed the next day for her interview, and intended to have an early night.

She was in frequent telephone contact with Aunt Hannah, but had not discussed her aunt's desire to move into a larger room, nor had she yet answered the letter from Lisa Browne at Keswick House. She knew, however, that she would have to ring Lisa Browne soon; courtesy if nothing else meant she should give some indication of whether or not Aunt Hannah could move. But pride, Emmie supposed, decreed that no one should know how desperately hard up she was but herself.

She was again early for her interview on Friday, and sat in her car for some minutes composing herself. She had on her best all wool charcoal-grey business suit, her crisp white shirt ironed immaculately.

She stepped from her car, knowing that she looked the

part of a cool, efficient PA in her neat two-and-a-half-inch heels, but felt glad that no one could know of the nervous commotion going on inside her. So much depended on this interview—and its outcome.

'My name's Emily Lawson. I've an appointment with Mr Cunningham at four-thirty,' she told the smart woman on the reception desk.

Emmie rode up in the lift, trying to stifle her nerves, desperate to make a good impression and hoping against hope that Mr Cunningham would turn out to be fatherly, like old Mr Denby. He hadn't sounded particularly fatherly over the phone, though.

Oh, she did so hope he was not another womaniser! She couldn't be that unlucky yet again, could she? Emmie pulled her mind away from such thoughts. She must concentrate only on this interview and Aunt Hannah, and the fact that if she was successful this afternoon Aunt Hannah could move into the double room she preferred.

Emmie made a vow there and then that, for Aunt Hannah's sake, if her prospective employer was yet another of the Casanova types she would keep a tight rein on her new-found temper. To do so would also mean that she kept her security—always supposing she was lucky enough to get the job. Having spent many years in a financially uncertain household, security was now more important to her than ever. She *had* to be self-reliant; she had no family but Aunt Hannah. And, having Aunt Hannah to look out for, Emmie knew she must think only of her career and, if all went well, the high salary being offered, which would afford both her and Aunt Hannah that security.

She was worrying needlessly, Emmie considered bracingly as she stepped out of the lift. This was a very different sort of company from the one she had walked out of on Monday—true, she had been told not to come back. But the very air about this place was vastly more professional.

Emmie found the door she was looking for, tapped on it

lightly and went in. A pale but pretty pregnant woman somewhere in her early thirties looked up. 'Emily Lawson?' she enquired.

'Am I too early?' Emmie's hopes suffered a bit of a dent. He'd want someone older; she felt sure of it.

'Not at all,' Dawn Obrey responded with a smile. And, leaving her chair, she went on, 'Reception rang to say you were on your way up. Mr Cunningham will see you now.'

Emmie flicked a hasty glance to the clock on the office wall, saw with relief that there were a few minutes to go before four-thirty and that neither her car clock nor her watch had played her false, and followed the PA over to a door which connected into another office.

'Miss Lawson,' the PA announced, and as Emmie went forward into the other room Dawn Obrey retreated and closed the door.

'Come in. Take a seat,' Barden Cunningham invited pleasantly, leaving his seat and shaking hands with her.

Ten out of ten for manners, Emmie noted with one part of her brain, while with another part she saw that Barden Cunningham was not old or fatherly, but was somewhere in his middle thirties. He was tall, had fairish hair and grey no-nonsense sort of eyes, but—and here was the minus— he was seriously good-looking. In her recent experience good-looking men were apt to think they were God's gift to women—and Barden Cunningham was more good-looking than most.

Emmie took a seat on one side of the desk and he resumed his seat on the other. His desk was clear, which indicated to her that he wouldn't be hanging about to start his weekend once this interview was over. Was she the last candidate?

She looked across at him and found he was studying her. She met his look, her large brown eyes steady, wishing she could read his mind, know what he was thinking. 'You're young,' he said. Was he accusing? He had obviously scanned the application form she had been asked to complete so knew she was twenty-two.

'I'm good,' she replied—this was no time to be modest!

He looked at her shrewdly, 'You trained at...' he began, and the interview was under way. His questions about her work experience, her views on confidentiality, were all clear, and most professional. 'What about your diplomacy skills?' he wanted to know.

Emmie knew that great tact was sometimes needed when dealing with awkward phone calls or difficult people. Now didn't seem the time to mention that earlier in the week diplomacy had gone by the board when she'd belted her previous boss and left him sprawled on the floor.

'Very good,' she answered, looking him in the eye. Well, they were—normally. Anybody who made a grab for her the way Clive Norris had, deserved what they got in her book. Barden Cunningham asked one or two more pertinent questions with regard to her general business knowledge, which she felt she answered more than adequately. 'When I worked at Usher Trading, communication skills were...' She went to expand when he stayed silent, only to be interrupted.

'Ah, yes, Usher Trading—they went into liquidation about a year ago,' he cut in—just as though it was her fault! As if she had been personally responsible!

Emmie clamped down hard on a small spurt of anger. Steady, steady, she needed this job. Perhaps he was just testing her to see how she reacted to the odd uncalled-for comment.

'Unfortunately, that's true,' she replied, and gave him the benefit of her full smile—which had once been called ravishing.

He was unimpressed. He looked at her, his eyes flicking from her eyes to her mouth and back to her eyes. He paused for a moment before, questions on her abilities seemingly over, he went on to refer to her work record over the past year. She'd had small hope that he would not do so. But, until she knew if this man was in the same womanising mould, Emmie didn't think she would be doing herself any favours if she gave the true reasons for her previous 'temporary' employment.

'As I mentioned to Mr Garratt—' she started down the path of untruth without falter '—I felt, having worked for the same firm for three years, that I should widen my work experience.' Usher Trading were no longer in existence, but if he wrote elsewhere for references—she was dead!

'Which is why you applied for this temporary post?'

There weren't any flies on him! 'I'm very keen to make a career in PA work,' she answered.

'You live with your parents?' he enquired out of the blue. She wasn't ready for it, and for a brief second felt unexpectedly choked.

She looked quickly down at her lap, swallowed, and then answered, 'My parents are dead.'

His expression softened marginally. 'That's tough,' he said gently. But after a moment he was back to being the interrogator. 'As I'm sure Mr Garratt mentioned, Mrs Obrey, my PA, is having an atrocious time of it at the moment. While in normal circumstances she would frequently accompany me when I need to visit our various other concerns, she isn't up to being driven around the country. That role will now fall to her assistant.' He fixed her with his straight no-nonsense look. 'Would that be a problem?'

Emmie shook her head. 'Not at all,' she answered unhesitatingly, hoping with all she had that Aunt Hannah's forgetful perambulations were a thing of the past. She'd been so good lately.

'It could be that I'd be late getting back to London,' Barden Cunningham stressed—and, those direct eyes on her still, he went on, 'You have no commitments?'

Emmie hesitated, but not for long. She guessed he meant

was she living with anyone. Now, if she was going to confide in him about Aunt Hannah, was the time to do so.
'None at all,' she replied, again managing to look him in
the eye. Well, her security was on the line here—her
chances of getting this job would go cascading down the
drain if he had so much as an inkling of her previous bad
time-keeping and the erratic work hours she'd kept.

'You'd have no problem working extra hours?'

Her heart lifted—the fact that this was turning out to be
no cursory interview gave her confidence that she was still
in there with a chance. 'Working extra hours, working late
has never been a problem,' she replied, back on the honesty
track, and glad that she was.

'You were called on to work late in your other temporary
job?' he questioned, before she'd barely finished speaking—was he sharp or was he sharp!

'I never liked to go home before I'd got everything
cleared,' she answered—oh, grief, that sounded smug and
self-satisfied! Better, though, than telling him she'd re-
garded her jobs more as permanent than temporary during
her short stays there.

Barden Cunningham had very few other questions he
wanted to ask, and then he caused her hopes to go sky-
high. 'When would you be available to start?' he wanted
to know.

'Straight away,' she answered promptly.

'You've nothing else lined up for Monday?'

Oh, crumbs—had she answered too promptly? Emmie
took a deep and steadying breath and then, her innate honesty rushed to the fore. 'Well, to be quite frank, I was
hoping this interview would go well enough for me not to
need to apply for anything else.'

Again Emmie wished she could have a clue as to what
he was thinking. But he was giving nothing away as he sat
and stared at her. Then, after some long moments, 'You
want the job?' he enquired.

He'd never know how much. She swallowed down the word 'desperately' and changed it to, 'Very much.'

Barden Cunningham's eyes searched her face for perhaps another couple of seconds. Then slowly he smiled, and it was the most wonderful smile she had ever seen. But better than that were the words that followed, for, as he stood up, indicating the interview was over, he said, 'Then, since you're going to be working with her for a while, you'd better come and have a chat to Dawn.'

'I've got the job?' she asked, hardly daring to believe it.

'Congratulations,' he said, and shook her hand.

CHAPTER TWO

FEBRUARY was on its way out and they were in the throes of some quite dreadful weather. Last week it had seemed to rain non-stop. Today it had gone colder, and snow was threatened. Emmie had not slept well, and got out of bed that Wednesday morning feeling oddly despondent. Oh, buck your ideas up, do. A month ago she had been overjoyed that she'd actually managed to be offered the job of assistant, shortly to be acting, PA to Mr Barden Cunningham. So—what had changed?

Emmie padded around her flat, trying to pin-point why she felt so—well, not exactly dissatisfied with her lot, but certainly sort of restless, out of sorts about something.

Which was odd, because she no longer had any worries about her step-grandmother. Aunt Hannah was now cheerfully established in the double room she had so wanted, and was more settled than Emmie could have hoped. Indeed, so content did Aunt Hannah seem that Emmie realised how right she had been to think it was important to the dear soul to feel safe during the long hours while Emmie was away at work. Safely ensconced in Keswick House, gradually, bit by bit, Aunt Hannah's confidence was returning. Her confidence—and her spirit of independence. Twice in the last month Aunt Hannah had declined to stay with Emmie for the weekend—though she had permitted Emmie to collect her for Sunday tea.

So it wasn't on Aunt Hannah's account that she felt so unsettled, Emmie decided. Her thoughts turned to her job, and how, without bothering to take up references—clearly he was a man confident in his own judgement, and that had

been one tremendous worrying hurdle out of the way—
Barden Cunningham had appointed her.

She had been working at the head office of Progress
Engineering for four weeks and two days now, and loved
the work. Had, in fact, taken to it like a duck to water.
Sometimes she worked under pressure but she absorbed it,
enjoyed the challenge—and felt that she did well enough
that her employer could not have one single solitary com-
plaint about her output.

She got on exceedingly well with Dawn and was glad to
be of help to her whenever she could, because, as well as
being a thoroughly nice person, Dawn was not having a
very easy pregnancy at all. 'I thought morning sickness was
something that happened early on—not now,' Dawn had
sighed only yesterday, after yet another visit to the ladies'
room.

'Why not go home? There's nothing here I can't cope
with,' Emmie had urged.

'I'll stick it out,' Dawn had said bravely. 'I'm having
tomorrow afternoon off for an antenatal appointment, as
you know. Thanks all the same, Emmie.'

Dawn had asked her that first Monday if she was called
Emily or if there was another name she was known by.
'I've been called Emmie for as long as I can remember,'
she'd answered, and had been Emmie to all at Progress
Engineering since then.

So, Emmie went back to trying to find the root cause of
what was making her so restless. She had no worries about
Aunt Hannah now, she liked her job and she liked Dawn,
and everything else was ticking along nicely. So why did
she feel…?

Her thoughts suddenly faltered. Everybody at Progress
Engineering called her Emmie—except *him*! To him, she
was still Emily. She wasn't terribly sure quite when Barden
Cunningham had become *him*. She had quite liked him during those first few hours of working for him. That was

before she had taken the first of his May-I-speak-with-Barden-please-Paula-here-type calls.

'Do I put Paula through?' she'd whispered to Dawn.

There had followed, over the next few weeks, Ingrid, Sarah, and a whole host of other females—it was a wonder to Emmie that he ever got any work done. But he did. That was the bitter pill. She couldn't fault him; given that—wouldn't you know, another wretched womaniser—he took time out to answer his calls, the amount of work he turned out was staggering.

'He's not married, then?' Emmie had asked Dawn, knowing she was going to hate him like the devil if he were.

Dawn had shaken her head. 'Why limit yourself to one pudding when you can have the whole dessert trolley?'

Emmie had managed a smile, but she'd had her fill of womanisers. She'd been sure, however, to keep her feelings well hidden, but happened to be in his office when a female she hadn't so far come across had telephoned him.

'Claudia!' he'd exclaimed with pleasure. And, charming the socks off Claudia—Emmie didn't want to know what else he charmed off her—he'd kept Emmie waiting while he dallied with his new love.

'If you'd just sign these papers for me!' Emmie had requested crisply, when he'd at last finished his call.

She'd ignored his raised eyebrow, that look that said, Who the blazes do you think you are? 'Anything else?' he'd asked sarcastically, and Emmie had felt sorely inclined to give him a taste of what she'd given Clive Norris.

'No, thank you,' she'd replied politely, if a shade aloofly, and returned to her desk. Men!

True, he hadn't attempted the womanising bit with her. Let him try! Not that she wanted him to. Heaven forbid! It irked, though, in some strange way that he still called her Emily, even though she knew for a fact that to him, Dawn always referred to her as Emmie.

Realising she was getting all huffy and puffy over nothing, Emmie got ready to face the day and drove herself to work. The morning went well, and Dawn went off at lunchtime to keep her hospital appointment.

Barden Cunningham was out of the office for the first hour of that afternoon, and Emmie quite enjoyed the challenge of being left in sole charge of the office. Her enjoyment, however, was somewhat dimmed by a telephone call she took around two-thirty.

'Mr Cunningham's office,' she said into the mouthpiece, on picking up the phone.

'Roberta Short,' the caller announced herself. 'That's Emmie, isn't it?' See—even Cunningham's friends knew she was called Emmie!

'Yes,' she answered, a smile in her voice. She liked Roberta Short, a striking woman in her early thirties. Emmie had met her and her husband, a man in his late forties, when they had called in to see her employer one day. 'I'm afraid Mr Cunningham isn't in.'

'Oh, drat! I particularly wanted to catch him.'

'May I get him to call you?' Emmie offered—and felt her blood go cold at Roberta Short's panicky reply.

'Lord, no!' she squeaked. 'Neville mustn't know I'm phoning Barden. I've an idea he already suspects—' She broke off. 'Oh, help, Neville's coming in… He mustn't find out…' The line went dead.

Slowly, feeling stunned, Emmie replaced her phone. No, she'd got it wrong. That call just now didn't really imply what she'd thought it might. Neville Short was Barden Cunningham's friend, for heaven's sake! Just because Cunningham was a womaniser of the first order, it didn't follow that even married women weren't safe from him. Emmie felt all churned up inside. Why didn't it? He had charm by the truckload—no woman was safe from him. Well, save for her, and she was sure that didn't bother her in the smallest degree!

But—his friend's wife? No! Emmie got on with some work, but time and again those words 'I've an idea he already suspects' and 'Neville's coming in… He mustn't find out…' before Roberta Short had abruptly ended her call returned to haunt her.

Ignore it. It's nothing to do with you even if he is having an affair with his friend's wife. Two-timing her too with Claudia whatever-her-name-was, who'd phoned him last week. The man was an out and out monster! Men like him wanted locking up!

The sound of the connecting door to the next office opening told her that the object of her sweet thoughts was back. Who had he been extending his lunch with? she'd like to know. Claudia? Paula?

Emmie looked up. 'Any messages?' Barden Cunningham wanted to know.

'Mrs Neville Short rang,' Emmie replied. 'She didn't want to leave a message.'

'She'll ring again, I expect.'

My stars! How about that for confidence? Though, since the diabolical hound most likely knew that Neville Short was at home, he wouldn't be likely to ring Roberta while her husband was there. Emmie concentrated solely on being an efficient PA, and then told her employer of a business enquiry she'd taken before he went back to his own office and closed the door. She carried on with what she had been doing.

It was just around half past three when her intercom went. 'Come in, Emily, please,' her employer instructed.

Certainly, your libertine-ness! Without a word Emmie picked up her pad and went in. And for the next half an hour she took dictation or jotted down his instructions. She was still writing when the phone in her office rang.

Cunningham indicated she should stay where she was, and, reaching for the phone on his desk, pressed the appropriate button. 'Cunningham,' he said, and then there was a

smile there in his voice as his caller announced herself.
'Roberta! You cunning vixen, how's it going?' he asked.

Emmie didn't like it. A kind of sickness hit her, and she
wanted to dash out of there. She made to leave—she could
come back later, when he'd finished chatting up the 'cunning vixen'. Cunning, no doubt, because she was successfully fooling her husband! But Barden Cunningham motioned her to sit down again. All too obviously he didn't
give a damn that Emmie overheard his philandering phone
calls. Why couldn't he conduct his wretched affair outside
business hours?

She had no idea what Roberta's replies were, but what
Cunningham was saying didn't leave Emmie in very much
doubt that the conclusions she'd drawn were correct.

'You're worrying too much!' Cunningham teased. 'I
promise you he's not likely to divorce you.'

Grief—how was that for confident! Even if Neville Short
did find out about the affair, the poor chap so loved his
wife he would never divorce her. Barden Cunningham was
taking advantage of that! Locking up! He should be put
down—preferably painfully! The call was coming to an
end.

'I'll somehow manage to snatch a few moments with you
tomorrow night at the theatre,' Barden promised. 'It
shouldn't be too difficult.'

There was a pause as Roberta replied—and Emmie
started to get angry. She knew full well that it was nothing
to do with her, but, confound it! Not content to play fast
and loose behind the cuckolded Neville's back, it sounded
very much as though Cunningham would be seeing them
both at the theatre tomorrow, and—given half a chance—
he would snatch his opportunity for a quick cuddle right
under her husband's—*his friend's*—nose. Oh, it was too
much!

'You've nothing to worry about. I promise you, Neville

has no idea what you're up to,' Barden soothed. 'Now stop
worrying. I'll see you tomorrow. Everything will be fine.'

She'd bet it would, Emmie fumed. Quite plainly Roberta
Short was getting the wind up that her poor husband might
find out what was going on. And Barden Cunningham, who
was no doubt no stranger to this sort of situation, was almost casual as he attempted to soothe Roberta's anxieties.

'Now what did I do?'

The tone was sharp. Emmie looked up—he had ended
his phone call, though she would have known that from his
tone of voice, which was oh, so very different from how it
had been now that he was no longer speaking to his lady-
love.

Emmie strove hard to keep a lid on her anger. 'Do?' she
countered.

'I've just about had it with you and your arrogance!'
Barden Cunningham snarled curtly. Arrogance? Her?
Emmie could feel herself fighting a losing battle with her
anger, even if she was desperate to keep her job. She sensed
from his statement, 'I've just about had it with you', that
she was on her way out, anyway. 'So tell me what I did
this time.' He gave her a direct look from those no-
nonsense cool grey eyes, and Emmie just knew that he was
going to pursue this until he had an answer.

'It's none of my business.' She felt forced, if she hoped
to hang on to this job, to give him some sort of a reply.

'What isn't?'

As she'd thought. He wanted more than that. 'When Mrs
Short rang earlier she was very anxious that her husband
didn't know about it.'

'So!'

Oh, abomination, he was immovable. 'Add that to the
conversation—well, your side anyway, which I've just
overheard—and it's obvious!'

'What is?'

She wanted to hit him. He wanted her to come right out

with it. Well, she'd be damned if she would. 'If you don't know, it's not up to me to tell you!' She could feel her temper getting away from her. Cool it, cool it, you can't afford a temper.

'You think—' He broke off, and, putting her remark about Mrs Short being anxious about her husband knowing, together with the exchange he'd just had with her, he suddenly had it all added up. 'How d—?' He was angry; she could tell. That made two of them. 'Why, you prissy little Miss Prim and Proper. You think I'm having an affair with—'

'It's nothing to do with me!' Emmie flared. Her on-the-loose temper had no chance while that 'prissy little Miss Prim and Proper' still floated in the air.

'You're damned right it isn't!' he barked. He was on his feet—so was she. 'What I do with my life, how I conduct my life, is absolutely, categorically, nothing whatsoever to do with you!' he snarled. *'Got that?'*

Who did he think he was? Who did he think he was talking to? Some mealy-mouthed, wouldn't-say-boo typist? 'It was you who insisted on knowing!' she erupted, her brown eyes sparking flashes of fire.

She refused to back down, even though she knew he was going to well and truly attempt to sort her out now. Strangely, though, as she waited for him to rain coals of wrath down about her head, all at once, as he looked into her storming brown eyes, it seemed he checked himself—and decided to sort her out using another tack. For suddenly his tone became more mocking than angry.

'Are you being fair, do you think, little Emily?' he enquired charmingly.

She blinked. 'Fair?' She owned she wasn't quite with him.

'I don't—scold—you over your affairs,' he drawled, and she looked at him, momentarily made speechless. 'But then,' he went on coolly, 'you've never had an affair, have you?'

She hadn't. But pride, some kind of inverted honour, was at stake here. 'I've…' she began, ready to lie and tell him she'd had dozens of affairs—only she faltered. Given that it seemed it was she who had instigated this conversation, was she really discussing her love-life—or his view that she didn't *have* a love life—with her employer? 'How many affairs I've had, or not had, is entirely nothing to do with you,' she jumped back up on her high horse, and told him loftily.

'Typical!' he rapped, soon back to snarling, she noted. 'You think you can pass judgement on my out-of-work activities, but the moment I enquire into yours, it's none of my business!'

'Out-of-work activities'. That was a new name for it! But she'd had enough, and grabbed up her notepad. 'Do you want this work back today or don't you?' she challenged hotly—and too late saw the glint in his eyes that clearly said he didn't take very kindly to attitude.

Oddly again, though—when some part of her already wanted to apologise, while another part wouldn't let her—instead of laying into her, as she'd fully expected, Barden Cunningham took a moment out to look down at her. She knew from her burning skin that she must have flares of pink in her cheeks. She was, however, already regretting her spurt of temper, and on the way to vowing never to get angry again, when still looking down at her, that glint of anger in those no-nonsense grey eyes suddenly became a mocking glint as he derided, 'And there was I, putting you down as a mouse.'

That did it! Mouse! Apologise? She'd see him hang first! Mouse! What self-respecting twenty-two-year-old would put up with that? 'Better a mouse than a *rat*!' she hissed—and was on her way.

She went storming through the connecting door, not

bothering to close it—she wasn't stopping—and straight to her coat peg on the far wall. Even as she reached for her coat, though, and started shrugging into it, she was regretting having lost her temper. What the dickens was the matter with her? She couldn't afford a temper!

Emmie dipped in the bottom drawer of her desk to retrieve her bag, knowing full well that even if she didn't want to go there was no way now, after calling Barden Cunningham a rat, that he was going to let her stay.

Or so she'd thought. She had just straightened, her shoulder bag in hand, when his voice enquired coolly, 'Where do you think you're going?'

She looked over to the doorway and saw he had come to lean nonchalantly against the doorframe. She hesitated, common practical sense intruding on what pride decreed. Oh, she did so like the work, and didn't want to leave. Her breath caught. Was he saying that, despite her poking her nose into his private life and making judgements on his morals, he wasn't telling her to go?

'Aren't I—dismissed?' she managed to query.

For answer Barden Cunningham stood away from the door. 'I'll let you know when,' he drawled—and added, with insincere charm, 'You'll be working late tonight.'

With that he went into his office, and, obviously utterly confident that she would do exactly as he said, and not bothering to wait to see if she took her coat off, closed the connecting door.

Emmie slowly put down her bag, relief rushing in because she still had this well-paid and, it had to be said, enjoyable job—while another part of her, the proud part, she rather suspected, made her wish she was in a position to walk and keep on walking.

A cold war ensued for the remainder of the day.

Working late was of no concern to Emmie, and she arrived at her flat around eight that evening, starting to feel quite astonished that, though her security was so vital to

her, she had today, because she had been unable to control
a suddenly erratic temper, put both her security and Aunt
Hannah's future tranquillity at risk!

Emmie got up the following morning, still wondering
what in creation had got into her. She was aware that she
had been tremendously shaken when her stepfather Alec
had died. Her emotions had received a terrible blow. Her
redundancy from Usher Trading around about the same
time hadn't helped. The worrying time she'd had of it when
each of her successive jobs had folded had been a strain
too. Had she perhaps grown too used to heading for the
door when something went wrong, and had it become a
habit with her?

But, not without cause, she mused as she drove to the
offices of Progress Engineering. She remembered Clive
Norris's attempt to kiss her. The way he'd hemmed her in
between the filing cabinet and the wall—was she supposed
to put up with that sort of nonsense? No, certainly not!

So what had Cunningham done that had made her so
angry? So angry that for emotional seconds at a time she
had been ready to forget her oh, so important security and
walk out of there. Made him so angry she had thought
herself about to be dismissed at any second—thought she
had really blown it when she'd more or less called him a
rat.

So he was, too. But was it any of her business? She
hadn't liked it when he'd said he thought of her as a mouse.
Nor had she liked it when he'd referred to her non-existent
love-life. But, and Emmie had to face it, she was employed
by Barden Cunningham to work, and only work. *She* had
been the one to bring the personal element into it. True,
the whole sorry business could have been avoided if he
hadn't enquired so sharply—in such a direct contrast to his
tone when talking to his lady-love, Roberta Short—'Now
what did I do?'

Or could it have been avoided? He'd caught her on the

raw with his tone, and negated any chance of her making use of the skills of diplomacy she'd assured him at her interview she possessed, without those sharp words telling her he'd just about had it with her and her arrogance. And, if that hadn't been enough, he'd insisted on knowing why she was being 'arrogant' this time.

Emmie went to her desk, aware by then that she was at fault. Anything that happened in the office that wasn't business was nothing to do with her. Unless the womanising hound made a pass at her—and she could be part of the furniture for all the notice he took of her; not that she wanted him taking notice of her, thank you very much—perish the thought. But she had no call to be remotely interested in anything else that went on which was unconnected with business.

'Everything all right?' she asked Dawn after their initial greeting.

'As it should be.' Dawn smiled.

'How are you feeling today?'

'Touch wood, so far, and in comparison to Tuesday, quite good.'

Emmie got on with some work, but the row she'd had with Barden Cunningham the previous afternoon came back again and again to haunt her. Somehow, when at around eleven he called her into his office, she knew that she was not going to forget it, or indeed feel any better about it, until she'd apologised.

But he was cool, aloof, as he stated, 'I have to go to Stratford—be ready at twelve.'

She felt niggled; no please, no thank you, no Could you be ready at twelve; I'd like you to accompany me? The cold war was still on, then? He was charm personified with everyone else.

'Will you require any file in particular?' she enquired politely, knowing by then that they had a product and design offshoot in Stratford-upon-Avon, about a hundred and ten miles away.

'Just a fresh notebook,' he replied. 'You're taking the minutes of what could be a lengthy, involved and very important meeting.'

Emmie returned to her desk, glad she was wearing the same smart charcoal suit she had worn for her interview. She knew she was looking good, and felt it was quite a feather in her cap that she had been appointed to go with the head of the group to take notes for this very important meeting. Although, on thinking about it, she had known from the first that Dawn wasn't able to go. Barden could easily have found someone else, though. Emmie cheered herself up. Make no mistake, please or offend, he would have found someone else if he thought for a moment that she wasn't up to it.

They made it to Stratford-upon-Avon in good time, and were greeted by the general manager, Jack Bryant, a pleasant man in his early thirties who, while totally businesslike with her employer, frequently rested his eyes on Emmie.

'I refuse to believe you're called Emily,' he commented, while Barden was having a word with the products manager.

'Would you believe Emmie?'

He smiled, and when Emmie was starting to wonder if she was going to last the whole afternoon, lunchless, he informed her, 'A meal's been laid on for you in the executive dining room.' He was just adding, 'I hope you won't mind if I have lunch with you too, Emmie,' when she became aware that Barden Cunningham had turned back to them.

He tossed her a sour look, which she took as an indication that he felt she hadn't wasted any time in giving the general manager leave to call her by the name all but he used. Then he looked from her to remark, a touch sarcastically, she felt, 'Good of you to wait lunch.'

They did not linger over the meal, and, having been given all of five minutes to wash her hands afterwards, they adjourned to the boardroom and the afternoon flew as fast as her fingers. Emmie had known she was good at her job, but at that meeting her skills were tested to the full. When it came to an end she felt as if she had done a full week's work in one afternoon.

Jack Bryant came over to her while Barden was shaking hands with a couple of the board members. 'I'm in London quite often, or could be.' Jack smiled. 'You wouldn't care to let me have your phone number, I suppose?'

'Your divorce through yet, Jack?' Barden appeared from nowhere to ask conversationally.

'Any time now,' he replied.

Barden smiled. 'Talk to my PA when it's absolute—she doesn't encourage married men.'

Why did she want to hit him? On the one hand she was thrilled to bits that he'd actually called her his PA, but on the other she wanted to land him one. For all it was true, and she didn't encourage married men, he somehow made it sound as if she really was the 'prissy little Miss Prim and Proper' he had called her yesterday. That still stung!

It was around seven-thirty when they arrived back at the Progress Engineering building, and by then the mixed feelings about her employer Emmie had been experiencing had calmed down, to the extent that she was again thinking of the apology she owed him.

Intending to lock her notes away in her desk overnight, Emmie went up to her office in the lift with Barden, and he took a short cut through her office to his own. Placing her bag and pad down on her desk, she heard him at his desk, and, acting on the impulse of the moment—and in a now-or-never attempt to get her apology over and done with—she went and paused in the doorway.

Barden Cunningham looked over to where she stood— and her words wouldn't come. He waited, his glance taking in her straight and shiny black hair, flicking over her suit, which concealed her slender figure. Unspeaking, his glance came back to her face, to her eyes, down to her mouth, where the words trembled, and then back up to her eyes.

Emmie knew then that if she didn't push those words out soon she was going to lose all dignity and feel a fool. 'I—I want to apologise for my—er—behaviour yesterday,' she forced out jerkily—and wished she hadn't bothered when, instantly aware of what she was referring to, but not looking at all friendly, he looked coolly back at her.

'You're still of the same view today as yesterday?' he enquired crisply.

The view that he was a rat for playing away with Neville Short's wife while pretending to be his good friend? Yes, she did still hold the same view. Why couldn't Cunningham just accept her apology and forget it? But—he was waiting, and Emmie just then discovered that, even though a lie, a simple no would have ended the matter, suddenly, lying was beyond her.

'Yes,' she said quietly, weathering the direct look from those no-nonsense steady grey eyes. 'My views haven't changed.'

The no-nonsense look went from cool to icy. 'Then your apology is worthless,' he stated curtly.

Emmie abruptly turned her back on him and marched stormily into her own office. She didn't know about losing dignity, but she did feel a fool—and humiliated into the bargain. Heartily did she wish she had never bothered, had ignored the plague of her conscience. Her apology was rejected. Huh! The way he talked, he would only accept her apology if it was sincere. *He* was so sincere! Stabbing his friend Neville in the back—it looked like it!

Fuming, Emmie tossed her notepad in her drawer and locked it away—only to feel like storming in and punching Barden Cunningham's head when his voice floated coolly from his office. 'Leave typing back your notes until the morning, Emily.'

Was he serious? He actually thought she had it in mind to type up those minutes *tonight*? There was a full day's work there! Resisting the temptation to go to his doorway and poke her tongue out at him, Emmie instead picked up her bag and went swiftly to her outer office door.

Afraid that if she opened her mouth something not very polite would come out, she decided against wishing him goodnight, but, by switching out the light and plunging her office in darkness, she let that be her farewell to him. The swine. He had an assignation with Roberta Short at the theatre that night. He must already be late—she hoped that he wouldn't be let in.

Emmie had difficulty in getting to sleep that night. It seemed to her that she only had to close her eyes to start wondering if Cunningham had managed to snatch some private time with his married lover. Perhaps even now, at this very moment, they were alone together. The thought made her feel quite wretched. She moved and thumped her pillow—wishing that it was his head.

She surfaced on Friday, after a very fractured night, and showered and donned a white silk shirt and her second-best suit of dark navy wool. Satisfied with her appearance, and aware that, since her notes from yesterday needed to be typed up she was in for a hard day, she was about to don her three-quarter-length car coat when her phone rang.

Aunt Hannah? She didn't normally ring in the morning on a weekday. Though since she did sometimes get her days mixed up, which was perfectly understandable, Emmie defended, perhaps Aunt Hannah thought today was Saturday.

Emmie went over to the phone, checking her watch and mentally noting she had five minutes to spare if it was Aunt Hannah.

The call *was* from Keswick House, she soon discovered.

However, it was not her step-grandmother—but Lisa Browne. Mrs Whitford was not to be found, and enquiries had revealed that one of the other residents had seen her letting herself out an hour ago. She hadn't told anyone where she was going.

An hour ago! Aunt Hannah didn't usually get up this early! Emmie took a quick glance to the window, trying not to panic. It was a grey day; snow was threatening. 'Was she wearing a coat?' she asked quickly.

'Apparently, yes.'

'She's probably gone back to our old apartment.' Emmie spoke her thoughts out loud, panic mixing with concern that Aunt Hannah might be getting confused again. 'I'll go there straight away,' she told Lisa Browne—and wasted no more time.

Only when the cold air hit her did it vaguely dawn on her that she had rushed out without actually putting her own coat on. But she had more important matters to worry about than that—she'd soon get warm in the car. She must get the car heated up for Aunt Hannah. Must collect her. Must return her to Keswick House. Must get to work. Oh, heck, all that work she had to do today! Barden Cunningham was just going to love her. She tried not to think about him. This was the last day of her fifth week at Progress—and the first time she'd been late.

Hoping that her five-week record for being on time, not to mention that she had uncomplainingly worked late when required, would see her employer—womanising toad—forgiving her this one lapse—she couldn't bear to think that there might be another—Emmie concentrated on her most immediate problem. Her present accommodation was just five miles away from Keswick House; the apartment where they'd used to live was seven miles distant from Aunt Hannah's new home. For someone so confused that she had in the past believed that she still lived in their old apartment, it was a source of surprise to Emmie that, even in the depths of confusion, Aunt Hannah remembered their previous address and how to get there.

Thinking she would soon have her step-relative safe in her car, Emmie was delayed by twenty minutes in traffic. When eventually she did make it to the area where she had lived happily with Alec and his mother, Emmie looked about for signs of the dear love.

With not a glimpse of her, she parked outside her old address and rang the doorbells of their former neighbours. No one answered. For the next hour Emmie scoured the streets, looking for Aunt Hannah. Starting to feel quite desperate, she went back to her present flat, hoping that Aunt Hannah had thought to go there.

She hadn't. Emmie rang Lisa Browne, crossing her fingers that her step-relative had made it back to Keswick House. 'I'm afraid not,' Lisa Browne answered.

By then Emmie was getting seriously worried. She thought of ringing the police, then decided she would give it one more try. Aunt Hannah had grown aggressive the last time she'd been in police 'custody'.

Emmie did also consider ringing Dawn at Progress Engineering, but, as distracted as Emmie felt, she remembered just in time how Barden Cunningham had specifically asked her at her interview if she had any commitments. She had an idea she was going to be in enough trouble when she did eventually reach her office without now confessing that she had lied at her interview.

Emmie was back on the road to her old home once more when it came to her that because of her lie about no commitments she would be unable to tell the truth. She suddenly realised she had no excuse to offer for her absence!

All that, however, went from her mind when, just as she reached their former apartment, she saw Aunt Hannah getting out of a delivery van. The van drove off. Emmie made it to the pavement just as Mrs Whitford was about to climb the steps to the front door.

'Aunt Hannah!' she called, loud enough for her to hear, but not enough to startle the old lady.

Aunt Hannah turned and, seeing Emmie, smiled. 'Hello, dear. Not at work today? I waited ages for a bus, but that driver stopped and—' She broke off, something of much greater importance occurring to her. 'Do you know, he used to have a Norton 16H too?'

Emmie smiled; her relief at having found Hannah was enormous! The dear love was motorbike crazy, and, in her unconventional younger years, had owned several machines. 'How are you?' Emmie enquired, as a precursor to getting her in the car and driving her back to Keswick House.

'Oh, very well. Mr Norton,' she went on, making Emmie smile—the van driver and ex-motorbike owner was obviously Mr Norton!—'was telling me about the National Motorcycle Museum in Birmingham. It's open seven days a week,' she hinted.

How could you not love her? Emmie smiled fondly. 'We'll go,' she promised. 'Not today,' she added quickly, 'but soon. It must be getting near to your lunchtime. Shall we go back to Keswick House?'

It was closer to twelve than eleven by the time Emmie had got Aunt Hannah cheerfully settled back at Keswick House, and nearer one than twelve when she made it to her office. She noted that Dawn wasn't around when she went in, and stowed her bag, glad that the door between her office and the next one was closed.

It did not stay closed for long. Trust *him* to have heard her. Barden Cunningham pulled back the door and took a pace into the room, his glance becoming more and more hostile the longer he looked at her. She swallowed. Oh, crumbs, it looked like fire and brimstone time!

It was. He took a long breath, as if needing control, 'Since you obviously haven't been rushed to hospital to have your appendix removed,' he began, silkily enough—

it didn't last. 'Would you mind telling me,' he went on toughly, 'just where the hell you've been?'

'I—er—had a domestic problem.' Emmie found her voice, hoping he would think her central heating system had malfunctioned.

'Don't tell me you've broken the habit of a lifetime and let some man into your bed!' he snarled, his idea of domesticity clearly on a very different plane from hers.

The cheek of it! 'According to you, I don't have an overnight life!' Emmie flared, not at all enamoured by his snarling sarcastic tone, but striving hard not to let it get to her.

'What was this "domestic" matter?' he went on, as if he hadn't heard her. 'Couldn't you get him to leave?'

Emmie lost it. 'Don't judge me by your own criteria!' she flew. Oh, grief, he looked ready to throttle her. All too obviously he hadn't cared for that. She wanted to back down, wanted to regret her words—but she found she couldn't. Oh, what was the matter with her? She had pushed her luck yesterday, and the day before—she couldn't hope to be so lucky again, and she needed this job! 'Er—has Dawn gone for an early lunch?' She attempted to cool both her temper and his. Fat chance!

'I've given her the day off!' he gritted. 'When *she*, despite how off-colour she's feeling, managed to get to a phone—' sarcastic swine! '—I decided we'd cope without her.'

Bully for you! Emmie, hoping, since she was still there, that she hadn't received her marching orders, offered, 'I'll make up my time off. I'll work late tonight and—'

'You're damned right you will,' Barden cut in bluntly. 'I want those minutes finished and in my hands before this day is over!'

Emmie stared at him. He *had* to be joking! Pride—she guessed that was what it was—wouldn't allow her to tell him she couldn't do it. She was supposed to be cooking a

meal for Adrian Payne that night. 'Do I take it that you'll
be staying late too?' she enquired, as evenly as she could.

He smiled then, an insincere smile. And she, who had
never hated anyone in her life, well and truly hated Barden
Cunningham then. She hated him particularly when, his
tone again silky, he replied, 'No way. I was here before
seven this morning. I'm just about to leave for a weekend
party.'

Fuming, while trying to hold her temper down, Emmie
stared belligerently at him. 'You're saying that you want
me to cancel my date tonight, to work until I'm ready to
drop, in order to lock those minutes away in a drawer for
your attention on Monday?'

He didn't smile, but his tone stayed pleasant as he admonished, 'You weren't listening, Emily. I said I want
those completed minutes *in my hands today*.'

'But—but you're going—er—partying!'

'True,' he answered, and, reaching for a sheet of office
stationery, swiftly wrote down an address and some directions. 'I don't doubt the party will still be thrashing gone
midnight. I'm sure you won't mind dropping off the
minutes on your way home.'

Emmie took the paper from him and stared at it. Then,
her eyes widening, she stared at him. The address—Neville
and Roberta Short's address—lay in an entirely different
direction from where she lived. And she was positive the
vile Cunningham *knew* it! She flicked her glance past him
to the window, where the first flakes of snow had started
to fall. A glance back at her employer showed he'd followed her eyes.

He looked back to her—and smiled. Then she hated him
afresh! He knew full well that she would be slaving away
until at least eight o'clock that night. And after that it would
take her an hour to drive to his *lady-love's* home!

She opened her mouth to protest, then all at once realised
from his silky look that it was just what he was expecting—

and she knew she'd see him in hell first! She swallowed down all hint of protest. 'Anything else?' she enquired prettily—and thought she caught a glimpse of something akin to admiration in his eyes.

It was gone in an instant, and she knew that she must have imagined it when he went to the door. Though, once there, he turned, and his agreeable tone beat hers by a mile when he reminded her, 'Don't forget to break your date, Emily,' and went off for his evil weekend. Emmie actually thought she heard him whistling as he went!

CHAPTER THREE

BY GOING without a lunchtime and working as fast as she
could, though telephone interruptions caused her to stop all
too often, Emmie completed her work just after eight that
evening. She felt drained and exhausted, but also triumphant.

She also felt extremely anti Mr Barden-womanising-
Cunningham. She hated him, and hated that he was actually
spending a partying weekend in his married lover's *home*.
How *could* he?

Emmie, still winter coat-less, dashed from her office to
her car, glad to note that there wasn't too much snow
around. She started the engine and headed the vehicle in
the direction of Neville and Roberta Short's home, making
herself calm down. For goodness' sake, it was nothing to
do with her what Cunningham did in his spare time.

She drove on, realising, since her security was so important to her, she should count herself lucky that after her
non-attendance this morning she still had a job. A well-
paid job, too.

All thoughts, however, of how grateful she should be that
she had kept her job began to disappear from her mind
when, clear of London, she started to drive into bad
weather. It started snowing again. It will stop soon, she told
herself, just as her stomach began to violently protest because, apart from breakfast, it hadn't been fed that day. The
snow kept falling.

After quite some while she saw a signpost, fortunately
not yet obscured by snow, which showed that her destination was not so far distant. Emmie turned off the major
road she was on and steered down a minor one.

By then food was starting to dominate. She had phoned Adrian and cancelled their meal, but felt hungry enough to eat a dry bread sandwich. She was aware that if she didn't stop now and have something to eat she might well be unlucky on the way back, if any pub she came across stopped serving food at nine-thirty.

She was almost at a pub when she knew she *must* eat something before she got home. For heaven's sake, she started to fume, *he'd* be so busy partying he was never going to notice what time she got to the Shorts'—and she was *starving*! Telling herself that, provided those minutes were in Barden's hands by midnight, it would still count as *today*, just like he had ordered—though of course she'd be handing them over well before then—within the next hour if the service in The Farmer's Arms was pretty smart—Emmie turned into the pub car park.

The service was not swift, and it seemed to take for ever for the prawn risotto she had ordered to arrive, though it was nicely presented, with a couple of decorative prawns on the side.

The taste left something to be desired, but Emmie was by then ravenous, and the risotto was filling. She felt much more cheerful as she made to leave the pub than when she had entered it.

Any feeling of cheerfulness abruptly vanished, however, when she opened the door to the outside elements. It was snowing a blizzard out there! Already the roads were well covered. Snowflakes as big as buckets charged straight for her.

The winter chill bit through the thin wool of her suit as, taking her life in her hands—in her two-and-a-half-inch heels—Emmie hurried over the snow-covered ground to her car. She turned the key in the ignition and saw from the clock that it was already half past nine. She just couldn't believe it!

According to her calculations at the outset, she should

have been back at her own home about ten-thirtyish. Well, she could forget that! She wished she could forget having to go to the Shorts' house. But she wanted this job, and *he* was a pig, and the sooner she got there the sooner she'd get back. By her reckoning, and with a fair wind, she would be heading back in little over half an hour.

Matters did not work out as planned. Her initial estimate had been that it would take around an hour for her to complete the distance to the Shorts' home. But she found that she was out by thirty minutes—and that would have been in normal weather conditions.

With the wind howling, the snow falling thick and fast and coming straight at her, visibility was next to nil. Having no wish to end up in a ditch, Emmie slowed her speed to a crawl. She was not happy. She felt isolated, alone, and very sorely tempted to give in to the instinct to turn around and head for home.

Doggedly, she pressed on, reminding herself again and again that *he* wanted those minutes, but, more importantly than that, she wanted, nay, needed quite desperately to keep this job.

Feeling both mentally and physically exhausted, while mutinying that she must be the only driver out on a night like this, for she hadn't seen so much as a glimpse of another vehicle since she had driven away from The Farmer's Arms, Emmie experienced a tremendous uplift of spirits when she found she had arrived at the edge of the village she was looking for.

She relaxed her concentration for the briefest of moments—it was a mistake. The worst happened. She skidded off the road down a gully and into a hedge. Her car, she knew instantly, was going no further. She tried anyway, put it into reverse and gently accelerated—but her wheels spun.

Emmie tried for the next ten minutes. Even while knowing it was hopeless she tried. It was going to take a tractor to pull her out. She glanced about, but couldn't see very much. But, though she didn't fancy at all getting out of her car—she'd freeze out there—common sense alerted that if she stayed in her car all night it was a near certainty she'd freeze to death anyway.

Grabbing up the minutes folder from the passenger seat, Emmie, with some difficulty, because of the angle of her car, managed to open her door sufficiently to be able to squeeze out.

Cold air hit her. Scrambling up the small incline, she fell over and measured her length. She scrabbled to her feet— her shoes were never going to be the same again—and started walking towards a distant glimmer of light.

Slithering and sliding on her smart shoes to what she saw now was a streetlamp, Emmie fell over once more in the ankle-deep snow before she reached the lamp. Then she saw a signpost and went to brush snow from it—and so get her bearings. The Shorts' home was on the outskirts of the village. Her good fortune was that she had 'parked' her car at the right end. If she took a left turn, the Shorts' place should be a hundred or so yards in that direction.

Mutiny entered Emmie's soul as she trudged, slithered and slid, and getting wetter by the second, doggedly ploughed on. *He* wanted the minutes; she'd give him the minutes! What did he want them for anyway during his partying weekend? Was he expecting there to be a dull moment or two? She hoped so.

She hoped it was the dullest weekend that he had ever spent. She hoped that Neville Short found out that Cunningham was having an affair with his wife and that Neville beat the hell out of him. Though, recalling Neville's gentle manner and average build, she supposed he'd have a bit of a job giving the taller, fitter-looking Cunningham a pasting.

Why didn't the Shorts have a fax machine anyway? Emmie fell over again, and got up feeling soaked to her skin—and fuming—but not defeated. If only she didn't need this rotten, stinking, foul pig of a job, given to her by that pig of a man… Calling him all the worst names she could think of got her through the last fifty yards. She trudged on—then saw it. A dim light at first, and then bit by tiny bit, as she drew closer, more light, in fact a whole house with all lights blazing.

She felt ready to drop as she went achingly up the drive, passing snow-covered parked cars—and wanted only her bed. She felt too tired even to think of what would happen once she'd handed over the by now soggy folder she had come to deliver.

Emmie struggled up the steps, and with fingers numb with cold managed to ring the bell. She could hear laughter and music going on inside—she wanted to sleep. The door opened. She recognised an astonished Roberta Short, the last word in elegance. Snow billowed into the beautifully carpeted hall.

'Come in, come in,' Roberta beckoned urgently. Emmie needed no further urging. It was only then, though, that she realised what a sight she must look, when Roberta peered into her face and, obviously having not recognised her but clearly being of such a charitable nature that she would not have left anyone standing on the doorstep on a night like this, exclaimed, 'Why, it's Emmie, isn't it? Barden's Emmie.'

Emmie was by then too fatigued to argue that she was neither Barden's Emmie nor anyone else's. But just then, as if his name being mentioned had conjured him up, Barden Cunningham appeared.

Dressed in crisp white shirt, and dinner-suited, he had never looked so handsome—nor so astounded. 'You… What are you doing here?' he asked—and if she'd had the energy Emmie was certain she would have set about him.

'You wanted these minutes!' she stated belligerently.

'You haven't driven out on a night like this purely to—' He broke off, plainly not crediting the evidence of his own eyes. 'Only an idiot would…' he was going on, when abruptly he changed his mind, and turned to Roberta. 'May we use the library?' he asked.

Emmie no more cared for being called an idiot than she cared to go to the library with him. But she had nowhere else just then that she particularly wanted to go. Though in any case he was taking a hold of her arm and…

'You're soaking!' he exclaimed.

'So would you be if you'd just walked ten miles.' She might be dead on her feet but discovered that there was still some life in her yet.

'You've walked ten miles—in this weather!'

No wonder he was incredulous. 'Superwoman I'm not! My car skidded into a hedge down the road and won't budge—the walk just seemed like ten miles.'

'Are you hurt?'

They were passing a hall mirror. She halted; her escort halted too. 'Is that me?' she asked croakily of the wreck with bedraggled, dripping hair and blue with cold that stared back at her.

Barden Cunningham did not answer her question, but repeated, 'Are you hurt anywhere?'

She stared, still disbelieving of her reflection. 'Just my pride,' she muttered miserably. But liked him when for a short moment he smiled gently at her in the mirror.

'I'm sure no one ever had such a loyal and trustworthy personal assistant,' he murmured, and moved her away from the mirror, taking her to the library and closing the door. He kept a hold of her arm as he switched on an electric fire. 'Stand there for a minute,' he instructed, 'I won't be long.'

With that he left her, and Emmie went closer to the fire, her teeth chattering as she stretched out her hands, hoping that some part of her would soon be warm. True to his word, Barden was not away long. He returned carrying towels and a towelling robe.

'Roberta wanted to come and look after you herself, but this is a special party for her husband. I told her you wouldn't mind putting up with me.' He smiled.

Emmie had never expected to be on the receiving end of his charm—she wasn't sure how she felt about it. 'I can look after myself,' she told him grumpily.

'I'm sure you can,' he soothed. 'But I'm your boss—humour me.' Her teeth started chattering again—and the teasing was over. 'Right,' he declared authoritatively. 'Get out of your wet clothes, rub yourself dry, and put that robe on.'

She wanted to argue, but didn't have the energy. To get out of her wet clothes seemed, just then, to be the best idea she'd heard in a long while. She raised her frozen hands to the buttons of her jacket, but her fingers were so cold, the material so wet, she couldn't undo so much as one.

Barden saw her plight and without fuss, without bother, came and stood in front of her. With deft fingers he undid her jacket and helped her out of it. He placed it on the floor and returned, raising his hands to the clinging dampness of her silk shirt.

'I—can...' she said quickly. But found she couldn't.

She felt she liked him a little bit more when, seeing the dreadful time her numbed fingers were having, he came forward again and almost tenderly murmured, 'I think I know that you're not used to men undressing you, little Emmie, but—I'm special.'

Somehow, though she had a kind of woolly feeling that all this was happening to someone else and not her, Emmie managed to find a bit of a smile—that was the first time he had ever called her Emmie! 'If you could just undo the fastenings, I can manage the rest.'

His answer was to raise his hands near her bosom and efficiently undo the tiny buttons of her silk shirt. Before she could make further protest, though for the moment she was feeling too defeated to say anything very much at all,

Barden made a workman-like job of unzipping her skirt. 'Anything else you need a hand with?' he enquired, his tone somehow impersonal, given that she knew he meant her only other problem: her bra fastening. She stepped back, shaking her head, and found his eyes on her eyes. But he accepted her refusal, and instructed, 'As quick as you can, then, out of your clothes, rub yourself dry and get into the robe.'

Emmie, not moving, continued to stare at him—and felt strangely weepy when those grey eyes which she was more used to seeing with chips of ice in them suddenly seemed warm as he smiled the gentlest of smiles.

'You're a rare one, Emily Lawson,' he said quietly—and turned and left her.

Emmie stared after him for a few moments. Was this man with the gentle way the same pig of a man she worked for? Her skirt started to steam. She moved six inches away from the fire and, suddenly afraid someone might come in and catch her naked, undressed as fast as she was able, opting to stay with her briefs and bra.

She found she didn't have the energy to give herself much of a rubbing, but did what she could, and rubbed at her hair. Shortly afterwards, wrapped in an over-large white towelling robe, and with a big white towel around her head, Emmie was starting to recover. She still felt very tired, but her brain, which had seemed as numbed by the wet and cold as the rest of her, was starting to come out of hibernation.

Sounds of a riotous party going on elsewhere in the house reached her as, seated on the carpet, she toasted herself by the fire. Emmie started to wonder if perhaps Roberta Short would lend her some of her old clothes. Although, remembering Roberta's elegance, Emmie doubted that she had any 'old' clothes.

The door behind her suddenly opened, and a gust of

laughter came in before the door was closed again. Emmie jerked round and saw her employer.

'Soup,' he explained about the mug he was carrying on a tray. 'You can thaw your insides with it while we talk.'

Talk? What was there to talk about? 'You're not intending to give me dictation, I hope?' She made to get up, but he motioned that she should stay where she was.

He handed her the soup, 'I see you've got your sauce back,' he commented mildly as he pulled round a padded chair and sat close by. 'Have you had any dinner?'

'I had a bite of something on the way. I didn't know then that the weather was going to be so bad,' she quickly excused. 'I'm—er—feeling warmer,' she added.

'Good. Drink your soup.'

He was back to being bossy. She didn't like him again. Absurdly, she felt she wanted him back being gentle. Abruptly she pulled herself together. Grief, the snow must have addled her brain!

'I'm sorry I've—er—been such a nuisance,' she apologised. Then truly got herself together. 'Only you did definitely say you wanted these minutes in your hands today.'

'It hadn't occurred to me you'd put your life at risk to deliver them,' he replied coolly.

'I only went off the road—I got out of my car in one piece!' she retorted sniffily, not caring in the least for his tone.

'A car that's going nowhere,' he stated, and added bluntly, 'And neither are you.'

She wanted to argue. Her frozen spirits had revived. She wanted to tell him that she wasn't at work now, so he could keep his bossy opinions to himself. But he'd said she was going nowhere and—since her car was stuck fast—what alternative did she have? If she said, as she felt like saying, that she was leaving she would confirm his previous opinion that only an idiot would be out on a night like this.

And, truth to tell, the idea of going out again in those night-marish elements while it was still dark was quite terrifying.

That didn't stop her from feeling mutinous, though, as she stared at Barden Cunningham and enquired snappily, 'You're suggesting I find myself a corner somewhere until morning?'

'We can do better than that,' he answered crisply. 'Though, as you can imagine, no one with any sense is driving very far tonight.' Rub it in! 'So, while Roberta and Neville's guests who have four-wheeled-drive vehicles will be returning to their homes in due time, others who hadn't planned to stay will be. As…' he paused '…will you.'

'Make me feel good, why don't you!' Oh, this was intolerable. 'I'm sorry,' she apologised. What in creation was the matter with her? She was feeling weepy again. 'I—I didn't mean to disrupt the whole household. I'll find a sofa somewhere and…'

'In case you hadn't noticed, there's a party going on,' he reminded her. 'A party you're welcome to join, but by the look of you I'd say you're too exhausted for anything but sleep.'

'I don't suppose I would get much sleep in the drawing room,' she answered, knowing full well that he was meaning that no one would want to party round a recumbent robe-clad female dossing down on the party room sofa.

He smiled then. It seemed to work some magic. Emmie found that she was smiling too. She was not smiling for long, however, and nor was he when he stated matter-of-factly, 'The situation is this: all the spare bedrooms have been taken, but…'

'But?' she questioned, somehow instinct telling her that she wasn't going to care very much for that 'but'.

'But there is a spare bed going.'

'Oh, yes?' she answered, feeling wary without knowing why. 'I'm not going to like this, am I?'

'You haven't very much choice,' he replied, and without

more ado announced, 'The spare bed happens to be in the room I'm using.'

'No way!'

'You can always go outside and try to hitch a lift home!' he rapped shortly.

'I didn't see one single solitary car after I left The Farmer's Arms,' she informed him rebelliously, hoping to let him know that if there was the remotest chance of her getting a lift in preference to using a bed in his room she would take it.

His expression softened suddenly. 'Trust me, Emmie,' he urged mildly. 'I know you've never shared a room with a man before, but—'

'You've soon changed your tune!' she erupted, interrupting him again. 'This morning you were of the opinion I was late because I was having too much fun in bed with some—'

'I didn't know for certain this morning—' he interrupted her this time '—that you were a virgin.'

That stopped Emmie dead in her tracks. Her cheeks went a bit pink, and she looked quickly away from him. She guessed he'd probably arrived at his correct assumption from the little he already knew of her, added to it her modesty when he tried to peel her out of her clothes.

'What—um—what about Roberta—Mrs Short?' Emmie quickly bolted up another avenue, away from her embarrassment at discussing such intimate matters.

'Naturally, as Roberta and Neville's guest myself, I've told her what I intend.'

'She—didn't object?'

He gave her a hard look, but if he was remembering that she knew he was having an affair with his hostess he gave no sign of it, but stated, 'Roberta was all for it. She's had a hot-water bottle put into your bed, and some nightwear slipped under your pillow.'

Roberta was all for it! Roberta—his mistress! Roberta,

his mistress, was all for him sharing his room with another woman! Emmie stared at him, stunned. But then she recalled how elegant Roberta had looked when she'd opened the door to her—and how bedraggled and unkempt *she* had looked, like something even the cat would have disdained to drag in—so much so Roberta hadn't recognised her. Emmie coloured again. Roberta would burst out laughing if anyone suggested Emmie was any competition!

Emmie pushed her second wave of embarrassment away, and looked at Barden Cunningham. From his tough appearance, she guessed he was expecting further argument. She recalled how—and it still stung—he had called her a prissy little Miss Prim and Proper—and suddenly, on top of her recent nightmare drive, she felt goaded beyond measure. She'd just about had enough.

She placed her empty soup mug down on the tray with a small bang, and stood up. Barden Cunningham stood up too. 'You lay just one finger on me and I'll kill you,' she hissed.

'In the unlikely event that I should ever feel that tempted,' he grunted, 'I'll kill myself!'

She hated him as they left the library, hated him as he escorted her up the long, winding staircase, and hated him with renewed ferocity when along the landing he opened a bedroom door and ushered her inside. A bedside lamp between the two beds had been switched on. Emmie was just about to antagonistically ask him which bed was his, when he left her to go into the adjoining bathroom. She heard bath water running, then he came back to her.

'Take a hot bath and get into bed,' he instructed.

But she'd had just about enough of him—and that went double for his orders. 'If it's all the same to you, I won't bother.'

He, it seemed, had equally had enough of her. 'Either I have your word that you'll have a hot bath, or I'll stay and dunk you in it myself.'

'You and whose army?'

He gave her a hard look, then without more ado took off his jacket. 'I refuse to have your pneumonia on my conscience!' he snarled, his hands at his cufflinks.

'It's news to me that you've got one!' She attempted to defy him, though backed away a step. 'Anyway…' She started to weaken when, cufflinks undone, he began to roll up his sleeves. 'It's a scientific fact that you can't catch cold from getting wet and frozen. You have to catch a virus before—' She broke off when, both sleeves rolled up, he went grimly back to the bathroom, presumably to test the temperature of the bath water. Emmie followed him. 'Oh, go back to your party!' she flung at him irritatedly.

Barden came over to her. 'Do I have your word?'

'You know you do.' She was forced to admit defeat. She led the way from the bathroom and watched as he turned his sleeves back down and did up his gold cufflinks. 'Would you really have? Dunked me in the bath, I mean?'

He smiled. 'You certainly know how to spoil a man's pleasure,' he replied, and, picking up his dinner jacket, he left her.

Spoil a man's pleasure? By giving her word and depriving him of the chance to dunk her in the bath? Oh, he'd have loved it, wouldn't he? Knowing him, he'd have had it in mind to push her head under, and hold it there for a good few seconds.

Roberta had been exceptionally kind, Emmie discovered, for alongside the masculine impedimenta in the bathroom was a fresh tablet of expensively scented soap, a new plastic-encased toothbrush and toothpaste. Perhaps out of kindness too, because of the wreck Emmie had looked, Roberta had loaned her a totally feminine concoction of a nightdress. It was of some diaphanous material that left little to the imagination. It crossed Emmie's mind to push the nightdress under Cunningham's pillow and snaffle his pyjamas.

She decided, however, that he was probably the type who went to bed *au naturel*, so didn't bother looking.

She had to admit she felt much more like her old self after taking a hot bath. So much so she even found enough energy to rinse through her smalls and place them on the hot rail to dry beneath her towel.

Her bed was bliss, the hot-water bottle a delight. Emmie was by then coming to terms with the fact that there had been absolutely no other option—she had to share a room with that womanising, two-timing swine. Womanising, but not with her, apparently—he'd die first. Well, that suited her perfectly, she fumed indignantly—though she had no idea why she should feel so indignant.

Oddly, although she felt too tired to keep her eyes open, sleep eluded her to start with. Emmie guessed it was the strangeness of having to occupy a bed in her employer's room that was making her fidget. But, thinking about it, with so many people staying over for breakfast, the party going on downstairs was probably the sort that would go on all night. By that reckoning, when Cunningham came upstairs to go to bed, she could get up and go down the stairs. Sleep arrived then. Gorgeous, much needed, energy-giving sleep.

Energy that Emmie very much required when, some time after two on Saturday morning, she was awakened by a horrendous feeling of nausea. The room was in darkness. She lay there, feeling ill and trying to adjust to where she was, what she was doing there and—oh, help, where was the bathroom!

She felt a violent surge in her stomach, and there was no time for her to wonder where the bathroom lay—seconds only to charge from her bed and hope she made it. More by luck than anything else, she instinctively bolted in the right direction; her hand found the bathroom light switch and she was just in time.

Emmie was unaware of anything as she bent over, other

than how awful she felt. So awful in fact did she feel that, instead of being alarmed when a pair of bare legs came and joined her in the bathroom, and she glanced up and saw Barden Cunningham, still tying his robe, she was more grateful than anything to see him.

'Oh, Emmie, Emmie,' he murmured, his grey eyes on her ashen complexion. Hurriedly she turned from him, feeling too ill to be embarrassed at the scantiness of her attire. A masculine hand came to hold her head—he would never know how comforting his action was.

'I'm—s-sorry,' she offered shakily, miserably, when it was over and he'd sat her on a bathroom stool.

'You've caught a chill,' he stated, for once his tone not accusing, but sensitive to how dreadful she looked and was feeling.

Emmie shook her head. 'Prawns,' she corrected. 'It has to be the prawns.'

'You had prawns?'

'A risotto—on my way here. One of them must have been off.'

'One?'

'It only takes one. Oh—excuse me!' she exclaimed urgently—and was off again. In fact, for the next three hours she was violently ill.

Twice during that time she had returned to her bed. And twice Barden, having opted to rest on his bed with the lamp between them aglow, was right there with her when she dived for the bathroom. Emmie was just beginning to wonder if it was ever going to end, when it did. Barden, too, seemed to recognise that it was finally all over as he once again helped her to sit on the bathroom stool.

She felt beaten, utterly exhausted, and was entirely without protest when he told her to look up at him. Obediently, she looked up. 'Poor little Emily,' he crooned, and gently sponged her face. 'How do you feel now?'

'Fine,' she said bravely. And went to stand up—only her legs felt weak.

Barden's arm came swiftly about her. 'Lean on me,' he suggested, and she was glad to. Slowly he took her back to her bed and sat her down. She felt his hand brush her hair back from her forehead, and knew that she was feeling better when she began to realise what a sight she must look.

'I'm a mess!' she exclaimed before she could stop herself.

Barden looked down at her, paused, and then said quietly, 'You're quite beautiful.'

That startled her. So much so she felt her heartbeat drumming. 'You're drunk,' she accused, and loved his laugh.

'You're obviously on the mend.' He smiled, and instructed her. 'Sit tight.' And while Emmie was thinking of lying down and sleeping until Christmas, he moved away and came back holding a fresh shirt. 'Your night gear's soaked,' he offered conversationally, and, vaguely aware that she had been perspiring freely while in the throes of food poisoning, Emmie, more aware of everything now than she had been, looked down to see that her nightdress was doing a very poor job of covering her.

'Oh!' she wailed. The thin straps were somewhere down her arms. Her bosom, while not over-large, was not at all small either, and her cleavage and the firm swell of her breasts were fully on display, their pink tips barely veiled by the thin damp material. With rapid haste she folded her arms in front of her.

But, while she was dying a thousand deaths, Barden took everything in his stride. 'Come on, Miss Modesty. Take that damp thing off and get into this. Okay, okay,' he said, and when she didn't move he did.

He turned his back on her and Emmie, having to stand up to do so, struggled out of her clammy nightdress and into the shirt. She hadn't buttoned it up when he turned round, so he matter-of-factly helped her. Then he was standing back, his eyes travelling over her and the long length of her legs.

'You look better in that than I do,' he commented, and, before she could think of anything to say, 'Are you going to behave yourself if I tuck you up in bed?'

She knew quite well that he was teasingly referring to her recent habit of leaving her bed to dash to the bathroom. 'Just let me sleep!' she begged, and did, more or less as soon as her head hit her pillow. She slept soundly.

Emmie surfaced around ten o'clock. She opened her eyes and, as everything came flooding back, swiftly turned, feeling utter relief—the other bed was empty. Somehow she wasn't ready to see Barden Cunningham just yet.

She checked her watch, and swung her feet over the side of the bed. Catching sight of the shirt she had on, she groaned. Oh, hang it—during the night, even though her employer had helped to button her up in his shirt, it hadn't bothered her! This morning she wanted to run away and hide.

She raised her eyes, and noticed for the first time that her suit and shirt, last seen on the library carpet, had been carefully dried and pressed and was hanging up on the outside of the wardrobe. Her never-to-be-the-same-again shoes had been dried too, and polished, and were by the dressing table. And there, on the dressing table itself, lay a fresh pack of tights.

Realising that the housekeeper must have organised everything for her, though only on Roberta Short's instructions, Emmie felt most grateful to the two of them. The more she learned about Roberta, the more she liked her—though how she and Cunningham could carry on so behind Neville Short's back was...

Emmie didn't care to think of Barden Cunningham's part in the affair, and abruptly left her bed. She discovered she was feeling a mite fragile, but told herself she was feeling fine, and, having more important things to do that day than stand around, she went to take a hasty shower. Somehow she had to get her car back on the road. She was picking up Aunt Hannah at three. Subject to road conditions, it might take Emmie all of that time to get to her.

She was dressed and was just slipping on her shoes when, opening the door very quietly, as if not to disturb her should she still be in a recovering sleep, Barden Cunningham came in. He seemed surprised to see her out of bed, and fully dressed into the bargain. But he saved his comments to ask, 'How are you feeling?'

'Fine,' she told him brightly—and found herself on the receiving end of a stern look.

'I asked how do you feel?' he repeated—a man who rarely went in for repeating himself.

He was starting to niggle her—and he'd been so good. 'How do I look?' she asked, ashamed that she could be so ungrateful, but pinning a smile on her face.

Barden studied her, and, too late remembering that she hadn't got a scrap of make-up on, that she was pale and had shadows under her eyes, Emmie sorely wished she hadn't invited his inspection.

'Delicate,' he pronounced when he'd finished his scrutiny.

Emmie pulled herself together. 'Like an orchid?' she queried with a grin, certain that she wasn't in the least bothered how he saw her.

His mouth twitched. 'You're lippy again—you're better,' he pronounced. 'Feel like some breakfast?'

That took the smile off her face. *'Don't!'* she implored, the mere thought of food making her stomach turn. She took a step away, then turned back. 'Thank you for staying with me and putting up with me—and for looking after me. You could easily have pulled your duvet over your head and let me get on with it.'

'What, and leave a maiden in distress?' he teased, and she found she liked it.

'Well, thank you anyway, Mr Cunningham,' she said sincerely—and saw his mouth twitch again. 'What...?' she
began.

'We sleep together—and I'm still Mr Cunningham?' His
grey eyes had the light of devilment in them.

'Not in that context!' she protested. 'We shared a room,
that's—' She broke off—it had to be said that he'd seen
more of her, in the literal sense, than any man she was on
first-name terms with.

'I really think, Emily—' he took over when she seemed
to be floundering '—that we know each other well enough
for you to use my first name.'

'Yes, well...' Where had this absurd habit of suddenly
blushing come from? She glanced from him, and caught
sight of her shoulder bag. She couldn't remember the last
time she'd had it, but, hoping she had automatically
dropped her car keys inside, she went to retrieve it. 'I'd
better go and rescue my car,' she announced.

'Your car's going nowhere until there's a thaw,' Barden
informed her. And, before she could begin to argue, he
continued, 'I've been to take a look.'

That didn't stop her. 'I thought I might get a tractor to
pull me out.'

'Apparently your car wasn't the only one that went off
the road last night. The non-urgent cases are being left till
last. If there's no thaw before, yours will be pulled out
around Monday.'

She stared at him. 'But mine *is* urgent. I have to get
home. I...'

'I'll take you home.'

How could he be so matter-of-fact? 'But you're at a
weekend party!' she protested. And, starting to feel all hot
and bothered suddenly, she went on, 'I've already ruined
last night's party for you, and...'

'Did I say you had?'

'No, but...'

'Look here, Emily Lawson, I'm driving you home today and that's it. You'll need all your concentration out there— and, frankly, you don't look up to it!'

Thanks! How did he expect her to look when she'd spent half the night being sick? Bossy swine! It hadn't taken him long to get into 'You'll do as I say' mode, had it? She'd walk first. Though, confound it, there was Aunt Hannah to think of. If she went with Cunningham now, she'd be able to take a taxi to pick her up from Keswick House. 'It's not fair to your hosts,' was the best defence she could come up with. 'You'll be gone hours, and—'

'The household's asleep, and unlikely to stir before noon,' he butted in.

Emmie realised then that all she was doing was delaying his return to his party weekend. She caved in. 'What are the roads like?'

'All main roads are clear, apparently, though getting to one is best done in daylight.'

Emmie picked up her bag. 'Is now a good time?' His answer was to escort her from the room. 'Would you thank Mr and Mrs Short for me, and their housekeeper?' she asked, as downstairs Barden undid the front door.

'Of course,' he promised, and, guiding her out to his car, kept a firm grip on her arm as they crunched over the snow.

Emmie closed her eyes from the glare of the snow—and was astonished when she opened them to find that they were leaving the main road and were heading for the area where she lived.

'I've been asleep!' she exclaimed unnecessarily. 'I'm sorry,' she quickly apologised.

'It will do you good,' Barden answered easily. 'I've an idea I must turn somewhere around here.'

Emmie came fully awake to give him directions to where she had her flat, and a short while afterwards he was steering his smart car into the run-down area where she lived, and pulling up in front of the dilapidated house where she had her flat.

'Would you like to come in for a cup of coffee before your journey back?' she asked politely, knowing in all fairness that she couldn't do anything else, but for some unknown reason, when he'd been so good, hoping he would say he had to dash back.

'Thanks,' he accepted, to her surprise, and went to the front door with her, and as she got out her keys he took them from her. Without commenting that the splintered door looked as though one slight shoulder-charge would have it open without the need for a key, he opened it and waited for her to go through.

He still had her keys when they crossed the floor to her apartment. 'This is it,' she said, and he opened the door. 'Come in,' she invited, and took him into her sitting room. The elegant contrast to the scruffy outside of the building was so marked Emmie wasn't surprised to see his glance flick over the expensive carpeting that had come first from the house where she had been born, and had then been taken to the apartment where she had lived with Alec and his mother.

'Have you lived alone long?' he enquired, his eyes skimming the good quality furniture before coming to rest on her liquid brown eyes.

That word 'commitment' reared its ugly head again. He mustn't know about Aunt Hannah! 'Not so long,' she replied. 'I'll—er—get that coffee.'

She went to move away, but Barden caught hold of her arm and detained her. 'What did I say?'

'Say?'

'You're touchy about something.'

'Pfff. You lost sleep too,' she pointed out loftily. Hoping he would read from that she thought his brain was suffering from his disturbed night, she jerked her arm out of his hold and went to her kitchen.

Had she thought, however, that by walking away from him she had put an end to the conversation, she found she was wrong. She hadn't even filled the kettle or set it to boil when Barden appeared behind her. Feeling on edge, her not-liking-him-very-much vibes on the loose again, she set about making him some coffee.

'Sugar?' she enquired, knowing full well that he didn't take it, but feeling the silence between them stretching. She didn't want him speculating on anything about her, thank you very much, but knew from the way he performed his business dealings that what he didn't know he made jolly sure he found out.

He didn't deign to reply to her sugar question, but asked instead—his tone mild, gentle even, it had to be said— 'When did your parents die, Emmie?'

She wasn't sure she was on any safer ground here, and, perversely, didn't want him using the more friendly version of her name just now. It was weakening somehow. But she could see no harm in telling him what he wanted to know. 'My father died when I was ten; my mother five years later.'

'You can't have lived alone since you were fifteen?'

Emmie stared at him, startled. Honestly! 'Is it *that* important?' she asked crossly.

He smiled. She hated him. 'Remember what I said about humouring me?' She'd like to take a hatchet and humour him by burying it in his skull!

'I had a stepfather!' she stated hostilely.

'You didn't get on?'

'We did,' she contradicted. 'I loved him. He…' her anger faded. 'He died about a year ago.' She glanced up at Barden, knowing she wasn't going to tell him another word about her family—her job was too precious to now tell him she had been sparing with the truth at her job interview.

His expression had taken on a gentle look. 'You've been

through a bad time. Have you any other family?' he asked softly.

Oh, crumbs! She turned her back on him. The answer had to be a straight yes or no. Did step-grandmothers count? Suddenly she realised she was hesitating too long. 'No!' she said quickly. And, turning to take a quick glance at him, didn't miss the shrewd look in his eyes. 'I'm sorry,' she apologised once more, and, hastily striving to excuse her delay in answering—he was sharp, too sharp; she didn't want him poking his nose in where it didn't belong; he'd ferreted enough into her background in her opinion—she said firmly, 'I think last night's performance must have taken more out of me than I realised. I've—er—come over very tired.'

Barden Cunningham stared down into her pale face. 'You're all eyes!' he murmured after a moment, and then, as decisive as ever, he announced, 'Forget the coffee—I'll get off. You, Emily Lawson, take yourself off to bed.' Having issued his orders, he unexpectedly took a hold of both her arms and, while she stared up at him, mesmerised, he bent down and laid a chaste kiss on her forehead.

Her heartbeat seemed to go into overdrive, and hastily she pushed him away. 'I haven't b-been *that* ill!' she exclaimed, feeling shaken as much by the agitated drumming of her heart as his action.

His answer was to give a smile that charmed her to the core. Without another word he went on his way. Emmie collapsed onto a chair. My stars—no wonder women fell for him like ninepins. Not that she would, of course, womanising swine!

CHAPTER FOUR

THERE was no time for Emmie to go to bed as ordered. In any case she was feeling better by the minute. She made sure everything was ready for Aunt Hannah, and decided to go and collect the old lady straight away. The major roads were clear, but the lesser ones still might not be, and in consequence she might not be the only one availing herself of a taxi service.

'Where's your car?' Aunt Hannah wanted to know.

'I ran off the road in last night's snow,' Emmie replied, and, having assured the dear love that she was fine and that nothing was broken, sat in the back of the taxi with her step-relative, who seemed to have motorcycles on the brain at the moment. Aunt Hannah regaled her with a tale of how once, she on her Norton and Piggy Etheridge on his Panther, they had both skidded on ice and ended up in a snowdrift.

Save for having some misguided notion that they would be paying a visit to the National Motorcycle Museum that very day, Aunt Hannah was quite alert, Emmie felt. True Aunt Hannah decided around six o'clock, despite the fact that it was dark, that she'd like to go for a walk...

'The pavements may be icy.' Emmie attempted to put Aunt Hannah off.

'We'll walk in the road.'

They took a stroll around the block, with Aunt Hannah in excellent spirits when Emmie suggested, weather permitting, that they could go to the Motorcycle Museum next Saturday. Feeling better for their walk, Emmie helped her step-grandmother out of the layers of outer clothing she'd insisted she wear and set about preparing an early dinner.

70

They were in the kitchen washing up afterwards when the phone rang. Emmie went to answer it. 'Hello?' she said—and experienced a sudden surge of adrenalin when she recognised Barden Cunningham's voice!

'I rang earlier. You must have been out,' he commented.

'Oh, yes. Yes, I was,' she replied, but hurriedly got herself together. 'Is there something wrong with the minutes?' she enquired. He was bothering with minutes? On a Saturday night? When he was partying!

'I wondered how you were? If your system was fully clear of its bug?'

'Oh, isn't that kind!' she exclaimed softly.

And heard a smile in his voice as he teased, 'I was concerned you might be doing an action replay—with no one there to hold your head.'

Emmie laughed, and felt so at ease with him suddenly that she was totally off her guard when she responded brightly, 'Oh, I'm not on my own. I—' She broke off. Oh Lord, he mustn't know about Aunt Hannah.

'You have company?' he questioned sharply. My word—what had happened to his teasing?

It was too late now to deny it. Emmie got herself together—her 'company' could be just about anybody, for goodness' sake! He wasn't to know *who!* 'Yes,' she replied. 'Yes, I have.' Had she anything to add to that, Emmie found she would have been talking to herself—the line went dead.

She went slowly back to the kitchen, pondering on the abrupt termination of the phone call. *Now* what had she done? For certain she had upset him in some way. In no time he'd gone from pleasant and teasing to terse and snarly. Perhaps, knowing now that she had someone with her, he was regretting that, out of concern for his employee, he had taken time away from his partying to check on her.

In compensation for not cooking a meal for Adrian Payne on Friday, Emmie popped up to his flat and invited him to

Sunday lunch. Aunt Hannah insisted on calling Adrian David a few times, but the lunch passed pleasantly enough. Adrian offered to drive Emmie to look at her car the evening of the following day, hopefully to retrieve it.

Adrian was a mature college student, and left them about four to finish a paper required for the next morning. 'David seems quite a nice boy,' Aunt Hannah muttered when he'd gone.

Adrian was twenty-six if he was a day. 'He is nice,' Emmie replied, aware that Aunt Hannah hadn't really taken to Adrian but was doing her charitable best.

Aunt Hannah decided at half past four that she wanted to go back to Keswick House. Emmie went with her in a taxi, and returned to her flat to check her wardrobe for the morning.

By Monday Emmie was almost fully recovered from her food poisoning, though she awakened with a splitting headache. She downed a couple of aspirin, sneezed, but refused to contemplate any notion that she might have a cold coming on.

Because she was going to have to use public transport, she left home much earlier than usual, and gave herself a pat on the back because she arrived at her office at ten to nine.

Both Barden Cunningham and Dawn Obrey were in the office Emmie shared with Dawn when she went in. Feeling cheerful—there might have been a blip on her attendance record on Friday morning, but her time-keeping, under difficult circumstances, was perfect today— She greeted them both cheerfully, 'Good morning!'

'Good morning.' Dawn smiled. Barden scowled.

Was it *her* fault he'd got a hangover? She'd found her aspirins, but Emmie hoped he never found his. Serve him right, partying the weekend away *and* abusing the hospitality of his lover's husband! How could he?

Emmie, her feelings of cheerfulness thoroughly dampened by thoughts of the affair Cunningham was having with his friend's wife, got on with some work. The only bright spot of that day was that a thaw had set in. Adrian was meeting her from work, and, all being well, she would be able to have her car back tonight.

Plans for collecting her car went from her mind, however, as she became more and more involved in her work. In fact she had forgotten most everything but the intricate job in hand when, just as Barden Cunningham's door opened and he came in to have a word with Dawn, the phone went. He'd had a wasted journey—Dawn was out of the office, so, sucks boo. Emmie answered the phone. The call was from Keswick House.

'Mrs Whitford's let herself out of the building again, without telling anyone where she's going,' Lisa Browne told her worriedly.

Emmie, aware that Barden was looking enquiringly, as if wanting to know whether the call was for him, looked down at her desk as she strove to stay calm. 'How long ago?'

'I've checked round. About an hour or more. Apparently her absence was noticed half an hour ago, but since it only takes five minutes to get to the local shops it was thought Mrs Whitford would soon be back. She's usually back, though, long before this.'

'Has…?' Emmie began, but Lisa Browne had read her thoughts.

'I sent someone to look locally for her—they've just come back now. They've scoured round—there's no sign. Do you think she's gone back to your old home?'

Emmie's concerns by then were centred solely on Aunt Hannah. She wasn't even aware that her employer, her busy employer, was in the same room with her when she answered, 'I think there's every chance. Leave it with me; I'll go and look.'

She replaced the phone, glanced up—and stark reality

hit. Cool grey eyes were studying her, watching, waiting. Oh, heavens, she was going to have to ask him for time off. Oh, crumbs, she needed this job! Only just then her need to find Aunt Hannah had priority.

Emmie was already reaching for her bag, while holding down her anxiety, as she told Barden, 'I'm sorry, I need an hour or so off.'

His look was cool. 'Man-friend trouble?' he rapped, and Emmie stared at him. Why would he think that? Probably because he was under the impression she had no family— and the fact she'd been 'entertaining' when he'd rung on Saturday evening, she realised.

But she hadn't time to bother with such things then. 'I— have to dash!' she stated stubbornly, on her feet and hoping with all she had that an hour off was all she would need.

'Your—errand seems urgent?' he questioned. Emmie refused to answer; she was worried—he was unsympathetic. 'You haven't a car!' he reminded her, clearly not liking her mulish silence.

'I'll get a taxi.'

'*That* urgent!'

Emmie nodded dumbly, feeling that her job was on the line here, but knowing she'd lose it for sure if he found out she had lied at her job interview. She knew, however, from the sudden look of purpose about him that he'd come to a decision—she prayed it wasn't one of the Don't-bother-to-come-back variety.

Emmie had her prayer answered, though nearly dropped with shock when, revealing his decision, Barden said crisply, 'No need for a taxi. I'll take you.'

'*No!*' rocketed from her in panic, before she could hold it back.

He smiled, an insincere smile. 'Get your coat,' he ordered. The door opened and Dawn came in, 'I have to go out for about an hour, Dawn. I'll take Emily with me. Contact me on my mobile if you need me.'

Emmie hated Barden-bossy-Cunningham as they crossed the car park. She loathed and detested him as she climbed into the passenger seat of his car. But, over and above all that, she was extremely anxious and stewed up about her missing step-relative.

The engine was running. 'Your flat?' Barden enquired pleasantly.

She didn't trust that pleasant tone—why couldn't he keep his nose out of her business? Emmie knew quite well that she should be grateful that he had volunteered to drive her, but she didn't feel at all so. The only reason he'd volunteered was because he had an over-large curiosity gene. All she'd done by refusing to explain why she wanted an hour off was to stir his proclivity to find out what he didn't know.

'No,' she replied frostily, and perforce was obliged to give him directions to her previous apartment—and found something more to worry about.

It was only last Friday that Aunt Hannah had once more taken off. While Emmie's main concern now was to get to her and find her safe, she couldn't help but wonder how Lisa Browne would view it if it happened much more. She wouldn't want to send her care assistants out looking every time the dear love decided that rules were only there to be broken. But Aunt Hannah was happy at Keswick House—what if they asked her to leave?

Realising she had enough to worry about for now, without looking for future problems, Emmie saw that they were driving through a very salubrious area and were almost at their destination. 'If you'll slow down here,' she found her voice to request, 'and take a right here.' Another left turn and they were at the terrace of elegant houses. 'If you'd let me out here,' she said quietly. There was no sign of Aunt Hannah anywhere, but she'd just get rid of Cunningham first—if she couldn't find her aunt in the area she'd taxi back to her current flat. 'Thank you for the lift. I'll get back to the office as soon as I can,' she added prettily—fingers crossed she'd still got a job. With that, and without turning to look at him, Emmie got out of the car and walked to the main door of her old home.

All the while, though, she was conscious that her employer had not driven by her. What was he playing at? She concentrated on more pressing matters and went up the steps to the front door.

Before she could ring the bell, however, the door opened and Johnnie Jeavons, a man of thirty-two years and one of the nicest people she knew, came out. 'Emmie!' he exclaimed, and, delighted to see her, he leaned over and kissed her cheek. 'Come in,' he invited. 'Jane's home; we're both having a day off work.'

Emmie quickly explained that she was only in the area because Mrs Whitford, who was perfectly fine, sometimes absently arrived at the wrong address.

'She always was a card!' Johnnie recollected. 'Do you remember that time she told the postman to change his route and send another one, because he never brought her any news but bad?'

Emmie did, but, much as she liked Johnnie, she was more concerned with finding Aunt Hannah. Emmie found a piece of paper in her bag and wrote down her home and office phone numbers. 'Would you mind giving me a ring if Mrs Whitford comes by?' she asked, handing the paper over, knowing for sure that Johnnie would invite Aunt Hannah in and give her a cup of tea while he rang her.

'With pleasure,' he smiled. 'I'll just slip up now and give this to Jane.'

Emmie thanked him, took a step to leave, and again thought what a nice person Johnnie was when he kissed her cheek again before letting her go. Her mind was back on Aunt Hannah before she reached the bottom of the steps. Emmie looked about and, not a sign of her aunt, caught sight instead of the long sleek car she had arrived in! Oh grief, she'd forgotten *him*!

That Barden Cunningham was still there, had sat there watching while she'd greeted Johnnie Jeavons, was no figment of her imagination. Why had he stayed? From the cold look on his face, the waiting had not given him any pleasure.

Ideally she would have liked to have walked on by him. Only the thought of how humiliating it would be if he took it into his head to follow her, with his car purring at a crawl, stopped her. She went up to the driver's window. The window slid down.

She opened her mouth to again appeasingly thank him, and hint he should be on his way, but he got in first. 'That it?' he clipped, which wrong-footed her.

'That what?'

He tossed her an exasperated look. 'Get in!' he rapped.

'I…' She looked away, her glance lighting on Johnnie, who smiled and waved. She found a smile and waved back. Humiliating! She went round to the passenger door and got in. Barden started up the car and moved off. By the time he had driven around the corner, however, Emmie had got herself into more of one piece. 'I—er—haven't finished my—business yet,' she informed him as evenly as she was able.

'That *wasn't* it?'

She had felt like hitting him before, but hadn't. Now she sorely felt like making up for lost time. 'I'll get a taxi!' she retorted.

He ignored her. 'Where to now?' he gritted.

She took a deep and steadying breath. She had an idea she was close to losing her job anyway—so what the heck? 'If you could just drive around the area for a few minutes.'

To his credit, he didn't demand to know why. 'Intriguing!' he commented.

'Look, you needn't…I can…'

'Wouldn't dream of letting you,' he came back with pho-
ney charm, adding pithily, 'I can't think of anything I'd
rather be doing!'

What could she say? Nothing. If she didn't so badly need
to hang on to her job, and the good salary it paid, she might
have told him to get lost anyway. But she did need to hang
on. Quite desperately did she need to. So she stayed silent,
and as he steered his car around the block, and while her
eyes scanned frantically for the person she was looking for,
Emmie at the same time tried to behave as if she was perfectly relaxed.

They returned to the point from where they had started.
'Again?' he enquired sardonically. She was going to hit
him soon!

Her searching eyes could see no sign of Aunt Hannah.
'Would you drive to my home, please?' she requested,
knowing by then she'd be wasting her breath if she again
suggested that he let her out so she might take a taxi.
'Would you drive slowly, please?'

He turned and cast a glance at her. 'Suddenly you're
carsick?'

She ignored him, sarcastic swine! She'd travelled miles
with him before with no ill effect, and he knew it. And, if
anything, she felt flushed rather than pale, so knew she
wasn't looking as if the car's motion was making her feel
queasy.

For all Barden had slowed his speed, it didn't take them
all that long to approach the decrepit area where Emmie
now lived. She was still scanning everywhere when, suddenly, her searching eyes were rewarded. 'Stop!' she ordered on catching sight of Aunt Hannah, standing admiring
a parked enormous motorcycle.

'What the…?' Barden's reactions were instant.

'I'm sorry.' Awash with relief, Emmie was ready to apologise ten times over, and more quietly requested, 'Would

you pull over please, Barden?' Where had his first name come from?

Feeling slightly shattered, and wondering if the worry of her missing step-relative had weakened her brain, Emmie waited only until he'd found a convenient place to park, and then she was out of the car.

Emmie hurried the first few yards, but then, not wanting to startle Aunt Hannah by pouncing on her, she slowed her pace.

'Hello, Aunt Hannah,' she greeted her quietly as she reached her.

Mrs Whitford dragged her gaze from the motorcycle. 'Hello, dear,' she answered, seeming not the least surprised to see her there when she should be at work. 'What do you think of that? It's a Harley,' she explained. 'A Harley-Davidson. Isn't it beautiful!'

'Quite beautiful,' Emmie agreed; to her non-mechanical mind, one piece of machinery was very like another.

She was just about to tactfully suggest Aunt Hannah came with her—for all there was a thaw it was still wintry, and the elderly lady shouldn't be standing about on a day like today—when Emmie realised they had company. Tall, good-looking, not saying a word, her employer had come to join them. The word 'commitment' jetted into her head, and as anxiety rushed in again her feelings of relief were short-lived. Why couldn't Barden Cunningham have stayed in his car? Another few minutes and she might have thought of something. As it was, with him so close, her thinking power seemed to have seized up.

But she had been very well brought up. 'Aunt Hannah.' She drew the dear love's attention away from the motor-bike. 'This is Barden Cunningham. Er, B-Barden...' She couldn't look at him, and, as more and more of her hopes of keeping her job went trickling down the drain, she said, 'this is my step-grandmother, Mrs Whitford.'

He appeared not a whit put out. Emmie guessed he never

would be. If her manners were good, his were impeccable as he extended his right hand to Aunt Hannah and shook hands with her, and enquired politely, 'May I give you a lift somewhere? My car is just here.'

'Are you Emmie's friend?' Aunt Hannah wanted to know.

'We see a lot of each other,' he fielded smoothly.

Mrs Whitford stared sternly at him. 'You're not her lover?' she questioned—making Emmie's ears go pink.

'Aunt Hannah,' she rushed in before he could answer, 'you'll get cold standing about in...'

'I won't,' she answered with a saintly smile. 'I remember what you said on Saturday about wrapping up warmly before we went out. I've got dozens of layers on.'

'You kept Emmie company on Saturday evening?' Barden asked, and Emmie felt her pugilistic tendencies rearing again. What he didn't know, he found out! Though why he should want to bother finding out if her step-relative was the person she had been with when he rang on Saturday stumped her.

But in any event Aunt Hannah wasn't in an answering frame of mind. 'Have you got the time?' she asked him, 'I believe I'm hungry.' And, not waiting to be told the time, she stated, 'I think I'll go back.'

'I'll take you, sweetheart,' Emmie said gently, fully aware that if Aunt Hannah had been wandering around for the last couple of hours she must be extremely tired.

Emmie was again thinking in terms of hailing a taxi when Barden took a hold of Mrs Whitford's arm. 'My car's the black one, just here,' he said, taking charge. 'Where do you live?' he asked conversationally.

'Keswick,' she answered brightly, and Emmie felt an insane desire to laugh. Keswick was a town miles away, in the Lake District—Barden, who'd got a full afternoon scheduled, as she well knew, would never make it to Keswick and back before dark!

As he began to steer Mrs Whitford to his car he glanced across at Emmie, as if seeking confirmation that her step-relative's destination truly was in the north of England, and Emmie had to quickly banish her serves-you-right look. Well—it was he who'd insisted she shouldn't take a taxi. He who had insisted he drove her around London. He who wouldn't take no for an answer. But—this wasn't funny! There were going to be repercussions—Emmie just knew it.

'It's about five miles away,' she informed him quietly, but was not thanked for the information. After he unlocked his car, either from courtesy to Aunt Hannah or because he'd had quite enough of one Emily Lawson, he assisted her step-relative into the front passenger seat.

I know my place, Emmie mused whimsically, and got into the rear of the car to discover that, while sometimes the needle on Aunt Hannah's memory groove occasionally slipped, she had no such problem in giving him directions to where she lived.

'Do you have a motorcycle?' she asked him chattily—and, not a word coming Emmie's way, the two in front carried on a pleasant conversation with regard to Aunt Hannah's long-term love affair with motorcycles.

They arrived at Keswick House, and Barden Cunningham again took charge. It was his arm Mrs Whitford leant on as he escorted her from his car to the front door. He to whom she turned and suggested he drop in for a cup of tea whenever he was passing.

But, to prove that her memory did occasionally get a little fogged—unless she was being deliberately forgetful, which wouldn't have surprised Emmie in this instance—she turned to her as they entered the building, and said affectionately, 'You're a good girl. Too good for that David.' Leaving Emmie undecided if she was being wicked or not. 'Are you going to marry him?'

Wicked, Emmie decided. 'I'll let you know when he asks me,' she smiled.

'Bye, darling. See you Saturday.'

'Shall I come to your room with you?' Emmie offered, wanting to help her aunt out of her coat, hat and scarf, but appreciating her independent spirit.

'No, thank you, dear. I want to go and have a word with Mrs Vellacott first.' She turned to Barden, 'Thank you for the lift,' she said graciously.

Vicky, one of the care assistants, came hurrying forward just then. 'Mrs Whitford!' she exclaimed in a relieved kind of voice. 'We've been so worried about you.'

'Absolutely no need, Victoria!' Aunt Hannah replied firmly. And, her voice carrying back loud and clear as she went off in search of her friend, to Emmie's horror, she added, 'I've been out with my granddaughter and her fi-ancé.'

It had been in Emmie's head to go and find Lisa Browne and have a quick word. But all such thoughts went flying as she turned scarlet with mortification, unable to look at Barden Cunningham to see how he was taking the news that he—free, a womaniser, and not looking to change that state of affairs—had just acquired an appendage likely to cramp his style.

She reeled out to his car and, because he held the door open for her, got into the front passenger seat, her pleasure that that was the first time she'd heard Aunt Hannah refer to her as her granddaughter spoilt by the rest of it. 'I'm so sorry—about that.' She found a choky kind of voice when he joined her in the car—was there ever such a foul pig of a day? 'Aunt H... Mrs Whitford—' Emmie broke off. She would defend Aunt Hannah to death, but had to give him some sort of an explanation. 'Mrs Whitford sometimes gets, just a bit confused,' she resumed. 'She'll have—'

'Forget it!' he clipped.

Emmie was happy to. But she feared the worst when she

noticed that they weren't driving in a direction that would take them back to the office, but away from it! Her heart sank down into her boots when she saw that they were nearing the area where she lived. And, the closer they got to her flat, the more she realised that her suspicions were correct. He could, she supposed, have left her to make her own way back from Keswick House. Though she hardly felt like thanking him, because by dropping her off at her home he had to be letting her know that there was no place for her at the office. This was it; she was sacked, fired, dismissed.

Barden pulled up outside the decrepit building where she had her home. Perhaps she should tell him goodbye, but she just couldn't find her voice. She stepped out of the car and went to her outer door, searching in her bag for her keys.

She found them, but jerked her head up when a cool hand stretched out and took them from her. She hadn't expected him to get out of the car too, and stared at him. She realised she must be feeling quite stunned because, as daft as you like, she handed her keys over.

Emmie had managed to retrieve a few of her scattered wits by the time he had the door unlocked. She held out her hand for the return of her keys, but was startled when he held on to them and, pushing the door open, indicated she should precede him into the building.

And that was when her stubborn streak reasserted itself. She refused to move another step. Her stubborn streak was short-lived, however—he killed it. Barden stared down at her immovable expression, his own expression tough.

'You owe me a cup of coffee!' he reminded her evenly— and Emmie understood then. Her dismissal was to be a verbal one, and, his manners impeccable, as already demonstrated—if one forgot what a rat he was when it came to other men's wives—it was not his intention to give her a dressing-down in the street.

Emmie, as proud as the next, was glad about that. 'Come in,' she invited, and went first.

Barden undid the door to her apartment while Emmie strove not to think of her perilous financial position, or the fact that he was highly unlikely to give her a decent reference—and how her future work prospects for anywhere that didn't pay peanuts looked bleak.

They were in her comfortable sitting room when Emmie turned to face him. 'Would you care to sit down?' she suggested, doing her best in the circumstances to be civil, to remember her own manners.

Barden stared at her from cool grey eyes. 'After you!' he replied curtly, and she knew then, as she took the seat nearest to her, that he was no more interested in a cup of coffee than she was. Nor was he wasting any more of his precious time. Taking the seat opposite, he at once demanded, 'Was the whole of your interview a lie?'

Straight to the nitty-gritty! Typical of him, of course. 'My qualifications were—are—as stated,' she replied.

'But not your reasons for taking temporary work after Usher Trading folded?'

Emmie didn't see why she should answer; her job with him was at an end, whatever she said, so why bother? Though, on second thoughts, he *had* taken a huge chunk out of his morning to take her around looking for Aunt Hannah—even though it must have seemed something like a wild-goose chase to him. And she had never liked being dishonest with him anyway. Nor did she need to be dishonest with him, she realised. He had found out about her commitment, her lie, and she was getting what she deserved. He was straightforward in all his business dealings—he wouldn't countenance having anyone in his office who didn't likewise measure up.

'No,' she admitted at long last.

'Your employment after Usher Trading always ended in dismissal?' he queried.

How did he know that? 'It got to be a habit,' she answered flippantly. Was all this necessary? He was termi-
nating her services, so…

'Why?' he wanted to know, ignoring her flippancy.

'Why what? Why did it become a habit?'

'I've no quarrel with your work,' he answered. 'You said
you were good, and you are.'

His compliment to her work was unexpected—and weakening. 'I wasn't always dismissed,' she told him. 'Sometimes I just walked out.'

'I'm aware you've a fiery temperament.' *Her? Fiery temperament?* 'But would you like to tell me why, when I
know you need work, you let your temper get the better of
you?'

Cunningham was a womaniser—like she was going to
tell *him*! 'No,' she replied, 'I wouldn't.'

Barden studied her speculatively for a moment or so, his
glance raking her flushed features, her wooden expression.
'Then I'll tell you,' he pronounced. Go on then, clever
clogs—bet you get it wrong. But, in the main, he didn't.
'You were sacked, mostly, for absenteeism and appalling
time-keeping.'

'You guessed!' she fumed—the headache with which she
had awakened was back again.

'I have it in writing,' he replied.

Astonished, she stared at him. 'In—writing?' she echoed
faintly.

'Personnel have a policy of sending for references,
whether requested by heads of departments or not.' Oh,
hang it! References! She'd thought she'd got away with…
'Usually they're just kept on file. But, despite the fact I
hadn't asked for them, when all your four references were
to hand, Garratt in Personnel felt I should take a look at
them.'

'How long…?'

'The last one arrived on Friday morning.'

'When I—didn't!' she said, and felt utterly miserable—until pride woke up and gave her a nudge. 'You're right, my time-keeping was appalling, but I always more than made up for any time I lost.'

'And your unmitigated rudeness,' he went on. 'According to Smythe and Wood International—'

'Unmitigated!' she flew. 'Mitigated, I'd say. Clive Norris was always hinting—without the smallest encouragement—that he and I could be doing better things than work. When he backed me into a corner, then made a lascivious grab for me, yes, I was rude!'

'He made advances?'

Emmie stared hostilely across at Barden. 'Not for nothing! I hit him, and walked—and kept on walking.' She thought his look had softened a little—but knew she would still be out of a job. 'And, yes, too, I'm sorry I lied to you about the reason I left my temporary jobs, but...'

'You felt you had to?' he questioned toughly, any softening she'd imagined clearly a mirage.

'I'm not usually a liar,' she stated. 'But—er—circumstances were against me.'

'Circumstances?'

He had a right to be answered, to be answered truthfully, she knew that, but his delving to the heart of the matter was starting to irritate her. She was out of a job, so you'd think he'd stop his probing!

Emmie shrugged. 'I've said I'm sorry I lied to you.' She was feeling stubborn again, and not intending to say anything more.

That was until she met his no-nonsense cool grey eyes again. 'You're sorry you lied about why you left your other *permanent* jobs?'

Swine! So, okay, she'd hoped they'd be permanent when she'd started them. Was it her fault that there were such womanising fiends about—not to mention the one in front of her? Though—her innate honesty tripped her up—in all fairness she hadn't left *every* job because of male lechery. In some cases her time-keeping *had* had something to do with it.

'I'm sorry as well,' she apologised, 'that when you asked if I had any commitments I said no. Not that I think of my step-grandmother as a commitment,' she said hurriedly. 'I just felt that in the context of your question I wouldn't have stood a chance if I'd told you the truth.'

He didn't give her any marks for perception, but questioned, 'Mrs Whitford is your *only* family?' In view of the fact she'd told him on Saturday that she didn't have any family at all, Emmie supposed she shouldn't be too surprised by the emphasis of his question.

'Yes,' she admitted quietly.

'And is Mrs Whitford the reason for your previous erratic time-keeping—the reason you didn't make it at all last Friday morning?'

Emmie nodded. 'I thought she was better. Aunt Hannah started to become a bit confused shortly after her son, my stepfather, died,' she explained. 'But she's been much more settled lately. Living at Keswick House, where she has company all day, seemed to be suiting her much better.'

'She's recently moved there?'

'Yes,' Emmie agreed. 'Aunt Hannah's supposed to write where she's going in the ''Out'' book, or at least tell someone where she's off to when she goes out, but on Friday, and again this morning, she didn't.'

'So Keswick House rang you?'

'They sent someone looking for her when they missed her. When they couldn't find her Mrs Browne rang me, wondering if Aunt Hannah had gone back to our old apartment. She—er—sometimes used to.'

'That would be the first address we went to?'

'As you saw, she wasn't there.'

'Who was the kissing doorman?' he enquired toughly, and Emmie blinked.

'Johnnie, you mean?' she asked, startled.

'We weren't introduced.'

'Johnnie's an old neighbour. I asked him to give me a ring if my step-grandmother turned up there.'

'How long ago did you leave that address?' Barden asked, and Emmie wondered what tack he was on now.

'Not so long ago,' she prevaricated, starting to feel antagonistic and deciding she'd answered enough of her ex-employer's questions.

Barden studied her for a few moments, and then caused her to realise that what he didn't know he was quite capable of correctly deducing. 'You left about the same time that Mrs Whitford moved into Keswick House,' he decided.

She decided she didn't like him. 'So?' she said mulishly.

'So you gave up your home because you could more easily afford to pay for Mrs Whitford's new accommodation if you moved somewhere less expensive.'

The sauce of it! Who did he think he was? Prodding and prying! Emmie was on her feet; she'd had enough. 'Wrong!' she corrected him coldly, and, glancing around at her mother's beautiful furniture, added, 'The walls may be different, but I still have the same home that I grew up with. And, for your information, Mrs Whitford has her own money with which to pay for her new accommodation.'

'All of it?' he enquired, on his feet too, and staring down at her. 'You don't help out at all?'

What a *pig* he was. 'I'll show you out!' was the best she could manage by way of a courteous reply. She took two paces—he didn't take one. He, it seemed, hadn't finished his inquisition yet.

'Who's David?' he wanted to know.

'David?' The question threw her, and took the edge off her anger. 'David?' she enquired again.

'The man you may marry,' he enlightened her crisply.

'Ah!' she exclaimed as light dawned. 'Adrian,' she corrected—welcome to my batty world. 'His name's Adrian, not David. Adrian's taking me to collect my car tonight.' She turned away and took another step towards showing her ex-employer out.

Only to halt in her tracks when he drawled. 'You'd better ring and cancel that arrangement.' Emmie turned. She had not the smallest intention of taking any more of his orders.

'Why would you imagine I'd do anything of the sort?' she questioned snappily.

Cool grey eyes stared down into fiery dark brown ones. 'We've a lot to do—I'm sure you won't want to keep him hanging about.'

Her heartbeat suddenly set up a hopeful commotion. She schooled herself to stay calm—this could be the biggest let-down of all time, a punishment. 'I'm—er—not quite with you?'

He smiled then, a smile she quite liked. 'I'll take you to pick up your car after we've finished.'

'Finished?' she questioned—was he saying he hadn't, after all, dismissed her?

Apparently he was. 'You're working late,' he replied succinctly, and stepped past her—leading the way out of her apartment building. Emmie, quickly overcoming her incredulity, hurried after him.

CHAPTER FIVE

EMMIE—her relief knowing no bounds that she still had a job—duly got in touch with Adrian to let him know that she wouldn't require his help that evening after all, then tried to concentrate on her work. Thoughts of Barden Cunningham, however, seemed continually to get in the way.

She quite liked him again, though she didn't want a repeat of the third degree he'd given her. A necessary third degree, she realised. He couldn't have anyone in his office who wasn't trustworthy. She rather thought that now he knew all that there was to know about her background, and why she'd found it necessary to lie to him about the commitment issue, he would also know that she *was* trustworthy. She did so hope so. Somehow, and she didn't know why, since he was being less than a trustworthy friend to Neville Short, it seemed important to her that Barden trusted her.

She continued to hold the view that if she *had* explained anything about her wandering step-grandparent at her job interview, then it would have ended right there. But by now she had apparently proved her capability—hadn't Barden agreed that her work was good?—and, miracle of miracles, *she still had her job*!

She was going to work hard and be better than good, she determined, and remembered how charming Barden had been to Aunt Hannah. She recalled the easy and well mannered way he'd behaved with her step-relative, the way he'd chatted about motorcycles with her on the way to Keswick House.

Emmie was just deciding that, yes, she really, really liked

Barden, when Dawn broke into her train of thought. 'It's ten past five. Unless you need help with anything, I think I'll make tracks for home.' Dawn smiled.

'You go, I'm fine here,' Emmie assured her.

'You haven't forgotten I've an appointment in the morning and won't be in until after eleven?'

Emmie hadn't forgotten, and wished Dawn well for her antenatal appointment in the morning. After Dawn had gone, she reflected that, regardless of the fact that his senior PA wouldn't be in for the first few hours tomorrow, if she, Emily Lawson, hadn't given Barden the answers he sought back at her flat—had he not assured himself of her integrity—then no way would he have told her, 'You're working late'. However, this was not the way to start being better than good.

For the next two and a half hours, Emmie put every effort into her tasks. She sneezed a couple of times, but she didn't have time to have a cold. Besides which, she was feeling on top of the world about just about everything. She no longer had to worry about keeping dear Aunt Hannah a dark and deadly secret. Hopefully, Aunt Hannah would settle down again and everything would go back to normal.

Emmie was just tidying her desk, and thinking that, with her security back, all was right, wonderfully right, with her world, when the connecting door opened and Barden came through.

'Much more to do?' he enquired pleasantly.

'Just finished,' she replied in kind, and a short while later they were travelling along the same route she had travelled on Friday night, though this time the difference in the road conditions was astonishing.

'Your car was pulled out, by the way,' Barden thought to mention as they turned off the main road.

'Did you arrange it?'

'It seemed the least I could do, considering you risked

life and limb on my behalf.' In the darkness his voice sounded as if it had a smile in it—she liked that too.

'You'd never think, tonight, that the roads were such a nightmare on Friday,' she commented.

'But the Mountie got through,' he teased, and Emmie felt her heart actually flutter with her liking for him.

They found her car parked on the side of the road. Barden went over with her to check it out. Her vehicle, illuminated by his car's headlights, seemed unscathed. He stayed with her while she got in and started up the engine.

Emmie wound down her window. 'How's that for a motor? Started first time,' she remarked happily.

Barden bent down to her, but while she thought that he had done so to listen to the engine, in order to gauge if she would make it home without problem, she found he was looking at her.

She stared at him, seemed hypnotised, couldn't look away. Nor could she move, she discovered when, his head coming nearer, he said, 'Do you know, Emily Lawson—I think—you're rather a very nice person.' Emmie was still sitting there in a kind of daze when Barden touched his wonderful mouth to hers. It was a gentle kiss, a brief kiss, and she had still not found a word of protest when, as he started to straighten up, he bade her, 'Drive carefully, Emmie.'

Emmie had been on the road a full five minutes before she came out of her shock. Not shock particularly that Barden had kissed her, brief and unexpected as it had been, but shock that when she would have objected strongly had some other employer tried it, she hadn't minded at all. In fact—she had quite liked the gentle feel of his mouth on hers!

Five minutes after that, Emmie had truly got herself back together. Stupid, stupid! The cold weather must have dramatically slowed down her reaction time. What she should have done was to have given him a mighty shove. For crying out loud—his mistress lived so close to where they'd rescued her car; the rotten hound was probably kissing her right this very minute! He might think one Emily Lawson was a rather nice person, but she wished she could say the same about him!

The fact, however, that she *could* say that about him, was brought home to her the very next morning. She awoke with a high temperature, sneezed several times and, as her head began to pound, didn't know which to reach for first— aspirin or tissues.

Feeling like death, she dragged herself to the office and was straight away called on the intercom. 'I'm not taking calls for the next hour,' Barden told her.

She swallowed so her voice should come out clear. 'Right,' she said. It was enough. Barden had nothing else to say; either he had some top executive with him, or he was working on complex matters.

During the next half-hour Emmie deflected several phone calls, then Roberta Short rang, wanting to have a word with Barden. Oh, goodness, now what did she do?

'I'm—sorry, Mrs Short, but Mr Cunningham asked not to be interrupted. May I...?'

'Not to worry.' Roberta Short was sounding joyful and disposed to have a chat. 'The house is so quiet now—the last of our *weekend* guests went on their way this morning, and this is the first chance I've had to speak to Barden. How are you, by the way? None the worse for being frozen on Friday, I hope?'

'No, I'm fine,' Emmie replied, aware that her voice was quite husky from her cold but doing her best to disguise it. 'Thank you very much for putting me up for the night,' she added courteously, suddenly most grateful to Barden, be- cause it seemed as though he hadn't shared the cringing secret of her ghastly parting with her supper with anyone.

'It was the least we could do,' Roberta answered, apparently not a bit put out that Emmie had slept in the same room as 'her' man.

Emmie wasn't happy with such thoughts, and quickly changed the subject, hoping to end the call, by saying, 'I'm sure your party was a tremendous success. I'll—'

'With Barden organising it, it couldn't have been anything else,' Roberta cut in before Emmie could tell her that she'd let him know she had rung.

'Barden?' Emmie found she couldn't hold back from querying—when really it was absolutely none of her business. Though it was true, Roberta Short *was* being very friendly.

'Didn't you know?' Roberta obviously thought she did. 'I was such a pain—I'd never have been able to pull off the surprise if Barden hadn't—' She broke off, but, in as chatty a mood as Emmie had supposed, she resumed enthusiastically, 'I wanted to give Neville a surprise birthday party, the best birthday weekend he'd ever had. He was fifty,' she confided, 'and he was really down in the doldrums about it—I suppose I'll be the same when my fiftieth looms. Anyhow, as Neville works from home, I knew I didn't stand a cat in Hades' chance of it being a total surprise if I sent out the invitations. There were several terrifying moments when I thought he'd rumbled—Sarah Birch nearly blew it when she rang here instead of ringing Barden, but luckily I was able to point her in Barden's direction without Neville being any the wiser.'

'The—party—was a total surprise to your husband?' Emmie asked chokily, her husky tone having little to do with her cold this time.

'Absolutely,' Roberta replied, sounding positively cock-a-hoop. 'My dear, dear man was totally stunned. He had been expecting a quiet night at home, but one after the other our friends turned up.'

By the sound of it Roberta Short utterly adored her husband, and would no more think of taking a lover than she would kick a lame dog!

'I'm glad,' was the best Emmie could manage, while snippets of conversation—and her misinterpretation of them—whizzed around in her head.

'Oh, so am I. Neville said—' Suddenly Roberta halted. 'I'm keeping you from your work! I'm sorry. Everything went off so well, I can—' She broke off again. 'I'm going,' she said firmly. 'No need to tell Barden I rang; I'll ring him later when he's not so busy. Though Neville said he'd... I'm going,' she said again. 'Bye, Emmie.'

'Bye, Mrs Short,' Emmie replied—but found she was talking to herself.

Oh, Lord—she wanted to die. She sneezed—but her death wish had nothing to do with her cold. How crass! How impudent! Oh, heck, how absolutely everything! Barden wasn't having an affair with his friend's wife! By the sound of it—probably because he felt they must have had their fill of visitors now the weekend was over— Barden hadn't even called in on the Shorts last night, when he'd only been a short distance down the road.

Snatches of conversation thundered back. 'Neville mustn't know I'm phoning,' Roberta had said when she'd called. 'I've an idea he already suspects... He mustn't find out.' And Barden had told Roberta, 'Neville has no idea what you're up to.' Of course he hadn't—that was the *whole point* of a surprise party! 'He's not likely to divorce you,' Barden had confidently assured her. Why would Neville divorce his wife? What man would? Her only crime was to arrange a wonderful party to cheer him when he was feeling down about being fifty.

Never had Emmie felt more guilt-ridden as everything slotted into place. Even Barden's promise to have a few words with Roberta at the theatre last Thursday took on a different meaning. It had been no snatched meeting between two lovers. With all the arrangements in place for the following evening, it had merely been Barden attempting to assure a jittery Roberta that nothing was going to go wrong at the last minute. Which, by the sound of Roberta's euphoria just now, it hadn't.

Except, Emmie thought miserably, *she* had got it all wrong. Feeling down in the depths, she tried to find some justification for the way she had got it wrong. Barden Cunningham might not be having an affair, but he was, without question, a womaniser. Just look at all those women who rang him—and to whom he was charming. Claudia and Ingrid, she ticked off. Not to mention Paula, Sarah, and…

Sarah! Oh, no! Was there no end to her shame? Roberta Short's words came back to her. 'Sarah Birch nearly blew it when she rang here…' Oh, grief, were all those women friends of the Shorts, who had rung to confirm they would be at the party?

By the time Barden was free to take calls, Emmie wanted to run away and hide. It was no use telling herself that Barden should have denied he was having an affair that day when he'd clearly known what she was thinking. Why should he have denied it? Who was she but, she recalled painfully, some prissy little Miss Prim and Proper?

Emmie sneezed, shivered, for all the office was warm, and couldn't remember the last time she'd felt so thoroughly dejected. She was going to have to apologise, that was for sure!

She was still sneezing and rehearsing her apology when a short while later the connecting door opened and Barden strode in. He took one glance at her watery eyes and red-tipped nose, took a step back when she grabbed a tissue and sneezed—and then, as she looked across at him, he actually smiled.

It was the smile, Emmie rather supposed, that was responsible for sending all thought of making her apology clear out of her head. His words, as he rocked back on his heels to study her, were not conducive to allowing her to recall that she had something she should be sorry for.

'Well, well, little Nellie-know-it-all, I thought you couldn't catch cold from getting frozen and wet. I thought it was a scientific fact that—'

'There's a virus going round!' she butted in—huskily, and with far more authority than her lie should have allowed.

Barden came nearer, 'You're going home!' he decreed, his authority beating hers into a cocked hat.

'No, I'm not!' she spluttered. But as again she sneezed he was getting her coat and was holding it out for her to put her arms in. 'I've too much to do,' she protested, not moving an inch.

'Am I wrong, or am I wrong?' Barden enquired smoothly. 'Do you really want to give Dawn—who already has more than enough problems in her pregnancy—a heavy cold to go with them?'

Pig! Emmie fumed, but stood up. 'Messages,' she muttered grumpily, pointing to her notepad. She had recorded that Roberta Short had phoned but had left no message. Emmie was not, as she put her arms into her coat, which Barden continued to hold out for her, in any mood to apologise for anything. Then she forgot everything as a thrill of a tingle went through the whole of her body when Barden's fingers had touched her neck as he'd pulled her hair away from her collar.

'You're burning up!' he stated as she jerked from him, not a sign of a smile about him. 'Are you all right to drive?'

'I've a cold, not pneumonia!'

'Make sure you don't get it!' he threatened. 'I don't want your pneumonia on my conscience.'

Emmie looked at him—he'd nothing on his conscience, she realised. Her apology hovered—'Barden, I...' Hastily she grabbed for a tissue and sneezed.

'Go home and get into bed—and stay there!' he ordered.

Suddenly it seemed the best idea she'd heard in a long while. She went.

Emmie spent the rest of the day in bed and awakened on Wednesday, accepting that she had a streaming cold but knowing that but for Dawn she would have left her bed and gone to the office.

She stayed home and rang Aunt Hannah and had a long, if occasionally slightly weird, chat with her. Adrian popped down to see her that evening, but didn't stay—he didn't want her cold and she didn't want company.

Dawn phoned her on Thursday to ask how she was feeling. By then Emmie's husky voice had turned into a croak. 'Don't try talking; I can hear how you are,' Dawn sympathised.

'How are you?' Emmie croaked.

'Believe me—much better than you,' Dawn assured her, and rang off.

Not long afterwards the phone rang again. 'Do you need a doctor?' Barden Cunningham asked without preamble.

'Good heavens, no!' Emmie exclaimed, while her heart started to thunder quite unnecessarily. 'I should be embarrassed to death!' she stated firmly, if croakily, a sneeze imminent.

'You sound like hell!'

'I look terrific!'

He rang off without another word. Emmie put her phone down and snuggled beneath the covers. She looked a wreck and she knew it. She closed her eyes, coughed, sneezed, and sat up in bed. She felt as if she could sleep for a week—but the cough she'd developed decreed otherwise.

Around an hour later her doorbell sounded. She was of half a mind not to answer it. It rang again. Emmie got out of bed, wrapped a silk robe around her, and went to the front door.

Her face was already flushed; she flushed some more. 'You lied!' Barden Cunningham said. So, okay, she didn't look terrific. She turned her back on him and went to her sitting room. Barden followed. 'Sit down before you fall down,' he ordered, and placed the various packages he was carrying down on a low table. 'I called in at the pharmacy,' he commented—and Emmie suddenly felt quite weepy.

'It's ages since—' She broke off, swallowing hard.

'Since?' he enquired, coming to join her on the sofa. Emmie shook her tousled head. 'Since—anyone last looked after you?' he suggested gently.

'I'm being feeble,' she commented, striving for a bright note.

Barden studied her for a moment, and then teased, 'Let me make the most of it. You're usually rearing up at me for something.'

'Oh, Barden,' she mourned regretfully. 'I owe you an apology.'

'What did you do?'

'You never did—were never having an affair with Roberta Short. I...' She swallowed on a sore throat. 'I should never have thought what I did. When Mrs Short phoned on Monday she referred to your part in her surprise party for her husband—and I feel dreadful.'

'You choose your moments!' Barden replied. 'Any other time I'd probably have had a few words with you on the subject of jumping to conclusions—let alone what the devil it's got to do with you. But look at you, all huge-eyed and with the very latest in pretty pink-tipped noses. Who could be angry with you?'

'You're more kind than I deserve,' she told him painfully.

'Steady! You'll be going into compliment mode if you aren't careful.' Emmie giggled, and Barden shook his head, 'How the blazes you manage to sound all giggly-girlish and incredibly sexy at the same time defeats me,' he stated.

'Blame it on my husky throat,' she laughed, and found herself adding, 'Am I light-headed?'

'Do you feel light-headed?'

'I feel—as though I—like you.'

Barden stared at her for some long, hard moments. Then all at once he smiled. 'I should bring you cough linctus more often,' he said, and stood up, asking, 'What are you doing for food?'

'I've plenty in,' she answered. 'Aunt Hannah and I make things for the freezer most weekends.'

'Be good,' he bade her, and let himself out.

He was in her head for the rest of the day. And there again when she awoke, feeling much better, the next morning. His kindness in bringing medication to soothe her throat, and a couple of other remedies, touched her greatly. She did so appreciate that, when in receipt of her apology, he hadn't blasted her ears for her audacity in daring to think what she had about something that was nothing to do with her anyway.

Emmie still had Barden popping into her head off and on when, early that evening, he telephoned her. 'How's my second-best PA?' he enquired.

'How good of you to ring!' she exclaimed, never stopping to wonder why she should be so exceedingly pleased to hear him. Had she really told him she liked him?

'You're sounding better.'

'Oh, I am. I'll be back at the office on Monday.'

'Only if you feel up to it,' he declared. 'And you'll have to take it quietly this weekend.'

'Yes, Doctor,' she smiled.

'You haven't got a madcap weekend planned, I trust?'

Was that a threatening note she detected? Well, she had just had nearly four days away from his office, so she supposed he was entitled to want her not to do anything that might prevent her from being fully fit come Monday.

'Nothing too madcap,' she agreed, and found herself confiding, 'I had planned to drive Aunt Hannah to the National Motorcycle Museum in Birmingham tomorrow.'

'You're not fit yet!' Barden objected.

Any other time Emmie might have been nettled by his attitude. She guessed her cold must have taken more out of her than she realised. 'I'm a bit concerned I may still be a little infectious,' she admitted. 'Though Aunt Hannah would have it that she and the rest of the elderly residents at Keswick House have lived long enough now to have built up a powerful immunity to the common cold.'

'But you're worried you may pass your germs on to the residents if you call there for her?'

'I suppose I could send a taxi for her,' Emmie considered.

'You realise, of course, that all the way to Birmingham your germs will be bouncing around the close confines of your car.'

He made it sound monstrous. 'Perhaps I'd better leave the trip until next week.' She reluctantly saw sense.

'A much better idea.'

'I can still have Aunt Hannah here with me, though. Still send a taxi for…'

'Why don't I go and see her?'

Astonished, Emmie was lost for words for a moment. 'I can't let you do that!' was her first reaction. Followed by, 'Why would you?'

'Because my very conscientious PA is getting all uptight about checking on her step-relative to see how she is after her adventurous episode last Monday, and because I happen to be passing that way tomorrow and also happen to have a free half-hour.'

'But—I couldn't allow…' Emmie began to protest.

'And also because Mrs Whitford invited me, only last Monday, to drop in for a cup of tea whenever I was passing.'

'Yes, but…'

'How can you argue?' There was a smile in his voice.

'It's in my nature. I must be getting better.'

'Keep warm,' he ordered, 'It's bitterly cold out,' and, so saying, he rang off, and Emmie became quite dreamy about him.

Emmie had recovered by Saturday morning, but when she rang Aunt Hannah the sweet love wouldn't hear of Emmie taking her anywhere. 'You haven't been well, and besides, we've got some entertainment here tonight. Amateurs, of course, but since they've kindly given up their free time to come and sing to us, it seems only polite to stay and listen to them.'

'Barden Cunningham, my *boss*,' Emmie emphasised, lest Aunt Hannah was still carrying the notion that Barden was her fiancé, 'may call and see you some time today.'

'That will be nice,' Aunt Hannah replied. And to prove her memory was as good as ever, she went on, 'I invited him to do that whenever he was passing.'

Emmie felt very much cheered after her phone call. She felt so much better, and her appetite suddenly returned, so she decided a walk to the corner shop to buy some fresh fruit, vegetables and milk would do her good.

As Barden had said last evening, it was bitterly cold out. She was glad to return to her flat to get warmed through again. She played with the idea in the late afternoon of phoning Aunt Hannah to enquire if Barden had called.

She decided against it, but found she could barely wait until she thought her step-relative would be up and on the move the next morning to ring her. When she did call, however, she received one almighty shock.

'Did Barden Cunningham call yesterday?' she asked, after their initial chat was over.

'Oh, yes, we had a most wonderful day!' Aunt Hannah informed her enthusiastically.

For a second or two Emmie feared her step-grandmother's memory was throwing another wobbly. 'Day?' she queried gently. 'Um, did you...did he stay for coffee or tea?'

'Oh, we didn't have time when he called!' Aunt Hannah replied. 'We had coffee on the way and lunch when we got there. Did you know his father is a classic car enthusiast and has several of them?'

Emmie didn't, but by then she was starting to grow seriously worried. 'Where—er—did you have lunch?' she probed casually.

'The museum.'

'The museum,' Emmie echoed faintly. 'The Motorcycle Museum?' Surely not?

'Of course. Oh, it was wonderful! Lovely!' Aunt Hannah went on and into raptures about the motorcycles she'd seen.

Emmie was utterly stunned, and came away from the phone not knowing what to believe. Feeling quite free of her cold now, her sore throat gone, she had intended to invite Aunt Hannah to lunch. But all that had gone out of her head and she collapsed into a chair. Had Barden *really* taken Aunt Hannah to the Motorcycle Museum yesterday? Or, having set her mind on going yesterday, had the dear soul imagined it?

Having thawed out food from the freezer, Emmie set it to cook with her mind in a chaotic whirl. She knew Barden's home number—should she give him a ring? She felt worried enough to do so, while at the same time she also felt an unaccountable overwhelming shyness about doing anything of the sort.

She went to the phone several times, but it was only when she began to see that the very plain likelihood was that Aunt Hannah had imagined her trip, and she was going to have to get some specialised help for her—and soon— that she went and dialled Barden's number.

It rang and rang—he wasn't in. Emmie replaced the phone and didn't like at all the images that came to mind of him out at lunch somewhere, with a Claudia, or Paula, Sarah or Ingrid. What on earth was the matter with her? Good grief!

Deciding she'd had too much time on her hands just lately, Emmie went and peeled some potatoes and put them on to boil. She next attended to the broccoli—and then the doorbell sounded.

Her thoughts went immediately to Aunt Hannah, and she rushed to the outer door—to discover that this was her day for shocks. Barden Cunningham stood there.

She opened her mouth, and closed it. He got in first. 'Up and dressed, I see,' he observed.

'I've just tried to ring you.'

'Happens all the time,' he replied, and Emmie felt just a touch ruffled. Clearly he expected women to ring him a lot, and he didn't seem bothered as to why she would try to ring him anyway. 'Something smells good,' he commented, sniffing the air.

She felt perverse. 'You wouldn't enjoy it.'

'Are you always this mean?'

'So stay to lunch!' she invited snappily—and nearly dropped to the floor when, by stepping over the threshold, he accepted.

She left him in the sitting room while she went and checked the boiling potatoes. It didn't surprise her that she had peeled more than enough for two—her brain just wasn't engaged that morning.

A sound behind her made her turn. 'So tell me?' he invited.

Why she had tried to phone him. Now that they were face to face, there in person, it seemed ridiculous to ask if he had taken Aunt Hannah to Birmingham yesterday. Of course he hadn't! Yet, remembering how pleasant he had been to Aunt Hannah on Monday, and his offer to call and see the old lady yesterday—notwithstanding his kindness to Emmie herself in calling on Thursday with medication, she reflected—she began to waver in her certainty that he hadn't taken Aunt Hannah out yesterday. He *was* kind—but could he be *extraordinarily* kind?

'Did you…?' She couldn't get it out. 'I rang Aunt
Hannah this morning.'

'She's nowhere near as mixed-up as I first supposed,'
Barden remarked affably, his grey eyes fixed on Emmie's
slightly anxious brown ones. 'You're looking better,' he
threw in. 'Restored to full beauty.'

She was sidetracked. Was he teasing? She wanted him
to think her beautiful. 'It's a gift,' she said, pulling herself
together. 'Did you call at Keswick House yesterday?'

'I said I would.'

'By the sound of it, you—um—had an intelligent conversation with my step-grandmother?'

'Mrs Whitford seldom seemed stuck for words,' he answered tactfully of Emmie's sometimes garrulous relation.

'Er—how long were you with her?'

Barden studied her and, while Emmie was beating all
around the bush, he, as she knew, was never one to dodge
anything. 'She enjoyed it,' he stated.

'Oh, Barden, no! You didn't?'

'I did,' he confirmed. 'I enjoyed it too.'

Emmie finished bush-beating. 'You took Aunt Hannah
to Birmingham?'

'It seemed a shame to disappoint her,' he replied, and
suddenly Emmie had the most horrendous thought.

'Aunt Hannah thought that was why you called yesterday, didn't she?'

'You've gone pink,' he observed.

'I'm going to die of embarrassment!'

'Not you!' he declared. 'What are we having for lunch?'

Emmie wasn't so easily deflected. 'Just a minute. You
called in at Keswick House, intending to stay only a half-
hour at the outside, but instead when Aunt…'

'I've told you, I enjoyed it. The dear lady's technical
knowledge is astonishing.' He took a glance at the glass-
fronted oven. 'Are you doing Yorkshire puddings to go
with that beef?'

She would have prepared some had Aunt Hannah been there, but it was too late now. She shook her head. 'You'll have to fill up on apple pie afterwards.'

Oddly, because Barden was her employer, not to mention the fact that he had more or less invited himself to lunch, Emmie would not have been a bit surprised had lunch been a stilted kind of affair. But not a bit of it. Barden had a wealth of charm, as she well knew, for all it was seldom directed at her. During the meal his manner was easy, charming and, save for her briefly mentioning the two-week working trip to the States he was to undertake in a fortnight's time, work was never discussed.

What was raised, though, was her family background. 'Your father was a scientist?' Barden enquired at one point.

Aunt Hannah had been talking! 'Your father has several classic cars,' Emmie countered—and loved it when Barden laughed.

'Do you remember your father?' he enquired softly a few moments later. 'You were ten when he died, you mentioned?'

Emmie gave in. 'My father was a gentle man—quiet, often preoccupied, but always there for me.'

'As was your stepfather.' It was a statement.

Emmie smiled, 'Alec was lovely. Exactly the opposite of my father, though.'

'Not so often preoccupied?' Barden suggested, and she wondered just how much Aunt Hannah had told him.

'He was fun.'

'What work did he do?'

Ah! 'He—um—was always busy,' Emmie prevaricated.

'He liked to gamble. Don't get uptight!' Barden instructed. 'I didn't ask. Mrs Whitford said she hadn't had a decent conversation for days, and chatted about anything that came to her on the way to Birmingham.'

'It was all motorcycles on the way back?' Emmie guessed.

'That and classic cars.' Emmie thought they had left behind talk of her family—but she should have known better. Didn't she know all about his 'dog with a bone' tenacity for finding out what he wanted to know? 'According to Mrs Whitford, her son sold many of your mother's antiques over the years.'

'We've still got a few pieces left,' she defended. 'And we've always managed…'

'I've an idea you always will manage, won't you, Emmie?' Barden said, his tone kindly. She wasn't sure she knew what he was getting at, and realised her uncertainty must have shown when he went on, 'You moved from a very comfortable area when needs dictated.'

Needs dictated? You could say that. 'Security, financial security, mine and Aunt Hannah's, has to be my first and highest priority,' Emmie admitted.

'You moved because you could no longer afford to live where you were—not when Mrs Whitford had moved into residential care.'

'She's free at Keswick House to come and go as she pleases,' Emmie told him.

'Provided she tells someone where she's going,' he put in—well, he had proof of that, didn't he?—and also proof that Aunt Hannah sometimes liked to bend the rules.

'It's important that Aunt Hannah feels safe,' Emmie revealed slowly. Barden knew so much, there seemed little point in pretending that matters were other than how they were.

'Was she not safe before?'

'I have to go to work—I like going to work,' she inserted, lest he should run away with the idea that she hated working in his office. 'But if I work it means I have to leave her on her own for too long for five days a week. Rather belatedly I saw, when Aunt Hannah had her first bout of being a little confused, that the dear love would be happier if she had company during the day.'

'So, to keep your financial security, you moved to some-where cheaper to r—'

'You make it sound like some tremendous sacrifice.' Emmie smiled. 'But it wasn't. Aunt Hannah pays the lion's share of living at Keswick House, and I can't say that the value I put on my financial security is anything new.'

'It isn't?'

Emmie felt she had said more than enough. 'It isn't,' she confirmed, and, the subject closed, prepared to collect up their pudding plates.

'When did it start?' he wanted to know.

'Do you never give up?' she asked exasperatedly.

'What do you think?' He grinned, such charm in his expression that she found herself actually thinking back and trying to remember when she had started to value her fi-nancial security so much.

'There was a point after Alec died when I realised the only family I had was Aunt Hannah, and that there was no one else to look after us. But, with dear Alec being the way he was, I probably felt the first threat to my security when he sold the house and...'

'It was his to sell?'

'It was when my mother died.'

'Oh, Emmie,' Barden said softly.

'What does that mean?'

'No wonder you're down on men.'

Her eyes widened. She stood up and busied herself with the dishes. 'I'm not down on men at all!' she denied, and found that Barden was on his feet too and was coming over.

'When did you last allow any man to kiss you?' he asked—just as if that was evidence that she didn't have a down on men!

'If memory serves—just last Monday!' she answered.

'Who?' he demanded.

'I see I left an indelible impression,' she smirked.

And knew he'd realised that *he* had been the man who

had last kissed her when he asked, 'You're sure you're no longer infectious?' A smile was there in his voice somewhere.

'Positive,' she replied.

And got the shock of her life when, taking the dishes from her and putting them back on the table, Barden then gathered her in his arms and, while her heart started to go like a trip-hammer, he murmured, 'I'll risk it,' and, his head coming down, he kissed her, tenderly, but thoroughly.

Emmie was fairly speechless when that wonderfully tender kiss ended. 'If—er—if that was a—um—thank-you for your lunch, you needn't hang around to do the washing up,' she told him huskily, giving herself a slight push away from him.

Barden let her go, his arms dropping to his sides. 'What sort of a cad do you think I am?' he growled, and she laughed, and they washed up together. But she was glad when, all chores done, he went—her legs had never felt more wobbly.

Emmie returned to work on Monday, having been fully able to convince herself that the only reason she had felt her legs go weak yesterday was because she hadn't been terribly well. She had trouble convincing herself that her heart didn't give a bit of a flutter when she first saw Barden that day, though.

He greeted her in friendly fashion, but was no more friendly to her than he was to anyone else. She was in his office later that morning when her eyes strayed to his rather superb mouth—those lips that had gently kissed hers yesterday. Hastily she flicked her glance from his mouth to his eyes—and saw that his glance was on her mouth.

Abruptly he turned his attention to the work on his desk. 'It looks as if I'll have to be in Stratford Thursday afternoon. I'll need you with me.'

'Fine,' she answered, aware that as well as telling her that they'd probably be back late he was also assuming that she wouldn't have any problem with that. And so a busy week got under way.

Emmie joined Adrian up at his flat for a meal on Tuesday. She liked him, but there was never any suggestion that they might be more than friends. She guessed that, as she felt safe with him, Adrian felt safe with her.

On Wednesday evening Emmie had a long telephone conversation with Aunt Hannah, who asked if she would mind if she didn't see her this Saturday as she and Mrs Vellacott were going to a play that one of the local schools was performing on Saturday evening.

'How are you getting there?' Emmie questioned, not happy at the thought of her step-grandmother walking the streets after dark.

'Mrs Vellacott's son-in-law is picking us up and bringing us back,' Aunt Hannah assured her.

'You'll come and have lunch with me on Sunday?' Emmie asked, and could only be pleased that Aunt Hannah seemed to be having more of a social life these days.

'I'm looking forward to it,' Aunt Hannah declared, and asked, 'How's Barden? Have you seen him this week?' Oh, dear, had she forgotten he was her employer?

'I work for him; I see him every day,' Emmie said carefully.

'Of course you do. What am I thinking of?' There was a pause and then, wickedly, 'He's rather dishy, isn't he? Oh, to be sixty years younger!'

'You're incorrigible!'

'Too late to change now. He's definitely got that certain something, though, that—without him having to lift a finger—has women falling all over him.'

Emmie went to bed that night determined that that was one club she wasn't going to join. And got up the next morning wondering what on earth she had been thinking about. Good heavens, of course she wasn't going to join

Barden Cunningham's fan club. The whole idea was pre-posterous.

She went to work realising that she had been feeling very unsettled since last Sunday when, so tenderly, Barden had gathered her into his arms and kissed her. Why he had was a trifle confusing. Probably it was some male ego thing, because he thought she didn't allow any man to kiss her. Though—it hadn't seemed like that. Truth to tell, it had been rather a lovely...

Pfff—she'd take jolly good care he didn't kiss her again. Not that he seemed remotely interested in doing so. If the one-sided conversation she overheard that morning, when he was on the phone to some female named Karla Nesbitt, was anything to go by, Barden Cunningham Esquire had other things on his mind than kissing his assistant acting PA.

They started out for Stratford-upon-Avon at two and managed to get there by four. Barden seemed preoccupied on the journey, his thoughts either on work or the date he'd arranged with the sultry-sounding Karla Nesbitt. He was taking her out somewhere tomorrow evening.

They finished their business in Stratford at six-thirty, and Jack Bryant walked with them to Barden's car. But it was to Emmie's side of the car that he came, and, in an under-tone, he informed her warmly, 'My divorce becomes absolute in two weeks.'

'Congratulations,' Emmie replied.

'What I'm telling you is that I'll be free in two weeks—a single man. I thought—'

Barden's voice, a touch impatient cut through what else Jack had to say. 'I wouldn't mind getting back to London before midnight!' he stated shortly.

What a pig! What an embarrassing pig! Trying to make her look small! 'Bye, Jack,' Emmie smiled, and only just stopped herself from inviting him to give her a call when the two weeks were up. She got into the car realising that, though she liked Jack Bryant, she didn't know that she wanted to go out with him.

'What was Bryant talking to you about?' Barden asked curtly.

'He was telling me the state of his divorce,' she answered coolly.

She was, by then, not feeling very friendly towards her employer, and when fifteen minutes later he—in her opinion—begrudgingly enquired, 'Do you want to stop for something to eat?' Emmie knew she'd sooner starve.

'Do you mind if we get on? I'm seeing someone later tonight.' Charming! His foot went down on the accelerator and they nearly took off at the sudden surge of power!

He remembered his manners, though, when they reached her flat, and Emmie, having calmed down somewhat, was prepared to give a few plus-marks because he got out of his car with her and took her door keys from her.

Unfortunately, probably in his haste to be away, Barden collected an over-large splinter from the splitting door-post—and in attempting to hurriedly extract it succeeded only in breaking it off, leaving part of the wood under the skin of his index finger.

Automatically Emmie took a hold of his hand. 'Have you got a nanny at home?' she enquired lightly.

'Are you being funny?'

She'd had it with him! It had been a long day—and they were still all too obviously not the best of friends. 'Apparently not,' she answered a touch waspishly. 'You'd better come in; I can't see a thing in this light.' She hoped it hurt!

She had expected, out of sheer perversity, that he'd decline her offer in no uncertain terms. But, rather to her surprise, he kept a hold of her keys and crossed the hall to open up her flat.

'I won't be a moment,' she informed him and, draping her car coat over the sofa, she left him in the sitting room while she went to collect her tweezers. She returned with a surgical-spirit-sterilised needle and took a hold of his hand again, to inspect the damage. 'It won't hurt half as much if you don't look,' she promised him, suddenly very ashamed of her hope that his finger hurt.

'Do I get a sweetie if I don't cry out?' he asked—and Emmie folded, her good humour back. The remains of the splinter came out cleanly—and, oh, she did so love him. *Love him?*

Her head jerked up—just as he lowered his head to inspect her handiwork. Their heads touched, then jerked away. Then suddenly, and she had no idea which of them had moved first, they were closer, his hands were reaching for her, and she again knew the bliss of being in his arms.

His kiss, when his lips met hers, was as tender as it had been on Sunday. But where on Sunday Barden had held her firmly, but not too closely, this time his arms seemed to be compelling her forward.

Emmie moved that little bit closer, and Barden kissed her again, his kiss deeper and gentler still, but starting to seek, seek, take and give. And all at once there was a fire flickering into life inside her. Emmie put her arms around him under his jacket; she wanted to be closer—she had never been in love before. His body, the warmth of him through his fine shirt, was dizzying. She had never imagined that to stand this close, to feel, to touch, while at the same time being held secure in the all-male arms of the man she loved, could be so utterly enthralling.

Then it seemed that to feel and to touch was not all one-sided. For, as though wanting to feel her warmth too, she sensed Barden's hands come beneath her jacket, and was mindless for ageless seconds as he caressed up to her rib-cage over the thin silk of her shirt.

He kissed her again deeply, and their bodies touched. He kissed her throat while, in a tender whisper of a caress, his hands moved on upwards. To Emmie, when she felt his hands cup her full breasts, felt his fingers tantalising the hardened firm tips, it was an experience like no other.

Which made it a mystery to her that, when in his arms was where she wanted to be, she should then, at that utterly blissful moment, strangle out the one word, 'Don't.' He stilled immediately. 'Don't, Barden,' she found from a reluctant somewhere.

He took his hands from her breasts, moved them to hold her by her waist, and raised his head to look down at her. Emmie couldn't take his scrutiny. She turned abruptly about, presenting him with her back—and had to swallow hard when she felt his hands leave her waist as he caught hold of her by her shoulders.

'That—wasn't supposed to happen,' he said in her ear— and Emmie knew then that he was already regretting it.

'It—didn't,' she answered, grateful for pride's helping hand.

'Are you all right?' he questioned gruffly.

No, she was not all right! She had just discovered that she loved him, was in love with him, and she knew that when she was alone, when he had gone, her love was going to start to hurt.

'Good heavens, yes,' she assured him lightly—but had to move a few steps until she was away from his tingling, yearning-making hold.

She heard him move, and fought desperately to breathe normally. Then realised that he had taken her at her word that she was all right, for the next sound she heard was the sound of the sitting room door closing as Barden let himself out of her flat. All right? Nothing was ever going to be all right ever again!

CHAPTER SIX

WITH the coming of the cold light of day, Emmie found that her love for Barden was no figment of her imagination. She got out of bed and supposed she must have had a few hours' sleep. It didn't feel like it.

She stood under the shower with the same realisations tormenting her that had tormented her through the night. She was in love with him, and in all honesty now knew that it had been coming on since the first time she met him.

Emmie no longer wondered what had happened to her certainty of only yesterday morning, that she'd take jolly good care Barden didn't kiss her again. He had only had to reach for her—and that certainty had caved in.

What would have happened had not some semblance of sanity panicked her into telling him 'Don't', she didn't want to consider. Barden had shown no sign of being the one to end the interlude, that was for sure.

Emmie left her bathroom no nearer to finding an explanation for why she had fallen in love with him. Perhaps there wasn't an explanation for loving someone you didn't want to love—she was going to find no joy in it; she knew that. She loved him, and that love was here to stay, was unshakeable. But Barden did not love her, she had to face up to that, nor was it possible that he ever would.

What could be explained now, though, were those tiny little pointers along the way—overlooked then, significant today. For instance, that sensation of feeling oddly let down, upset when—and it happened a lot, as she well knew—she had believed he was having an affair with his friend's wife.

Emmie recalled, too, how she hadn't liked it when she'd

thought he was a womaniser. Well, she had been proved wrong there. Or had she? He might not have been lusting after *mesdames* Ingrid, Paula and Co, but he wasn't staying home nights, was he? She knew for a fact he would be out with Karla Nesbitt tonight.

Jealousy, cruel, spiteful jealousy, nipped, and Emmie drove herself to work determining she was going to overcome it—as she was going to overcome her love for Barden. She'd get herself a social life. Everyone had one bar her—well, there was Adrian. Even Aunt Hannah had a better social life than she did. Emmie decided right then that there was nothing to stop her from going out once in a while. And she would! In fact she'd go out with the very next person who asked her.

In remembering Aunt Hannah, though, Emmie had to wonder if *that* was the reason why when, close to Barden, and experiencing such wild and wonderful emotions, emotions such as she had never experienced before, she had found that awful word 'don't'. Had her subconscious been battering at her even then, while she had been thrilling to Barden's touch? Had her subconscious been alerting her to the fact that she mustn't let herself be another of Barden's women because, should they ever indulge in any sort of an affair, when it ended there was every probability that her job would end with it too?

Her security, and that of Aunt Hannah, was still paramount, Emmie mused disconsolately as she parked her car and made for her office. Not that Barden had done much more than kiss her—so that hardly meant he wanted a full-blown affair. But he was a man of the world—and she couldn't take that risk.

'Good morning,' she greeted Dawn cheerfully, pleased to see that her colleague was looking better than she had of late.

Barden came in to their office long before Emmie was ready to see him again. When would she ever be ready to see him again? She managed to meet his eyes, but felt his glance taking in her blush. 'If you'd bring through your notes from Stratford,' he suggested, and from there it was all work.

Emmie returned to her desk feeling very much anti the man she loved. Do this, do that—you'd never have known that less than twenty-four hours ago he had kissed her, laid so much as a finger on her, so impersonal was he. She hoped she hadn't got all of the splinter out—hoped that his finger turned septic.

She was, of course, hating herself for thinking anything so disgraceful by the time it came for her to go home. He was good and kind and had overturned a lot of her earlier not-so-nice opinions of him—and now she wouldn't see him for *two whole days*. It was unbearable.

With a very bleak weekend stretching before her, Emmie made her way to the car park, only to be waylaid by Simon Elsworth, one of the management trainees whom she knew slightly and who had obviously been hanging around waiting for her.

'I wondered if you'd like to come out to dinner with me?' he asked, and Emmie's determination to get herself a social life abruptly disintegrated. He wasn't Barden.

'I—er—I'm a little busy this weekend.' She tried to let him down gently.

'It doesn't have to be this weekend,' Simon said eagerly. 'How about next Tuesday?'

Emmie searched for tact, then remembered how Mr I-don't-even-remember-kissing-you Cunningham was dating all and sundry—well, she knew about Karla Nesbitt for a fact. 'I think I should like that,' she answered.

She was regretting having agreed to go out with Simon before she had so much as made it out of the car park, though Simon was soon gone from her mind.

With a long, long day stretching before her, Emmie got up on Saturday and decided that she wasn't going to waste another minute in thinking about Barden. Easier said than done. To keep herself occupied she cleaned and polished, had a brief respite when Adrian came down and cadged a cup of coffee, then stripped beds and remade them, washed and baked, then, physically tired, but mentally alert, she had a soak in the bath and went to bed.

But, as tired as she felt, Emmie found she couldn't sleep. She would not, not, not, not, *not* think about *him*! She picked up her current book and opened it, but, absorbed in thoughts of Barden, was suddenly startled when her door-bell rang.

Aunt Hannah! A hurried glance at her bedside clock showed eleven-forty. Worried that Aunt Hannah might have decided not to wait until she was collected tomorrow, Emmie quickly pulled on her silk robe and dashed to answer the door.

It was not, however, Aunt Hannah who stood there when Emmie pulled back the door, but, to her utter astonishment, Barden Cunningham! He had on a lounge suit, shirt and tie, and while her mouth fell open, so her heart went wild.

Speechlessly she stared at him, which made it just as well that he was the first to speak. 'I'm starting with a migraine,' he explained. 'I don't think I'm going to make it home before my vision's affected.'

Oh, my poor darling! Instantly Emmie went into action. He was, she realised, not the best colour she had ever seen. 'You do look a bit green around the gills,' she murmured, striving to hide her sudden agitation at seeing him so stricken. 'Come in.'

He appeared to make automatically for her sitting room while she secured the outer door. 'If I could borrow a chair for a while?' he asked, seeming to notice only then that she was in her night attire.

'You look as if you'd be better lying down than standing up!' It was decision time, only the decision was already made for her. She had never expected to see him so vulnerable, and her heart ached. She had once shared a bedroom with him and not come to the slightest harm. Poor darling. It wouldn't come to that, he could have a room to himself. 'Luckily for you Aunt Hannah's bed's made up.'

'She's not with you this weekend?'

'You're swaying!' Emmie took charge. 'Come on,' she said, but guessed he was having trouble focusing and did the only thing possible. 'This way,' she said, more gently, and caught a hold of his right arm and led him into Aunt Hannah's room. 'Have you been able to take anything for it?' she asked as she guided him to sit on the bed.

'I don't get cursed this way that often to need to carry medication, but I'll take anything you've got,' he answered. Emmie, who had an idea from somewhere that once a migraine got started it was too late to take medication, went quickly all the same to get him painkillers and some water.

'Have you had much to drink?' she thought to ask, before she handed the tablets over.

'A glass of something red and foul enough for me to refuse a second.'

Emmie didn't know much about it but wondered briefly if the foul red wine had triggered his migraine attack. She handed a couple of tablets over, and waited while he downed them. 'It doesn't sound as if it was too scintillating an evening,' she commented, taking the glass of water from him.

'A party,' he answered briefly, and she could tell he was having a problem in concentrating, though he added, 'I was driving near here on my way home when I realised I was in trouble.'

'Don't talk any more.' Emmie shushed him, and bent to remove his shoes and socks. Then, straightening, she went to help him out of his jacket. She could tell that he was really suffering when, his eyes closed, all movement seemed painful to him.

His eyes were still shut when she held him to her as,

almost unaided, she removed his jacket. She felt the side of his face against the swell of her breasts, and belatedly became aware that her robe had gaped open as she bent over him.

She held on to him, but very nearly let go of him when, almost into her breasts, he commented wearily, 'I trust you aren't planning to have your wicked way with me.'

Emmie smiled—dead, but refusing to stay down! A feeling of utter love and tenderness for him engulfed her, and she placed a whisper of a kiss on the top of his head. Then, with an arm around his shoulders, she managed to remove his tie.

Emmie wondered about removing his shirt, but felt he would prefer to be left alone. 'Lie down,' she instructed softly, and when he complied she settled for unfastening the buttons on his shirt. She also undid the waistband of his trousers. If he felt better shortly, it would not be too troublesome for him to take the remainder of his clothes off.

Emmie pulled the duvet up around him, and had just laid a cooling hand on his head when she saw that he had his eyes open. 'Kiss me, Emmie,' he requested, but sounded drained of energy.

Oh, she loved him, loved him! 'Promise you're harmless?'

'For the moment,' he answered.

'Sounds encouraging,' she teased, and because she wanted to she bent closer and, as he closed his eyes, she tenderly kissed him.

'Goodnight,' he murmured, and Emmie straightened, seeing that he didn't look any better. But, since he still had his eyes closed, she hoped he might drop off into pain-relieving sleep.

Emmie stayed only long enough to hang his jacket over the back of a chair, then, putting the light out as she went, she silently left the room.

She went back to bed, hoping that he would get some rest, some sleep. She couldn't. She admitted she liked having him so close. He hadn't been out with some female, then? Or had he? Had he just taken his date home when he'd felt the first vicious nip of migraine? A female who lived in this area?

Unable to settle to sleep, Emmie got out of bed and tiptoed to the next-door room. She had closed his door, and didn't want to disturb him if he had managed to fall asleep, so she listened, but heard no sound.

She returned to her bed, her ears attuned for any noises, but none came, and around four o'clock she finally succumbed to sleep.

It did not surprise her that she slept later than she normally did on a Sunday morning. What did surprise her was to awake and find the man she loved in her room.

As Emmie had assumed he might, Barden had removed the rest of his clothes and was now somewhat incongruously clad in the spare robe Aunt Hannah kept on a door hook. Emmie, her black shiny hair all over the place, struggled to sit up, while noticing that the robe, with its sleeves halfway up his arms, was far from a perfect fit. Her eyes travelled down to his bare feet, and then up past his quite handsome legs, his knees just covered, and on up to his face—more healthily complexioned this morning.

More because she was overly conscious of her tousled hair and feeling suddenly shy rather than because she needed an answer, she asked, 'How are you feeling?' She was able to see for herself that he looked fully fit again this morning.

His answer initially was to let his gaze travel slowly over her sleep-mussed hair and her pinkened complexion. Then he smiled, that leg-weakening smile, and answered, 'Never better.' And, leaning casually against a solid chest of drawers, he continued, 'Though...' He hesitated.

'Though?' she prompted slowly, her senses somehow alert for mischief.

'Though I think it's possible I've just ruined your love-life.'

He didn't, Emmie noticed, look devastatedly worried about that. 'Oh?' she queried warily, as yet without an inkling as to what he could mean.

'Know anybody by the name of Adrian?' he enquired nicely.

He knew full well she did. But—all sorts of clicks were clicking! It was not unknown for Adrian to come down to borrow something or other as soon as he thought she was up on a Sunday morning—or any other morning for that matter—be it milk, sugar or yesterday's paper.

Her eyes did a more detailed study of the tall, all-masculine, bristly-chinned man, his arms shooting out from the fit-where-it-touched robe, and his bare feet, bare, strong legs.

'You answered the door—looking like that?'

'I thought you'd want me to put on a robe,' he answered pleasantly, confirmation there, she realised, that he probably hadn't a stitch on underneath!

'You realise you've just ruined my reputation?' she told him severely, to hide how wonderful it was to see him; she had thought she would have to wait until tomorrow for a glimpse of him.

Barden stared back at her for long seconds, then mockingly drawled, 'You're not suggesting I marry you?'

And that made her mad. Clearly she was the very last person he would ever consider marrying! Who did he think he was? 'You should be so lucky!' she flared. She wouldn't marry him if he asked her—oh, to have the chance! 'You've obviously recovered,' she snapped. 'Let yourself out!'

'I'm not allowed to stay for breakfast?'

'Make it a first!' she erupted—but, crazy as it was, from having just fumed, she now had to laugh.

Barden stilled, his glance on her happy face and merry eyes. Then abruptly he moved from the chest of drawers and took a few steps to the doorway. Then, however, he turned, and suddenly his eyes were filled with devilment when he said, 'Permit me to tell you, Miss Lawson, that you have an exceedingly snuggleworthy bosom.'

She went scarlet—he seemed to enjoy her blush. She had thought him more or less out for the count when she had cradled him to her semi-naked breasts last night.

What was a girl to do? Emmie did the only thing possible. Regardless that he was her boss, she ordered, 'Clear off, Cunningham!' To her surprise, he went.

Emmie heard him moving around, but, though she wanted to leave her bed, she stayed where she was until she eventually heard him letting himself out of the flat. She got up then—and found she had wandered into the next-door room. He had made the bed he had slept in, she noted, and she fell in love with him all over again.

Aunt Hannah was in a talkative mood when Emmie went to collect her, telling her all about last night's play, and did Emmie mind if she didn't come next Saturday either; they were having a whist drive at Keswick House in the afternoon and it might go on until rather late.

In all the years Emmie had known her she had never known Aunt Hannah was interested in cards, much less a game of whist. But Emmie couldn't help but be pleased that—given a lapse here and there—the dear love seemed to be really, really settling in and treating Keswick House as her home.

Aunt Hannah had a nap after lunch, and Emmie picked up the paper to read. But she did not read very much. Barden was in her head again, dominating her thoughts. He'd looked so ill last night, barely able to stand. Of course he'd been well again this morning and—remembering that

comment about her 'snuggleworthy bosom'—full of devilment.

She found she was grinning, and straightened her face
behind her newspaper. Then, recalling how a week tomorrow Barden was going to fly to the States for two weeks,
she did not have to make a conscious effort to stop smiling.
There wasn't a smile about her as she wondered how she
was going to cope for *two whole weeks* without seeing him!

It had been bad enough on Friday, when she had believed
she wouldn't see him again for two days. But two weeks!
Why couldn't he have asked her to go with him? He could
take a PA to Stratford; why couldn't he take a PA to the
States?

She went to work on Monday knowing she couldn't have
gone away—she had to be there for Aunt Hannah. To her
delight, Emmie found Barden in good spirits. 'How's the
fair Emily this morning?' he enquired, when she took some
paperwork in to him.

Fair-complexioned but with black hair! She loved him.
'Very well,' she answered sedately, but just had to ask,
'Yourself?'

'Never had nursing like it,' he murmured, his expression
dead-pan.

Emmie went a trifle pink and returned to her office, fairly
certain Barden had been referring to her 'snuggleworthy
bosom'.

He was in the same amiable mood the next day too, and,
while he made no mention or hint again of having been in
need on Saturday of what nursing skills she had, she had
never known him so friendly and pleasant. All in all, she
found him pretty wonderful.

So wonderful, so much in her head, that, had she not
bumped into Simon Elsworth in one of the corridors,
Emmie had an idea she'd have forgotten she had a date
with him later that evening.

It was not a good evening. Simon Elsworth was a snob.

It showed in his face when he called for her, looking down his nose at the area where she had her flat. 'I'm glad you're ready,' he greeted her when she answered the door, 'I wouldn't want to leave my car unattended around here for more than a minute.'

Guess who wasn't going to be invited in for coffee at the end of the evening! 'Very wise,' she replied, and her love for Barden soared—he'd left his extremely expensive car outside for hours on end—all night once, only recently—and had never looked down at where she lived.

Because her heart wasn't in it, and that wasn't fair to her escort, Emmie put herself out to be a pleasing companion. She realised she'd succeeded when her enquiries caused Simon to talk expansively about himself.

'Would you like to come back to my place?' he asked at the end of the evening.

No mention of coffee! This is where I bale out! 'It's been a super evening.' Emmie smiled, and having learned that Simon Elsworth was very career-orientated, added, 'but it's rather late, and we both have to give of our best tomorrow.'

He tried to kiss her when they parted. She found the idea appalling! She'd hit him if he did. 'Goodnight,' she said firmly, pushing him away.

'Shall I see you again?'

Not if I see you first. 'You will,' she managed. 'Probably tomorrow, at work. Goodnight.' She went in. If he had anything to add she wasn't staying around to hear it.

Simon Elsworth had been a mistake, she mused as she went to work the next day. She had thought him shy and perhaps a little sensitive when she'd agreed to go out with him. She had been wrong. She recalled how he had attempted to kiss her last night—and her appalled reaction. Had falling in love with Barden spoiled her for other men? She rather thought so.

The day started well. Dawn seemed to be having a better time of it now, in the latter stage of her pregnancy. She seemed, too, to feel more and more confident about passing work over to her assistant.

So it was that Dawn left it mainly to her to deal with the paperwork their employer would be wanting on his American trip. Emmie still didn't know how she was going to cope with not seeing him for two weeks—sixteen days if you counted the Saturday and Sunday prior.

She decided to live for the moment and, breezing in cheerfully to Barden's office, saw him look up as she entered, his glance on her alive face. She went all weak and pathetic inside at just seeing him, and, knowing she'd be with him for some time, was glad to be able to turn away and close the door, taking the opportunity to pull herself together.

'The figures on…' she began as she turned back and took a seat—only to find that, for the moment, Barden had no interest in the information she had for him.

'Your love-life hasn't suffered, I trust?' he enquired affably.

Emmie did a massive switch to get on to his wavelength and realised he was referring to the fact that, having opened the door to Adrian early on Sunday morning trouserless, with only a robe for modesty, Adrian must know he'd stayed the night. 'Can't say that it has,' she replied calmly.

'He's forgiven you—Adrian?' Barden asked sharply.

His tone annoyed her. 'I don't know what happened in your dream, but according to my memory he didn't have anything to forgive!'

'You've been out with him again since last Thursday?'

Thursday! She vaguely recalled telling Barden that she was meeting someone when they got back from Stratford—the rest of it would never go from her mind. Barden had kissed her, had…

'I'm trying to forget Thursday!' she said shortly.

And could have punched his head when he just wouldn't leave it alone. 'Him or me?' he grated.

Adrian had never figured. But these were dangerous waters—the very place for a red herring. 'Neither of you should get your hopes up,' she retorted loftily. 'I was out with Simon last night.'

Oh, dear—he was not a happy bunny! Barden positively glowered at her, and she knew then that he objected to her familiarity in telling him not to get his hopes up. She knew all too well that Barden hoped for nothing from her, but what was she supposed to do—sit there meekly and say nothing? To be that meek, she had discovered, was not in her nature. Besides, it was he who had started this personal discussion, not her. But apparently he was bored with the subject.

'Let me see your paperwork,' he ordered bossily—she'd have liked to have poked him in the eye with it!

Wednesday ended badly. Her employer was in a pig of a mood for the rest of the day. Even a call from his 'friend' Karla didn't seem to cheer him any, and Emmie went home of the view that if Barden Cunningham went to the States and never came back that would be fine by her.

The feeling didn't last. Within half an hour of reaching her flat, she wanted to be back with him whatever his mood.

Aunt Hannah rang her that night, and, again proving how independent and settled in her new environment she was becoming, asked if Emmie would mind if she didn't come to lunch on Sunday.

'You're going somewhere nice?' Emmie asked, knowing she would miss her while at the same time being glad for her.

'We're having a residents' meeting to discuss what we can do for a charity fayre. Everyone does so much for us,' Aunt Hannah explained, 'we thought we'd like to pay something back. They'll take a bit of organising, of course,' she said, of her fellow residents, obviously one of the leaders, 'but everyone seems to be keen.'

'Let me know if I can help,' Emmie offered, and had to

smile when Aunt Hannah declared stoutly that she would,
and meant it.

To Emmie's delight Barden seemed to have recovered
his good humour the next day, and was back to being
friendly, and, as far as Emmie was concerned, at his most
endearing.

She heartily hoped he was the same when the following
morning, while Dawn was in with him, Lisa Browne rang
to say that Mrs Whitford had left without saying where she
was going and had been away some while.

Emmie had just put the phone down when the connecting
door opened and, standing back to allow Dawn to precede
him, Barden came into her office.

Barden's glance went straight to Emmie. 'Problem,
Emmie?' he enquired calmly, observing her anxious expression.

'Aunt Hannah, she's…'

'Decamped?' he finished for her. Emmie nodded.
'You've got your car?' he questioned.

'Yes.'

'Off you go, then,' he instructed kindly.

'I'm sorry,' she apologised, feeling suddenly wretched.

'Don't be—you'll be here until eight tonight.'

He smiled, she found a smile, and Dawn, who by then
knew all about Aunt Hannah and her penchant for tripping
the light fantastic, smiled warmly too—and Emmie wasted
no more time.

She eventually found her absconding step-relative back
at her flat, having let herself in. 'I thought, as I wouldn't
be seeing you this weekend, that I'd come and see you
today,' she announced, appearing totally oblivious that
Emmie had a job to go to. 'Been shopping?' she enquired.

Emmie phoned Keswick House, then made some coffee
and chatted, and at last was able to drive her much loved
step-grandmother back to Keswick House. Emmie returned
to her place of work to find that Dawn—who would be

back later—had already left for her medical appointment, and that Barden, this being his last day in the office before his trip on Monday, was extremely busy.

He had time to ask if everything was all right, though, and Emmie was pleased to be able to tell him she had found Aunt Hannah at her flat. 'Which has to be a good sign,' she added. 'While it's a bit worrying that the rebel in her lets herself out of Keswick House without writing down where she's going in the ''Out'' book, it's good that she's remembered where I now live.'

She went back to her office and got on with some work, and was busily trying to make up for time lost when Barden strolled into her office. She looked up, expecting instruction of some sort, while trying to pretend that the next sixteen days without seeing him weren't going to be as bleak as she knew they were going to be.

But she was totally staggered when what Barden had come to see her about turned out to be nothing at all to do with work. He stated, 'I was very interested in some of the motorcycles on display the other Saturday.'

'The other Saturday when you were conned into taking Aunt Hannah to the Motorcycle Museum?' she asked, endeavouring her hardest to keep up.

'I wouldn't have put it exactly like that myself,' he murmured charmingly. 'I wonder, though, since I wouldn't mind going again tomorrow, if Mrs Whitford would like to come with me?'

'You want to take Aunt Hannah to Birmingham, to the…' Emmie stared at him, open-mouthed.

'We'll let you come with us if you promise to behave yourself,' he offered casually—and her heart sang, her spirits soared. If she saw him again tomorrow, that would make it only fifteen days.

Then her spirits sank. She could have wept. It wasn't fair. She loved him, and it just wasn't fair. 'Normally Aunt Hannah would have loved it.' She smiled—that or cry, and a girl did have some pride. 'But I'm not seeing her this weekend. That's part of the reason she came to see me today—she forgot I go to work.' Oh, crumbs, he wasn't interested in that; pull yourself together, do. 'I'm sorry.' Emmie rose above her crushing disappointment, 'I really appreciate your kindness, but Aunt Hannah has other plans for Saturday and Sunday, and I won't see her at all this weekend.'

'It was just a thought,' he said, and with that he returned to his office and, while feeling like howling, Emmie pretended to be never happier. But her feeling of utter wretchedness was compounded by a giant-size green blip when Karla Nesbitt rang to speak to Barden. Emmie put her through and knew that motorcycle museums would be the last thing on his mind for tomorrow.

Dawn left at five, but Emmie stayed on working with Barden until, just after seven, she took in the last of her paperwork and prepared to go home. 'That's everything,' she confirmed. 'I hope you have a good trip.' Take me with you, oh, please take me with you. 'I'll see you when you get back,' she chirruped lightly, and he'd never know how leaden her heart felt.

Barden was on his feet, his expression solemn, 'Be good, Emily Lawson,' he bade her.

'You too,' she smiled, and turned quickly away so he shouldn't see how her smile was slipping. She went home.

Emmie had seen Adrian briefly a couple of times in the week, and had been grateful that if he was curious about her ill-fitting-robe-clad overnight visitor he'd held his curiosity down. He dropped in for a coffee on Saturday morning, and was again unprying. But it was a sad fact that seeing Adrian was about the biggest highlight of that miserable Saturday for Emmie. She was certain that Barden was out with Karla Nesbitt.

She got out of bed on Sunday determined to keep busy,

but her flat was clean and shining from her efforts yesterday, and what chores she could find were soon completed.

Feeling unbearably restless, she took herself off for a walk—Barden was with her every step of the way. She found it was no use telling herself no good could come of her love for Barden; she already knew that. But it didn't make her feelings for him go away.

She returned to her flat, resolved her love for him was not going to make the slightest difference to her, and cooked a meal which she couldn't eat. Which was ridiculous. Womanising swine. She'd bet he never lost his appetite. He was probably tucking into his lunch right this minute—most likely with Karla Nesbitt as his companion. Emmie felt sick at heart when her mind ballooned to what else he might have an appetite for.

It was later that day, when the time had dragged around to just after six, when the phone rang in her silent flat, and Emmie nearly jumped out of her skin. She went to answer it.

'Hello?' she said, and nearly jumped again when she heard Barden's voice.

'You're not with anyone, I trust?' he enquired.

Like who? Pride arrived and shored up her melting bones. What about him? Was Karla with him? Oh, clear off, jealousy, you're making me ill. 'Why?' she asked, not about to let him know there wasn't a man about the place.

'I wondered if you could possibly come over and take some notes.'

Notes! They'd completed all his work Friday! Or so she'd thought. Perhaps, though, he'd spent the afternoon in his study and… The sun suddenly came out. His only appetite was—for work?

'Can't I take notes over the phone?' Instantly she wanted the words back. Clown! She'd just die if he said yes, and she lost this precious chance to see him again before he flew off.

'I'll give you dinner,' he coaxed, and Emmie loved him so much that, on hearing that friendly coaxing note, she felt she would do anything he asked.

'You're cooking it?' She couldn't keep a smile out of her voice.

'My housekeeper,' he replied.

She knew his home was called Hazeldene and was about an hour's run away. 'You'd better give me some directions,' she agreed, and delayed only long enough after his call to take a rapid shower, apply a little make-up and do a hasty check of her wardrobe.

Her red dress of fine wool won. She knew it suited her. It had short sleeves, a round neck and was perfectly plain. Emmie surveyed her reflection prior to donning her coat; her night-black hair was shiny and she had an excited light in her eyes. She'd have to watch that. But—she couldn't wait any longer. And, all right, so it was work, but—Barden was waiting to see her.

Her heart raced all the time while, following his directions, she drove nearer to his home. It seemed to race even faster when she turned into the driveway of Hazeldene, a large Georgian residence in its own grounds.

Leaving her car, she crossed the gravelled drive to the stout front door and rang the bell, but was not left waiting long before it was answered. She had supposed it would be his housekeeper who might open the door. But, and before Emmie was ready, it was Barden himself who stood there.

Swiftly she lowered her eyes—oh, how she loved him. 'Oh, hello,' she offered casually. 'Your housekeeper's busy in the kitchen?' she followed up, wanting to die at the inanity of her remark, feeling it was going to rank as one of those idiotic comments that come back again and again to haunt you.

'Dinner's all prepared—I've given Mrs Trevor the rest of the evening off,' Barden replied easily. If he thought her comment idiotic, he wasn't showing it for a moment.

'Come in, Emmie. I was beginning to think my directions were at fault.'

Emmie crossed the threshold into a wide and thickly carpeted hall, a smile playing around her mouth when, thinking she might have got there a trifle too quickly, it seemed Barden had expected her sooner.

'Let me have your coat,' he suggested, guiding her further along the hall and opening one of the many doors to reveal a downstairs cloakroom. Emmie shrugged out of her coat and he took it from her and hung it up, his eyes flicking over her and her red dress as he turned back to her. 'You've never worn that to the office,' he commented briefly.

'You'd have remembered?' She hadn't meant to be provocative—the words had just slipped out. 'I m-mean,' she stammered, 'I don't remember every suit you wear.'

'But then I never look anywhere as noteworthy as you,' he answered, his mouth curving slightly upwards at the corners.

She was in a meltdown situation again. He thought her noteworthy! She fought valiantly against his least little pleasantry affecting her, and managed some semblance of a brain cell by uttering, 'Talking of notes, I forgot to bring a notepad.'

'Not an insurmountable problem—I hardly expected you to.' He smiled, charmed her to her marrow, and, touching her lightly on her elbow, he led the way across the hall to a small kind of ante-room that housed an over-large thickly padded deep-cushioned sofa, an equally over-large thickly padded and deep-cushioned chair, and a couple of tables, one of which was close up to the sofa and carried a telephone and a sheaf of paperwork. 'I thought we'd work in here,' he informed her. 'A bit more congenial for a Sunday than my study.'

He made it seem more personal than business, and

Emmie was delighted. 'Anything you say,' she answered agreeably.

'According to Mrs Trevor, I'm to do things domestic in half an hour.'

'Has she written it down?' Emmie heard herself tease. Oh, Lord—get a grip!

Barden's mouth twitched. 'For that, you can have the burned bit,' he threatened, and she loved him. Then he said, 'We'll sit over there and I can give you an outline before we eat, then you can ask any questions during our meal.'

'Fine,' she answered, 'over there' being the over-large sofa. She went over to it and tried to calm the wild drumming of her heart when Barden, taking up the sheaf of paperwork, came and sat beside her.

'This is a list of...' he began, and Emmie realised why he was sitting that bit nearer to her when he extended the paper he had in his hand so she should read it with him.

Donning her professional hat, she moved in closer, raising a hand to the paper to get the view she wanted. Unfortunately her fingers touched his, and a kind of tingly sensation shot through her. She jerked back—and bumped against Barden.

And he, as she knew, never missed a thing. He turned in his seat to look at her. 'You're—twitchy,' he accused, his tone gentle, surprised even.

He was too close; his body, his face were too close. 'No, I'm not,' she denied, but for all she was trying desperately to stay professional her voice came out sounding all husky, and every bit as though she felt far from relaxed.

Barden's expression softened, and tenderly almost he trailed the back of his left hand down the side of her face. 'I'm sorry, Emmie,' he said kindly, 'perhaps working in here wasn't such a very good idea after all.'

'Are you deliberately trying to embarrass me?' she demanded, waking up with a vengeance—good grief, he was as good as saying that he was aware he had some kind of

effect on her, over and above their employer-employee relationship.

'What a sensitive soul you are!' Barden's tone was still
kindly. 'Of course I'm not trying to embarrass you. Though
I have to say that I'm—aware,' he selected, as if choosing
his words carefully, 'of a chemistry between you and me
that I'd prefer we kept under control.'

Talk about telling the truth and shaming the devil! She
felt red up to the top of her ears. 'Speak for yourself, Mr
Cunningham,' she stated bluntly. 'In the past you have
kissed me; I don't recall that I reciprocated in any way!'
She was ready to go home. To blazes with his notes!

What she wasn't ready for was that Barden should look
at her, slightly amazed, and then give a short bark of laughter. 'A gentleman might let that pass, but...'

'But you're no gentleman,' she finished for him, having
to cast her mind back to only a week last Thursday to recall
how he had kissed her and how she had put her arms
around him and had wanted more of his kisses.

'You'd prefer I lied—let you lie?'

'I prefer nothing—I'm going home!' she snapped, and
hated him and his wretched over-cushioned sofa because,
when she went to struggle out of its depths, it seemed determined to hang on to her.

Needing a bit of leverage, she pressed her hands down,
one to the sofa at one side of her, the other down somehow
on him—his well-muscled thigh. As though scalded she
snatched her hand away, and Barden stretched out a hand
to steady her—and somehow they ended up being closer
than ever.

'Don't let's part bad friends,' he said softly—and her
backbone went liquid again.

'Barden...' she murmured helplessly. The only thing in
her head then was that he was going away tomorrow for
two weeks, for two whole miserable, agonising tortoise-
ticking weeks, and she didn't want to part bad friends.

'Shall we kiss and make up?' he teased gently. It was the best suggestion she'd heard in a long while.

'As long as you don't accuse me of over-reciprocating,' she laughed—and reciprocated fully at the first touch of his mouth against her own.

He was going away. Two endlessly long weeks would pass before she saw him again was all she could think of as Barden gathered her into his arms. And, when one kiss just wasn't enough, she was enraptured by their mutual reciprocation.

'I shall miss you while I'm away,' he said against her mouth—and it was the nicest thing anyone had ever said to her. She wanted to tell him that she would miss him too, but she was shy, and then the moment was past, because his lips claimed hers once more and she couldn't have spoken had she been able to overcome that shyness.

'Barden.' She said his name breathlessly as that kiss ended.

'Emmie,' he murmured, just that, and nothing more. Nothing more was needed as his head came near again and he looked deeply into her warm and giving velvety brown eyes.

He kissed her then, gently at first before, his kiss gaining in intensity at her response, he held her yet closer to him and touched her lips with his tongue. While she clutched at him and her lips parted so passion flared again, soared, and Emmie was then mindless of all and everything save him and how he made her feel.

She wanted him, wanted him with everything that was in her. Mutually they seemed to lie down together, wrapped together in the cushions of the sofa. She felt the hard length of him as body to body, thigh to thigh they pressed against each other.

With a gentle, unhurried touch, Barden caressed her, and when his hands moved to the fastening of her dress Emmie felt not the slightest alarm. She kissed him as, without haste, he took her dress from her, excitement drumming in her temples. She unbuttoned his shirt, vaguely aware he had been wearing a light sweater when she'd arrived but having no notion as to when he had disposed of it.

'You're beautiful, Emmie, so beautiful,' he breathed, staring down at her. She smiled, an all-giving smile, and he lowered his head, and thrilled her with more kisses, a hand whisperingly caressing her right shoulder, to gradually move her bra strap to one side.

Barden kissed the satin-smooth skin of her shoulder, and trailed his mouth down to her breast. She felt a surge of shyness again when he caressed her breast and then undid her bra fastening.

'Barden!' she exclaimed huskily.

'Is that a ''don't''?' he said softly.

She melted again. 'I think—I'm not so used to this,' she said on a little gulp of breath.

'I know,' he answered understandingly.

'Oh, Barden,' she sighed, and, every movement unhurried, he gently removed her bra.

'May I look?' he requested, a teasing kind of note there, for all—or maybe because—he must know she had never been this intimate with a man before.

She almost told him then that she loved him. But swallowed once more instead, and asked, 'May I look at you?' and loved him some more when he understood that too, because he removed his shirt, and Emmie, in a kind of awe, stared at his broad manly chest—naked except for a liberal sprinkling of darkish hair. 'Oh,' she said, and liked as well as loved it when he didn't ask what the 'oh' was about.

Instead, he lowered his gaze to her entirely uncovered breasts. 'Oh, Emmie,' he murmured. 'Emmie, sweetheart.' And while she thrilled at his endearment he bent and kissed her lips, and she felt the warmth of his naked chest against her naked skin.

She had an idea she sighed his name again, but she

couldn't be sure about anything any more because while he kissed her, Barden's hands were caressing and stroking the swollen globes of her breasts, and desire for him was rising and rising in her. She wanted him; more than anything she wanted him. She loved him and wanted him.

He lowered his head to her breasts, nibbled at the hardened pink tip and must have known as she clutched at his naked back that he was making her mindless with wanting.

They lay close again, and as their legs entwined she suddenly realised—strangely without panic—that while she had been unaware of everything, save him and the riot of emotions he was evoking in her, he had parted with his trousers. Then was when she experienced a few moments of panic. But then, too, she experienced a person she had never known she could be—an aroused woman who delighted in stroking his hair-roughened chest, who delighted in touching him. Instinctively she stretched, to nibble and kiss his manly nipples, and heard a groan of wanting leave him. She felt his hands on her behind—if she'd been wearing tights, and she had been, she had no idea where they were now.

The intimacy of the warmth of his hands as they caressed inside her briefs made her clutch on to him, and she heard a sound of joyous delight as he pulled her to lie over him, just as if he was saying, At your pace, Emmie, at your pace. Again, as she lay over him, their legs entwined; she kissed him.

From far off she heard the sound of a telephone ringing, but it had nothing to do with her and Barden. She kissed him, touched her tongue to his lips the way his had touched hers. The phone continued to ring. She halted.

'Ignore it—and do that again,' Barden commanded.

Emmie was happy to oblige. She pressed herself to him, kissing him—and heard a groan that was most definitely the sound, even to her novice ears, of a man desirous of making complete love to her. His hands under her remaining garment pulled her yet closer to him, and—had it not been for the unremitting ring of the unanswered phone—Emmie would have been utterly captivated, utterly his for the taking.

But that phone, nearer at hand than she'd realised when she raised her head, was an unwanted intrusion in this new and enchanted land.

Emmie stretched out a hand to the offending instrument with no idea if she meant to merely stop it ringing or whether, perhaps from habit, to route the caller to Barden so that he, in the fewest words possible, should end the intrusion. Her mind, she had to admit, was totally elsewhere when, receiver in hand, she raised it in passing against her ear.

Only—she didn't get to proceed with the manoeuvre. Not then. For, chortling across the airwaves, she distinctly heard an all-male voice order in jocular fashion, 'Stop seducing your secretary, Barden, and speak to me!' And shock waves immediately swamped her.

As if someone had just thrown a bucket of icy water over her, Emmie came rocketing to her senses. Though not much was making sense to her just then—other than the appalling truth. Barden must have been in this situation many times before! Barden, to the caller's certain knowledge, was no stranger to the seduction couch! Barden—Barden the womaniser—had *planned* this seduction, *her* seduction! But she, she meant nothing to him!

Horrified, sick at heart at his treachery, she threw the phone at him and grabbed for her clothes. 'What...?' he began, moving to sit up as she leapt from the sofa. But she was off—if he had anything else to add, Emmie was in no mood to hear it.

CHAPTER SEVEN

AT LEAST if Emmie had had her way she would have shot out of Barden's home without saying another word to him. But there was the small matter of getting dressed and collecting her coat from the cloakroom first, and she hadn't so much as got the zip of her dress done up before she heard him tell his caller, 'I'll ring you,' and, that dealt with, Barden was off the sofa and trying to take a hold of her right arm.

'Don't touch me!' she yelled, backing, fumbling with her zip, her agitation wild. 'And put some clothes on!' she snapped—what she didn't need was to see him so deliciously near naked; her wayward senses were still threatening to make a nonsense of her.

To her surprise, though she was sure that it wasn't in order to calm her, Barden complied. By the time she was properly zipped up and attired—and making for the door—he was once more trouser- and shirt-clad, and having the effrontery to try to detain her.

'Don't go!' He attempted to halt her at the door.

'Would you mind getting out of my way?' Emmie demanded icily. She had to go; she was barely thinking straight—and she *needed* to think.

'You're in no state to drive,' he declared, refusing to allow her to open the door. 'Stay…'

'Like hell!' she breathed, and with power she hadn't known she possessed she wrenched the door open and sprinted across the hall to the cloakroom.

She had the cloakroom door open, and was reaching for her coat, when Barden's hand on her wrist stopped her.

140

'You're scared,' he gentled, his tone soothing. 'I've frightened you. I'm sorry, but I wouldn't…'

She snatched her wrist out of his grasp—he was just *too* much. 'You're darned right you wouldn't!' she yelled, still fearing that if he didn't let go she might yet give in to him. 'I wouldn't let you!' she stormed, and, her coat in her hand, she went flying to the door, yanking it open—only to be stunned by the sight of a most ravishing blonde who was just about to ring the doorbell.

'Karla!' Barden exclaimed, and Emmie didn't wait to hear any more.

Without a please or thank you, she pushed past Karla Nesbitt, hating her, hating him, and hoping to make it to her car before she broke down.

Emmie was in her car and had it moving, realising she had reserves of strength she'd never known about, because she wasn't yet in floods of tears. Someone banged on the driver's window.

She jerkily glanced up to see Barden, in his shirtsleeves on a freezing night, standing there clearly demanding she opened her window. She did—just sufficiently so he should hear. 'Do me a favour—catch pneumonia!' Then she put her foot down.

She saw him in her rearview mirror, just standing there. The next time she looked he'd gone. Five minutes later, though, and she saw there was a car following her. She had to slow down at some traffic lights—it was Barden's car. Obviously the cold night hadn't cooled his ardour!

Emmie jetted away from the lights and drove speedily and erratically and, she had to admit, just a little crazily for the next five or so miles. She had been paying pretty constant attention to her rearview mirror, but the next time she looked, there was no other car in sight.

Nor, as she proceeded the rest of the way more soberly, did Barden appear behind her again. No doubt he'd gone back to the waiting Karla, Emmie fumed, thoughts rattling around in her head about the way Barden had set the scene—even to the extent of giving his housekeeper the night off! And how more than likely, at this very moment, Karla Nesbitt would have taken her place on that well-padded deeply cushioned sofa.

By the time Emmie reached her flat she had convinced herself that Barden Cunningham was 'celebrating' his departure for the States tomorrow with someone else—namely Karla.

Emmie had only just got in when her phone started to ring. It wouldn't be him? Would it? Don't be stupid; he was busy finding his way around Karla's zippers and fasteners. Oh, how she hated him.

Her phone continued to ring—she determined not to answer it. That was until conscience-twisting thoughts that it might be Aunt Hannah phoning for a chat started to plague her.

She'd answer it—but she wasn't going to speak to *him*—if him it was. Emmie picked up the phone and said not a word—neither did the party at the other end. Which told her that it wasn't Aunt Hannah—it was unknown for her aunt to hold back.

The silence grew, persisted—Emmie broke first. 'And you can stuff your dinner!' she yelled. Silently, her caller terminated the call. A swift dialling of 1471 revealed that the caller's number was not known.

She knew then that it hadn't been Aunt Hannah, and, glad to feel hate for Barden Cunningham, Emmie went and got ready for bed. Then discovered that it was pointless having an early night—her head was too busy for sleep.

So much for that loathsome rat saying he'd prefer to keep the chemistry between them under control! All he'd been doing had been lulling her into a false sense of security—she could see that now. No wonder he'd given his housekeeper the rest of the night off. He wouldn't want his Mrs

Trevor bursting into that small and—what was it?—'more congenial for a Sunday' ante-room, would he? I'll say it was congenial. Just nice and cosy for a 'congenial' seduction.

Which brought her straight back to the stunning-looking Karla Nesbitt. Oh, how she wished she had never laid eyes on her. It had been enough to know of Karla's existence— to see for sure, as anticipated, that Karla was elegant and sophisticated into the bargain, was something Emmie just hadn't needed. What Karla was doing ringing the doorbell at Hazeldene Emmie had no wish to speculate. But—didn't seem able to stop herself from doing so. Had Barden thought her 'note-taking' wouldn't take all that long? Had he arranged for Karla to call later? Hang on, though, even as fresh spiteful jealous barbs speared her Emmie was recalling that Barden had definitely mentioned dinner. He'd definitely invited her to dinner. So where did Karla come in? Perhaps for the sweet course, Emmie thought sourly.

Endeavouring to get both Barden Cunningham and Karla Nesbitt out of her head, Emmie was forced to come to the sad conclusion that if Barden had *not* been expecting Karla to call—and from the way Emmie remembered it Karla hadn't been on his mind at the time—then the blonde sophisticate must be on *very* friendly terms with him. Who but a very good female friend would just drop by without thinking to make a prior arrangement? He had, Emmie recalled—remembering his exclaimed 'Karla!' when he'd seen her—been a shade surprised to see her on his doorstep.

After a fitful night with Barden, and a liberal sprinkling of Karla, filling her head, Emmie got up at her usual time the next morning, but had never felt less like going to work. She got ready just the same, and was within ten minutes of leaving her flat when her phone rang. She knew it wouldn't be Barden this time—by her reckoning he was on his way to the airport.

'Hello?' she queried, on lifting the receiver—and nearly dropped it when Barden answered.

'I hoped I'd get you before you left for the office,' he informed her, sounding cool and in charge and just the same as he always did—and, while she had spent the most wretched of nights, it was all too plain that he hadn't missed a wink of sleep.

It just wasn't fair! Her pride came rushing to the fore, refusing to be stamped down when all logic would have advised caution. 'I'm not going to the office,' she told him loftily—put that in your flute and play it!

'You're not?'

Oh, dear, there was a definite edge coming to his voice. 'Not!' She refused to back down—and pride pushed her on. 'I'm leaving,' announced pride, when its owner knew she just couldn't afford to give up this job that paid so well.

But she had angered him, she realised, either by her words or the lofty way she'd said them. Before she could retract her statement that she intended leaving he, to her absolute dismay, was snarling furiously, 'Correction, Miss Lawson—you've left!'

'Left!' she gasped witlessly. 'How…?' She started to get herself together. 'You're dismissing me?' she challenged—her own anger not very far behind his. 'On what grounds?' she demanded. If he so much as mentioned their 'chemistry' last night, she'd…

'Try misinformation at job interview!' He stopped her dead in her tracks.

'You *pig*! You utter pig! You know…'

'I know that you were lying your pretty little head off at your job interview when you were misinforming me about your lack of commitments. I've since learned for myself of your tardiness with regard to time-keeping, I—'

'I was late *once*!' she butted in stormily.

'Not to mention your absenteeism,' he went on, as though he hadn't heard her.

'I've always made that lost time up!' she flared angrily.

Only to have her pride rear up totally out of her control when, his anger dipping slightly, he mockingly drawled, 'Anyone would think you didn't want to leave after all, Emily.'

And that taunt was just too much. 'You can keep your job, Cunningham!'' she yelled. 'I wouldn't work for you if you paid me triple and in diamonds!' It was a toss-up which one of them ended the call first.

For all of five minutes after the call ended Emmie fumed about her ex-employer. The reality started to descend. Oh, pride, wretched, wretched pride—I just can't afford you, Emmie realised.

Where Dawn was concerned there were several people who sprang to mind who would be more than willing to help her out, Emmie knew. Which didn't make Emmie feel any less guilty for not being there to help the mother-to-be. From her own point of view, though, she needed that job—oh, what an idiot, love, pride and all else had made her.

Although, thinking about it, she had to be glad she had acted the way she had. Because, on playing back her conversation with Barden, as she did many times in the next hour, Emmie came to realise that, starting with 'I hoped I'd get you before you left for the office' Barden had only been ringing anyway to tell her not to go to the office—ever again.

She was glad, glad, glad she'd got in first to tell him she was leaving. Which was not at all conducive to her earning her living. She toyed with the idea of ringing Dawn and apologising for leaving so abruptly, but guessed that Mr Efficiency would have been in touch—either before or after his call to her—acquainting Dawn with the news. And anyhow, Dawn might well ask awkward questions, such as why, if Barden hadn't told Dawn why he'd sacked her, she had left. She could hardly tell Dawn that Barden had been in the middle of seducing her when, almost too late, she'd come to her senses.

Instead of ringing Dawn, Emmie rang a temping agency, went for interview, and found work to keep her busy to the end of that week. She rang Lisa Browne at Keswick House to tell her where she could be contacted, and found the temporary work uncomplicated and unchallenging. She bought a paper on her way home to check the 'Situations Vacant' column.

There was nothing remotely as good as the job she had that very morning been dismissed from. Emmie determined she would not be down-hearted. She invited Adrian for a meal the next night, and heard he had bumped into his ex-girlfriend and had her new phone number—and was hopeful.

Emmie wished him well, it was a little cheering to hear of someone else's love-life taking a bit of an upward swing—hers was at rock-bottom, as were her spirits. There were no Situations Vacant that sounded in the least appealing that night either.

Determined to look on the bright side, she rang Aunt Hannah after her meal on Wednesday evening. 'You've nothing planned for this weekend, I hope?' she managed to tease.

'I'll come to you Saturday afternoon, if I may—I'll be glad of a break. We've got a meeting here on Saturday morning, but trying to get this lot here to agree to anything is impossible—they're worse than a lot of schoolchildren.'

For all her step-relative was having a general moan, she sounded in a happy frame of mind, and positive about having been elected to be part of the recently formed residents' committee.

Emmie came away from the phone resolving to be more positive herself. To that end she circled three possibles in that evening's Situations Vacant column, and took out her writing materials.

She had penned only one application, however, when her phone rang. She wasn't expecting a call, and had just spoken with Aunt Hannah. But it was not unknown for Aunt Hannah to ring back with something she had forgotten. Emmie answered the phone with a warm and pleasant, 'Hello?'

She immediately went from warm and pleasant to shocked and stunned when her call turned out to be of the transatlantic variety. 'Hello, Emmie,' Barden greeted her, his tone a shade on the cool side, she rather thought, but hadn't got her head sufficiently together to be very sure about that. But, whatever his tone, hers was non-existent when her voice failed her completely. 'It occurred to me,' he went on, when nothing at all came from her, 'that perhaps we were both a little over-hasty the last time I rang.'

Her heart was racing. What was he saying? She tried desperately to fight against the love-weakened shell she had become, who wanted to agree with everything he said. 'You may have been—I wasn't!' she found out of a stubborn somewhere. Was he saying that she wasn't dismissed after all? Her brain started to stir—she wanted to work for him, she did, she did, but...

'Oh, come on, Emmie, you know you need to work,' Barden said toughly—and Emmie woke up with a bang.

He was *pitying* her! How *dared* he? He knew her financial situation, the fact that she needed the kind of salary he paid but—how dared he pity her? She wanted his love, not his pity.

'I *am* working!' she snapped, proud and starting to be furious into the bargain.

'*Where?*'

It hadn't taken long for his aggression to arrive on the scene, had it! 'That's none of your business!' she retorted hotly. 'I shan't be asking you for a reference!' With that, afraid her tongue might run away with her, and that she might reveal some of her hurt, Emmie slammed down her phone.

It did not ring again that night, and Emmie spent the rest of the evening—her letters of application forgotten—in knowing she had done the only thing possible. But that didn't make her feel any better.

Logic, screaming logic, stabbed at her the whole of the time, reminding her—as if she needed any reminding—that she just couldn't afford to turn down the chance of rein-statement in a job that paid so well.

But, ignoring logic, her emotions well and truly out of gear, she had turned down that chance. She wished Barden had not telephoned, and yet—and she owned that love had made her a mass of contradictions—she hungered for the sound of his voice.

But she couldn't take his pity. No way did she *want* his pity. She had seen his kindness before, and guessed that his motive in calling her had probably stemmed from that quality she had witnessed in him.

For ageless minutes Emmie dwelt on his goodness of heart—only to come to minutes later to recall the enchant-ment of being in his arms on Sunday, and to start to dis-count entirely that his motives had been kindness at all.

The miserable toad had set her up last Sunday—don't forget that, Emily Lawson. For heaven's sake, was she so naive that she couldn't see further than the end of her nose? Seduction was the name of the game here, not kindness.

Well, forget it, Mr Won't-take-no-for-an-answer Cunningham. She was not going to be 'one of his women'. Just as she was not going back to work for him. Neither was she going to have an affair with him—the ultimate outcome of which would only mean job loss anyway—and Aunt Hannah's security was still, as it had to be, of prime importance.

Emmie sighed—perhaps she'd got it wrong and he didn't want an affair. But what did she know? What she *did* know was that she loved him so, and that from the way their telephone conversation had ended she reckoned there was a good chance that an affair was off the menu. She went to bed with a throbbing head.

The weekend arrived on leaden feet, and on Saturday morning, after a few chores, Emmie took herself off bright and early to the shops. She would be picking up Aunt Hannah that afternoon—Aunt Hannah, different to the last, preferred 'shop' cake to home-made. Emmie was quite laden by the time she got back.

She was just about to go up the steps to the house when Adrian came bounding out—she had never seen him looking so happy! 'I saw you from my window!' he announced, smiling broadly.

'You've passed all your exams!' she teased.

'Is it obvious?' he asked, automatically taking some of her plastic carriers. 'Better than that—' he grinned joyously '—I've just rung Tina—she's agreed to go out with me tonight!'

They were standing at the bottom of the steps and, had her hands not been full, Emmie felt so pleased for him she might have given him a hug. She settled for giving him a beaming smile—and discovered that Adrian was so ecstatic he could barely contain himself and, on impulse, leaned forward and kissed her.

He had never done such a thing before, but, while she was unoffended, he looked a little startled by his own behaviour. He was still on cloud nine, though, when he suggested, 'Fancy a cup of coffee?'

'I'd better make it,' she agreed. 'From the look of you, you'd probably end up scalding yourself.'

Adrian helped carry her shopping into her flat, but could talk of little else but Tina and his good fortune. 'She's not the sort of woman who would accept an invitation to go out with me if she was only playing,' he opined, and regaled Emmie with his hopes for the future and how he would take great care not to neglect Tina ever again if they ever did get back together again, as he so sincerely hoped.

He was still on a high, whistling his little head off, as she saw him out and he went up to his own flat. Emmie couldn't have been more pleased for him. But, with Barden ever a dominant force, Adrian was soon forgotten. It seemed to be a waste of effort trying to out Barden from her mind. Perhaps one day soon more than thirty seconds would tick by without him paying her head a visit.

She was never hungry these days, but forced herself to eat a snack before she left her flat just after two to go and pick up Aunt Hannah. The weather had improved, and while still cold it was sunny as Emmie parked her car and rang the bell at Keswick House.

A care assistant Emmie hadn't seen before answered the door to her. 'Mrs Whitford is expecting me,' Emmie began to explain.

'She's gone out,' June, according to her lapel badge, replied.

'Out?' Oh, crumbs—keep calm. She might have taken it into her head to come to her by taxi. 'Er—did Mrs Whitford say where she was going?' Emmie asked.

'She did,' June replied, and Emmie began to relax a little—at least Aunt Hannah hadn't done one of her little flits. 'She wrote the address down in the book,' the care assistant added, though she did pause to ask what her connection with Mrs Whitford was, and, when Emmie enlightened her, she invited her in.

'I expect Mrs Whitford has taken a taxi to see me.' Emmie smiled, wanting to be on her way and to get back home before Aunt Hannah should take it into her head to wander off. But, fully expecting that when June had inspected the 'Out' book she would say Aunt Hannah had filled in Emmie's address, Emmie got the shock of her life when June read an entirely different address from the book.

'She's gone to… Can't read her writing. Hazeldene. That's it. Is that where you live?'

'*Hazeldene!*' Emmie gasped.

'Yes, it's in…'

Emmie knew full well where Hazeldene was. 'Let me see,' she requested, more sharply than she'd meant to, hoping against hope that June had read it incorrectly—though since the house where she lived didn't have a name she feared the worst.

The care assistant, starting to look concerned, showed her the book—and there it was, Hazeldene, followed by most of the rest of Barden's address. 'There's nothing wrong, is there?' June asked. 'I mean, she told Mrs Vellacott she'd been invited to lunch and…'

To lunch! Ye gods! 'No, everything's fine,' Emmie assured her—and got out of there as quickly as she could.

She drove fast, trying not to panic. Invited to lunch? Where on earth had Aunt Hannah got that idea from? Emmie sped towards Hazeldene, trying to remember when she had ever told Aunt Hannah where her employer lived.

She couldn't actually remember ever having told her. That wasn't to say, though, that she never had, because she and Aunt Hannah discussed all sorts of inconsequential matters. And, of course, since Barden had been out for hours with Aunt Hannah that day he had taken her to the Motorcycle Museum, he could very likely have revealed to her himself where he lived.

With her mind in a turmoil Emmie slowed down as she turned into the drive at Hazeldene, her eyes scanning right and left and everywhere, hoping for a sight of Aunt Hannah. But of Aunt Hannah she saw not a sign.

Emmie parked her car and got out, her eyes still searching. She approached the stout front door and stood at the doorbell she had rung what seemed a lifetime away but was in fact only last Sunday. Perhaps the housekeeper would tell her if Aunt Hannah had called. Perhaps she could leave a message if she hadn't.

Emmie stretched a hand and rang the bell, hoping against hope that Mrs Trevor was in. Her only relief in any of this was that Barden, thank goodness, was absent in America, and with luck would never get to hear of any of it.

The stout front door began to open, and as her heart started to thunder so, with ever-widening astonished eyes, Emmie stared at the tall, no-nonsense grey-eyed man who stood there. Luck! Emmie knew then that her luck had just run out. What was Barden doing here? He was supposed to be on the other side of the Atlantic!

Without speaking, Barden, since it was she who had slammed the phone down on him the last time they had been in communication, politely waited for her to speak. For no reason—though half a dozen presented themselves, not least the one that the last time he had seen her she had been as near naked as made no difference—Emmie went scarlet.

'Is Aunt Hannah here?' came hurtling from her like a shot from a cannon.

Her question went unanswered—but he wasn't cutting her dead. 'Come in,' Barden invited, his eyes on her flushed skin, a smile lurking there somewhere.

Emmie had enough to cope with without her heart racing energetically to see him so unexpectedly. But she was grateful that he wasn't ordering her off his premises, and entered his home. She had thought he might ask while they were where they stood why she thought her step-relative might be paying him a visit, but he led the way into a superb drawing room that had several rather special-looking oil paintings adorning its walls, was thickly carpeted and housed several deeply cushioned sofas, similar to the one she had seen—experienced—in the ante-room.

She needed a clear head, and didn't want to think about the sofa experience, or any of it. 'Aunt Hannah...' she be-

gan rapidly. Only the rest of the sentence got lost somewhere when she saw Barden turn at the drawing room door
and firmly close it.

He turned back to her. 'Take a seat, Emmie,' he invited,
calm, where a riot of emotions were battering at *her*.

She declined. 'Aunt H—'

'Mrs Whitford is safe.' He put her mind at rest straight
away.

'You've seen her? She's been here?' She was gabbling;
Emmie slowed down. 'You say she's safe. Safe where?'

The smile that had been promising didn't make it. Seriously Barden studied her for long, silent moments before
he at last revealed, 'Mrs Whitford's out with my father,
actually.'

Emmie's wide eyes grew larger. 'Your—father?' she
gasped, feeling a need to check on her hearing.

'He's taken her for a spin in his Austin Healey,' Barden
stunned her further. 'She was delighted to go,' he added
pleasantly.

Austin Healey! Delighted…! Of course she would be.
She'd be tickled pink at the thought of having a drive in
his father's classic car. Oh, heavens, this was so embarrassing. Obviously Barden's father had been paying him a
visit when Aunt Hannah had arrived. Just as she'd conned
Barden into taking her to Birmingham that time, she had
probably seen the Austin Healey parked outside and had
persuaded his father to take her for a drive in it.

'I'm sorry,' she mumbled miserably, loyalty to her step-
relative preventing her from adding more of an apology
than that. 'Um—have you any idea how long they'll be?'

Barden studied his watch. 'About an hour or so, I should
think,' he answered, still in that same pleasant tone.

'Thank you,' Emmie said primly, making for the door
and expecting him to move away from it. 'I'll come back
later, if I may,' she stated politely.

Barden was already shaking his head, and had not moved

so much as a half-inch to let her out from the door. 'I don't think so,' he informed her coolly.

'You—don't think…' She halted. She was shaking inside already. *This* close was close enough. She got herself into more of one piece. 'Surely you can't object if I wait outside for my step-grandmother to return,' she challenged firmly—and was totally foxed for several seconds when it appeared that that was exactly what he did do.

'I object most strongly,' Barden replied, and made her eyes shoot wide when he added, 'I haven't set this up only for you to—'

Emmie stopped him right there, her feelings of being totally foxed rapidly starting to clear in that last half-sentence. 'Set this up?' It was she who challenged this time. My stars—was he a master at 'setting things up' or wasn't he?

But any scant notion which flitted into her head that Barden was again setting her up for seduction swiftly evaporated when he elucidated, 'Because it is of some—very great importance to me—I purposely rang my father and asked if he would drive over in one of his classic cars.'

'To— In order…' This was crazy. She tried again. 'So he should give Aunt Hannah…' It didn't make sense.

'So you and I could have a—talk.'

That didn't make sense either. But what did? Her heart-beat was racing like an express train. 'Talk?' she questioned, with what few wits she could find.

'We need to discuss a few matters, Emily Lawson—you and I.'

'Discuss?' She knew she was sounding like a parrot—but that was how she was starting to feel—bird-brained.

'Our discussion has waited much too long from my point of view.'

She strove to string a sentence together. 'You—you're—um—not due back for another week,' she reminded him, knowing that had got nothing to do with it, but it was the best she could manage.

'I came in a hurry,' Barden replied. And very nearly shattered her completely, when he added, 'I came in a hurry—to see you.'

She wasn't sure her mouth didn't fall open. 'You came—to see me!' she exclaimed. And suddenly all her instincts were on guard. She might not be doing very well in the intelligence department just then. But all her instincts were alert and telling her that the womanising swine was up to something. Oh, very definitely he was up to something—a pity she wasn't playing!

CHAPTER EIGHT

'WELL I'm not here to see you!' Emmie stated belligerently. Confound it! He thought he could set her up and she'd go along with it! 'I'm here to collect Aunt Hannah!' she told him firmly. He could play what game he liked—she hoped he liked solitaire. 'I don't know why you've gone to—to the lengths you have to—to…and I'm not in the slightest interested,' she inserted heatedly, lest he should think differently. 'But—but…' She was running out of steam. 'But I think it's diabolical of you to make an elderly lady get into a t-taxi and come over h—'

'Mrs Whitford didn't arrive by taxi,' Barden cut in mildly, his eyes seeming very watchful.

Emmie knew her agitation was showing—well, why wouldn't it? 'Well, it's for sure she never walked it!' she erupted.

'I do wish you'd calm down, Emmie. I'm fully aware of your fiery temper, but we'll get nowhere…'

'In case you hadn't noticed, I'm not interested in getting anywhere with…er—where you're concerned,' she blew. Oh, grief, she'd nearly said 'with you'. But what the heck was he meaning anyway?

She turned her back on him and tried to find some semblance of calm. She needed to be calm; she had nearly slipped up in temper then and coupled them together. She couldn't afford such slips. She just wanted to collect Aunt Hannah and get out of there.

'Look,' Barden addressed her back—patiently for him, she realised. 'Mrs Whitford isn't going to be back for quite a while yet. Why don't you take a seat? We could use the time while we're waiting to…' He hesitated—that wasn't

156

like him; Emmie didn't like it. 'To iron out a few misunderstandings,' he continued.

Emmie didn't like that any better. She hadn't misunder-
stood a thing. For heaven's sake, they'd both been near
naked! What was there to misunderstand about that? Had
it not been for that phone call at that timely moment—or
untimely moment, depending on your viewpoint—Barden's
last little set-up would have worked a treat.

She turned to face him then, her anger renewed.
Apparently she still wasn't going to be allowed to go outside and wait for Aunt Hannah. Emmie took a few paces
away from him—it seemed ridiculous, suddenly, to stand
glaring at him for the next sixty minutes, or however long
it took for her step-relative to return. She went over to one
of the sofas and, as he had earlier invited, took a seat.

She was not too happy when Barden, looking pleased at
his small victory, came and pulled up a chair not two yards
away. 'So, if Aunt Hannah didn't come by taxi, how *did*
she get here?' Emmie demanded to know. He wanted to
talk, to discuss? They'd talk all right, but only about matters *she* wanted to raise.

Knowing him, however, and his get-to-the-bottom-of-ev-
erything kind of brain, she had to own to feeling a mite
surprised when he allowed her that same right. Instead of
embarking on his own discussion, he answered her.

His answer, however, stunned her into a brief silence
when, his eyes on her, he stated, 'I drove her here.'

She stared at him, blinked, and managed a two-word sentence. '*You* did?'

'I may have mentioned that I wanted to—discuss...'
There it was, that hesitation again—as if he was selecting
his words very carefully! '...something, with you,' he continued slowly, going on to stun her further when, having—
skilfully, it seemed to her—brought the subject away from
what she wanted to discuss, he added, 'I called at your flat
early on this morning—you weren't in.'

'You called at…' Her brain seized up momentarily. She just couldn't get the hang of this. Barden could have practically any woman he chose. His desire for her in particular wouldn't have him going to these extraordinary lengths, would it? 'I—er—was out shopping,' she said witlessly, while she mentally scoffed at the notion that Barden was so desirous of a fling with her that he had raced home from the States a week early to get it under way. For goodness' sake, wake up, do!

'I know,' Barden commented—but she was at a loss to know *what* he knew. 'It was—urgent that I see you,' he stated, which didn't help. 'When you weren't in I went to call on Mrs Whitford.'

Emmie's brain started to stir. 'You went to ask her where I was?'

'I didn't get to see her then, but I saw a care assistant who remembered me from that time we dropped Mrs Whitford back at Keswick House.' Oh, don't remind me! Aunt Hannah had referred to him as her 'granddaughter's fiancé'. 'She told me that Mrs Whitford was chairing a meeting and that she didn't have the nerve to interrupt unless it was dreadfully important—and would it wait until my fiancée collected her grandmother that afternoon?'

Spare my blushes, why don't you! 'You want me to apologise again for that?' Emmie asked shortly.

'How could I when you blush so beautifully?' Barden asked softly.

She almost smiled—then realised she was being seduced! 'Cut that out, Cunningham!' she snapped, refusing to blush ever again.

'You're beautiful,' he said quietly, but before she could fire up again he continued, 'I was heartily relieved after my visit to Keswick House to know that you hadn't gone away somewhere for the weekend, but—'

'Relieved?' Emmie questioned, deciding it was time she bucked her ideas up. Barden was clever; she'd seen him in action. But just because she craved to be in his arms, that didn't mean she was all weak and feeble and ready to give in. She would fight it, and him, all the way. Challenge him all the way—because she was now growing more and more convinced that Barden was either building her up so he could drop her down again from a great height—though why he would do that she hadn't worked out yet—or he was on the way to asking her to have an affair with him. She loved him too much to be able to bear it when, as would happen in a very short space of time—she knew it— he would move on to the next refusing, and therefore challenging, female in his orbit.

'I have a meeting in New York on Monday—it's important to the company and its employees that I be there.'

'You're going back to the States?' she questioned seriously.

Barden looked at her steadily. 'I flew back only to see you, Emmie,' he said.

Her heart, which had been beating erratically since he had opened the door to her, gave a lurch, and another excited racing beat. 'W-when did you arrive?' she stammered.

'I flew in on Concorde last night,' he replied.

He'd said he had come in a hurry to see her, but—in *that* much of a hurry? She was starting to be more confused than ever! Perhaps she'd got it all wrong. Barden flying home wasn't about business, by the sound of it. But surely a man of his standing, his sophistication, wouldn't break into an important two-week business trip to jet home on Concorde merely because he wanted an affair with *her*?

'You flew in last night, you said?' she recapped, feeling her way.

'I did,' he agreed firmly, his eyes ever watchful on her.

'Forgive me for being slow—I'm feeling a mite confused here,' she confessed.

'Take all the time you need,' he invited kindly, surprisingly kind for a man in such a hurry—though he did seem a trifle pleased to see that she had, for the moment, lost her fiery edge.

'And you flew in to—only to talk to me, to have a discussion with me?' She was still feeling her way.

'I felt it vital—feel it of the utmost importance—to have—a discussion with you, Emmie.'

She was starting to melt again. He only had to say her name in that gentle-sounding way and she was about to crumble. But this would never do. 'Don't they have telephones in New York?' she asked sharply. My stars, he'd had her going there for a moment!

'They do, and if you remember I tried that. Last Wednesday I rang—and had the phone slammed down in my ear for my trouble.'

So this *was* about business. Emmie didn't know if she was disappointed or what she was, but her anger with him was on the loose again when she flared hotly, 'If you've come personally to offer me my job back out of pity again, you can jolly well—'

'Pity!' he broke in, seeming amazed that she had put that interpretation on his phone call. 'I don't pity you, you proud nitwit.'

'Thanks!'

'You're sweet and kind and uncomplaining of your lot, and I admire you tremendously.' Oh, she wished he wouldn't; she was feeling all shaky inside again. 'But never have I pitied you,' he went on, then hesitated, began again, 'I…' Then he seemed to change his mind, and said, 'I rang because I needed to talk to you. To open with a small discussion on work seemed at the time to be quite a good introduction to—'

'When have *you* ever been backward about coming to the point?' She managed to find sufficient backbone to challenge him.

'Never—until I met you. I didn't know what nerves

were—until you came along,' he half pole-axed her by
saying.

Emmie stared at him in amazement. She admitted he
seemed to hold the exclusive rights on scattering her brain-
power, but was he truly saying that he had needed an introductory subject because he'd been *nervous* about coming
to the point?

'You—um—surprise me,' was about all she could find
to say. Surprised? Dumbfounded, more like!

'I've surprised myself countlessly since I've known you,'
Barden revealed. And it was all too much. He was trying
to tell her something here. She didn't know what it was;
she had gone past hoping to be able to work it out.

'I'm—listening,' she mumbled. It was the small encouragement he had been looking for.

'After that phone call—that disastrous phone call when
you more or less told me I could forget any idea of your
coming back to work for me—I knew then that as much as
needing to talk to you I—needed to *see* you.'

Warily she stared at him. 'You needed to—see—me?'
she checked.

'I almost rang you back and asked you to fly out to me.'

Stunned, her eyes huge in her face, she looked at him.
'But—you decided against it?'

'I had to. I'd been thinking in terms of asking you to
join me in your PA capacity.'

'Naturally.'

He allowed himself a half-smile. 'Naturally,' he agreed.
'But you'd just as good as told me you'd starve before
you'd come back to work for me. And it was then that I
knew I was done with pretence anyway.' He broke off to
study her seriously for some long moments. And then, after
that short while, 'I wanted to see you—because you're you,
Emmie,' he stated quietly, his eyes holding hers, searching
hers as if seeking some kind of reaction. Numbly, Emmie

stared back. 'Which is why I flew in last night—to see and to talk to you.'

Emmie coughed to clear a suddenly nervous throat. 'And—it has nothing to do with work?' she asked, feeling her way again.

'Not one solitary thing,' Barden assured her.

And suddenly, with what sense of comprehension he had left her with, Emmie realised she had been right in her first supposition. 'I'm sorry to disappoint you, Barden—' she began, as steadily as she could, doing her best to keep things civil, polite.

'*Disappoint!*' The word seemed strangled from him; he even seemed to her eyes to have lost some of his colour. 'You're saying you aren't interested in—'

'I'm not!' she interrupted quietly, loving him so much it hurt—as did it hurt to see how his jaw tensed, as if he was striving for some kind of control. 'I can't have an affair with you...'

'*Affair!*' he exclaimed, startling her by the strength of his tone. 'Who the hell's asking you to have an affair?' he demanded.

And that was just the end for Emmie—she'd got it wrong. She had determined never to blush again—but she blushed furiously to the roots of her hair. 'I'm sorry!' she gasped, shooting to her feet and diving for the door. 'I'll go and wait in my car!'

She was at the door when Barden caught her. She struggled to be free—he refused to let her go. 'Be still.' He tried to hush her.

'Let me go.' She struggled and pushed, but found she was going nowhere.

'Not yet—not ever, you daft crackpot.'

Emmie stilled, found the nerve to pull back and look at him. He was looking encouragingly down at her. She wanted to question that 'not ever' but couldn't, so she repeated, 'Daft crackpot?'

'Forgive me.' He smiled. 'But you did get it all so wrong.'

'I...' She couldn't finish.

'Don't be embarrassed, little love,' he urged gently, and she was glad he was still holding her because that 'little love', even without his gentle tone, was threatening to turn her legs to water.

'I'm—sorry. I got it wrong,' she said, with what dignity she could muster.

'The fault is mine,' he accepted. 'This is new territory for me. Take that, and a pinch of nerves—and I'm succeeding in making a total hash of everything I've rehearsed since I made up my mind to come and g— see you.' Helplessly, her heart once more reacting like crazy, Emmie stared at him. 'Be kind to me, Emmie,' he requested. 'And give me the chance I need to tell you what it is I *do* want.'

If it wasn't work, and it wasn't an affair... Her brain seemed stymied, unable to take her any further. But, since she was no longer struggling or resisting, Barden, keeping one arm about her, as if still not convinced she would not bolt, turned her back towards the sofa.

He seated himself next to her this time, and Emmie, striving to get herself together, pulled out of his arm. Not that it did much good. He was so dear to her, and so close.

He half turned in his seat so he could look at her. 'To save any more misunderstandings, Emmie, I'll start at the beginning. But first of all I think I've got to bite the bullet, and risk you laughing your beautiful head off, by telling you that...' He took a long breath, and then, to her utter astonishment, very clearly said, '...that—I love you.'

Emmie stared at him solemnly, in shock at what he had just said, while every scrap of intelligence she possessed was battling to take it in. He loved her—oh, the joy if that was true. She had always known him honest and straightforward, but—despite his vehement denial—was it really an affair he wanted after all? Was 'I love you' just the way he went in pursuit of a conquest? She had no way of knowing. What she *did* know, though, was that she did not want to be just another of his conquests.

'You're not laughing,' he said.

She was afraid to give him too much encouragement in case he saw how it was with her. And yet if he did care for her, as he said, and this wasn't all part of the 'affair' scenario, she just had to find out more of his 'love' for her.

She found her voice—albeit that it was so husky suddenly it didn't sound like her voice at all. 'That's probably because I'm not experienced in these matters.'

'That makes two of us.' He smiled.

Emmie felt on extremely shaky ground. 'Er—when—um—did it start?' she wanted to know, looking at him, trying to gauge him, trying to use her brain and not her heart. 'This…' She coughed; the word 'love' had got stuck. 'This—um—caring…?'

Barden took over. 'There am I, sitting at my desk one Tuesday, with a job application form in front of me completed by a Miss Emily Lawson. On the face of it she was eminently suited for the position. Would her voice match up?'

'No point in having an efficient assistant PA if she's got a voice like Donald Duck,' Emmie murmured. So far, so good. Though she felt overwhelmingly stressed to know more of Barden's stated 'I love you'—oh, he couldn't, could he?—she felt she could cope in these neutral waters. He might, of course, only be talking to get her to feel more comfortable with him before he went for the big crunch of telling her what all this was about. But for the moment she was prepared to go along with him. 'So, you—um—invited me for interview?'

'I knew you had a lovely voice. The surprise was that you were equally lovely,' he commented. 'Even if you so nearly didn't get the job.'

'There were other applicants just as well qualified?' Emmie supplied.

'True, but that wasn't the reason. I knew you were hiding something when I put that question about commitments.'

'Did you?' she gasped.

'You're not a very good liar.'

'I do my best,' she said, and he smiled—almost as if he loved her. But she mustn't think about that; the let-down would be too intolerable.

'I should have ruled you out there and then,' Barden continued. 'Normally I would have. But I was just about to discover that nothing I thought of as normal would ever be normal again.'

'Because—of me?'

'Oh, yes, because of you,' he replied. 'There you are at interview—pleasant, in a detached kind of way, but hiding something. I should have known then—when I went against my better judgement and took you on—that I was taking on trouble.'

'Trouble?' she questioned. 'I didn't think there was too much wrong with my work.'

'There was nothing at all the matter with your work,' he told her. 'In fact you were very soon proving you were every bit as good as you'd said you were. The trouble you caused me had nothing to do with work.'

'You're saying—er—that I was trouble to you—personally?' she questioned nervously.

'From day one,' he confirmed unhesitatingly. 'Your aloofness I could just about go along with—in fact I told myself it was preferable than to have someone in my office who was over-friendly. But your colossal arrogance was something else again.'

'You're referring to my getting it all wrong about you and Roberta Short?' Emmie guessed, and confessed, 'I thought you were going to sack me when we had that row.'

'And I couldn't think why the hell I hadn't—though of course I know why now.'

Emmie shot him a startled look. Was he saying—because he loved her? She wanted oh, so very badly to believe that. But it still seemed much too incredible to be true—she needed to hear more, much more. She needed to question, and pry—with what intelligence he'd left her.

'I think I did apologise—eventually,' she commented, and when Barden returned her look unwaveringly she felt she had to explain. 'I'd—er—had my fill of womanising employers. With all those women ringing you up, aside from the fact that into the bargain I was soon certain you were having an affair with your friend's wife, I...'

'You thought I was set in the same mould,' he inserted gently.

Remembering Karla, she still didn't know that he wasn't. 'Karla Nesbitt.' The name seemed to leave Emmie's lips before she could stop it.

'Is no longer—' He broke off. 'You're jealous?' he questioned quickly, and appeared to take tremendous heart from that notice.

'Not at all!' she denied crisply. Oh, watch it, Emmie, watch it, do. He's smarter than you by half—do you really think he could be in love with you?

She saw his expression become deeply serious. But again, to her surprise, that patience she had noticed in him earlier was there again, when, after a moment or two of just studying her, he asked softly, 'Would it be of any help if I mentioned that I've been half off my head with jealousy over you?'

Her eyes shot wide. 'No!' she gasped. 'Who?' she asked, not believing it for a minute. For pity's sake—who did she see?

'Trust me?' Barden requested. 'First there's Jack Bryant, annoying me when within hours of meeting you he's asking you for your phone number. Then...'

'But—but that was ages ago! You're not saying you were—jealous of Jack…?'

Barden smiled at her stunned expression, and owned, 'I wasn't admitting to myself then that it was more jealousy than annoyance.'

'But—you think it was?'

'I know it was. We'd had a row the day before, you and I, and from that moment it seemed you were forever coming between me and my work. Devil take you, I thought— yet found you were in no time turning my world upside down.'

Her mouth fell open a little. 'I—was?'

'You were.'

Emmie swallowed. She wanted to believe—dared she believe? She needed to know more. 'G-go on,' she invited huskily.

Barden needed no further invitation. He moved his position on the sofa to sit closer to her still, and began to tell her of the upside-down world she had made for him. 'Why, when I found I wanted only your good opinion, was I behaving in the exact opposite way? Being as aloof with you as you'd been with me? Damned if I'd explain about the surprise party Roberta Short had asked my aid with. How dare this beautiful assistant PA pass judgement on me? Hell, without you having to say a word there you were, your disapproving looks saying it all! I hadn't had my wrists slapped since childhood.'

'I made you angry.'

'I found you—irksome. But it was too late then to get rid of you. I couldn't, you wretched woman—there was something about you that was getting to me.'

'Oh.' A hint of a smile was coming through. Barden spotted it immediately, and seemed encouraged by it.

He wasted no time in going on. 'From that first day, dear Emmie, I was drawn to you. Which meant, love being the perverse animal it is, that when I wanted you to only see me in a good light I seemed only able to let you see the opposite.' He shook his head slightly, as though still a little mystified by the whole of it. 'Logic, my dear, walked out of the door the day you walked in.'

'But—you're the most logical man I've ever met!'

'What can I tell you? You, thoughts of you, kept insinuating their way into my head, and I'd find while at times I was astonished by your kindness and sweetness, at others I was furious with this prim and proper little miss.'

'I thought you were two-timing your friend, and then, when all those women rang up, two-timing your friend's wife.'

'Were you just a bit jealous?' he wanted to know. 'Just a tiny bit?'

'Angry,' Emmie admitted. 'I was angry…' She looked at him. He was rather wonderful, and he was giving so much—would it hurt to give back, just a small fraction? 'Angry and, on reflection,' she owned, 'a wee bit jealous.'

'Little love.' Barden caught hold of one of her hands and brought it to his lips and kissed it. 'I'm not a saint, Emmie, I don't profess to be, but those phone calls were, with one exception, in response to the invitations Roberta had sent out. You—um—didn't seem to notice that twice as many *men* as women phoned me with their acceptances?' he teased, and she had to laugh. She had put those male calls down as business calls.

But he'd said 'with one exception'. 'Karla Nesbitt,' she said, laughter gone.

'Karla and I went out a few times. But I had to tell her last Sunday, when she turned up at my home uninvited to wish me Happy Landings, that I wouldn't be seeing her again.'

'You've—finished with her?'

'To be frank—and I want only openness between you and me—there wasn't a lot to finish. It doesn't reflect well on me, I know, but because of the openness I want I have to tell you I only went out with Karla a few times—and then mainly because you had, by then, taken complete possession of my every waking thought.'

'I—had?'

'You had,' he agreed. 'This was all new to me, Emmie. It made me vulnerable—I didn't like it.'

'I'm sorry,' she smiled.

'I love you,' he said.

'Oh, Barden,' she whispered tremulously.

'You—love me?' he asked, his eyes on her eyes, seeming as if they would penetrate her very soul.

She couldn't tell him. Nerves were taking great enormous bites at her. She shook her head. 'I…' Words failed her.

'You don't!' he exclaimed hoarsely.

'I…' she tried again.

'You're not ready yet?' His eyes searched her face, as though trying to read her answer. 'So—what else can I tell you of the anxiety and jealousy you've stirred in me?' he asked. 'Shall I tell you how, on the very morning Personnel deliver a clutch of dreadful references from your previous employers stating your rudeness—and didn't I have first-hand knowledge of your astonishing impudence?—and referring to your erratic time-keeping you don't turn up at all?'

'You were so angry,' Emmie recalled.

'Why wouldn't I be? Dawn had phoned in and was suffering. I'd said not to come in, so there am I, minus PA *and* assistant PA. If I'd wanted proof of your erratic time-keeping—I had it. I tried to phone you, but…'

'You did?'

'You weren't answering. Either you'd left for the office or you were in bed and didn't want to get out of it. Your references were not lying. And I was not liking you at all, my dear Emmie, when you eventually turned up and gave me that "domestic problem" for an excuse.'

'It showed,' she murmured.

'I was a swine to you,' he said contritely. 'After all the anxiety you must have been through until you found Mrs Whitford too.'

'You didn't know about Aunt Hannah then.' Emmie smiled.

'Which doesn't make me feel the least bit better that—when I didn't *need* those minutes of the Stratford meeting—I, out of sheer bloody-mindedness, all but caused you to catch pneumonia by insisting you get them typed back and delivered to me at Neville Short's house that evening.'

'Pneumonia's a bit of an exaggeration,' she murmured, then asked, 'You didn't need them?'

'Sheer bloody-mindedness,' he repeated. 'How was I to know you'd trudge through the snow to get them to me? But I should have known—I'd seen and admired your spirit.' Her backbone was so much water again. 'I shall never forget seeing you standing there that night—blue with cold.' He risked a gentle kiss to her cheek. 'Your loyalty alone redeemed your dreadful references,' he said softly. Emmie, a kind of trembling going on inside her, was incapable of speech, and Barden, perhaps taking heart that she wasn't moving away after the liberty of his kiss, looked into her wide brown eyes and told her, 'I think, looking back, that it was that night that I started to fall in love with you.'

Emmie swallowed. Oh, she loved him so. She was going to burst if he said much more. 'I—w-woke you up—puking,' she stammered, needing to inject a stern dose of reality into the conversation if she wasn't to hurl herself into his arms.

'And I,' he took up, 'who'd never thought the day would come which would see me holding someone's head while they parted with their stomach contents, felt quite overwhelmed by the feeling of wanting to protect you which came over me.'

'Oh, Barden,' she whispered.

'Sweet Emmie,' he breathed, his look on her so tender she just couldn't doubt that he had some caring for her. And her heart was racing when he revealed, 'That protective feeling for you stayed with me the next day, as I drove you home—though naturally I told myself that it was only because you'd been so ill during the night.'

'Naturally,' she murmured, and at last a feeling of belief in the warmth of his love was starting to come through.

'I knew, of course, when we reached your flat that you, shocking liar that you are, were avoiding telling me something.'

'Aunt Hannah.' Emmie smiled.

'Aunt Hannah,' he agreed. 'I wish I'd known about Mrs Whitford when, feeling fidgety that you might still be unwell, I rang you that evening. You said you had company—and I was as jealous as hell.'

'You weren't!' she gasped—though she clearly remembered how the line had gone dead immediately after she had told him she had company.

'I was sure it was some man.' He smiled. 'Not that I was admitting *then* that I was jealous. Heaven forbid—that sort of thing doesn't happen to me. So why am I again suffering the same emotion when, the following Monday at the office, you get a phone call and ask for an hour off and I immediately think it's some man? Why, if it's not jealousy, do I feel all uptight when I see your old neighbour kissing you? And I'm still in the silent throes of wondering what the devil's the matter with me when you're introducing me to Mrs Whitford and I'm starting to realise what a truly wonderful person you are.'

'Oh, Barden, I'm not,' she whispered, loving him so much, wanting only his good opinion, but— She became aware suddenly that something of her feelings for him might be showing in her eyes, for, ever alert, a new sort of light seemed to enter his.

'When did you know?' he asked quickly.

'What?' she answered, totally foxed for the moment.

'That you loved me,' he answered.

'It was—' She broke off, horrified, too late—he was not about to let her off the hook, not now.

He smiled, the most fantastic loving and giving smile she had ever seen. 'You do!' he exclaimed in delight. 'Oh, my love, you do! I've so hoped. I thought last night when I lay sleepless that perhaps you might, that I might have seen—then I was sure I hadn't. But you do, don't you? You do love me, Emmie, don't you?'

He seemed to be almost pleading—how could she deny him? 'I—d-do,' she managed, from a strangled kind of throat. It was all he waited to hear.

The next second she was in his arms, being held up against him. Held and held, and adored. 'This past week's been hell,' he murmured against her hair, and then, pulling back and looking deeply into her eyes, 'Say it, dear love,' he pressed, 'and put me out of my misery.'

What could she do? 'I love you,' she replied tremulously—and was rewarded by the most loving and adoring kiss.

Barden refused to let her go, still held her in his arms, drawing back so he could feast his eyes on her. 'When?' he insisted on knowing.

Emmie smiled. Oh, never had there been such a wonderful feeling as knowing that the one you loved loved you. 'It crept up on me while I wasn't looking,' she answered shyly.

'I know all about that one.' He nodded, and, as if he still couldn't believe it, bent nearer to touch his lips to hers. 'When did you get the first inkling?' he wanted to know.

She could hold back no longer. 'I suppose something started very early on,' she answered openly. 'I certainly wasn't liking that bevy of females who rang you—though I didn't consider my dislike might be jealousy. I was certain

I didn't care for the fact it seemed I was again working for a womaniser.'

'Oh, sweetheart—I got that sort of thing out of my system in my late teens.'

'Did you?' she asked.

'Poor love, you've had a bad time of it, haven't you?' he sympathised gently. 'Believe me, darling, I left that kind of thing behind years ago, when I learned to prefer more substance in a relationship.'

'Have there been many?' She immediately wished she hadn't asked the question, but it was out now.

'Relationships?' he replied. 'A few, over the years,' he allowed, ready, it seemed, to answer her every question. 'But all over now—and none of them were like you and me, Emmie.' He kissed her gently. 'You've absolutely nothing to be jealous of.'

She believed him, knew she could trust him, and returned his smile. 'Jealousy seems to go with the territory.'

'Tell me about it!' he commented. 'But you're not telling me what I need to know, little Emmie. I've just stated I'm a grown man—but I've got this terrible anxiety to be assured that you love me.'

She had to smile again. Indeed the whole of her being seemed to be wreathed in a smile. But she knew the feeling Barden was going through, of needing to be assured of love, so she wasted no more time and told him, 'I love you, Barden Cunningham—and I hardly know why.'

'Tell me more,' he ordered.

'You've been a bossy pig a lot of the time,' she informed him lovingly.

'I'm not sure I want to hear that bit.' He smiled—as if he too felt a mass of burgeoning smiles.

'And yet, at the same time, you've been unbelievably kind.'

'I like this better,' he murmured, and Emmie looked at him. Gathering her nerve, she just had to lean forward and kiss him. 'Oh, Emmie, Emmie, I love you so,' he said against her mouth—and she thought she might burst into tears from the sheer joy of it.

She swallowed hard on a knot of emotion and pulled back. She swallowed again, and was then able to resume. 'I thought you'd dismissed me—given me the sack that Monday you discovered all about Aunt Hannah—and yet you didn't. We went back to work, and that evening you gave me a lift to collect my car, and...'

'I certainly wasn't having any David-cum-Adrian muscling in!'

'You—were jealous—of Adrian?' she asked in surprise, remembering then that she had originally arranged for Adrian to take her to collect her car.

'I wasn't calling it jealousy,' Barden answered with a self-deprecating look. 'To my mind it was the least I could do, since your car had only gone off the road when you were doing business for me. Though I wasn't entirely thrilled, I have to admit, when earlier Mrs Whitford asked were you going to marry him.'

'There was never any question of that,' Emmie promised.

'So why were you and he all lovey-dovey and shopping together this morning?' Barden startled her by asking seriously.

'We weren't!' she answered.

And she actually saw Barden blanch at what he thought he knew to be an outright lie. 'I saw you, Emmie,' he stated, oh, so dreadfully quietly.

'Me—and Adrian—shopping?'

'You were both carrying plastic bags of shopping—this morning, outside your flat,' he reminded her. And suddenly Emmie knew what he was talking about.

'We hadn't been shopping!' she exclaimed, going on quickly—anything to take the hint of doubt from Barden's face, 'Adrian has the flat above mine, and—'

'Does he?'

'Didn't you know? That's how he came to be calling that morning—after you slept in Aunt Hannah's bed. He'd probably come down to borrow something—he does sometimes. Anyhow,' she rushed on, 'he's still very much in love with his ex-live-in-girlfriend. He had just finished talking to her on the phone, having got her to agree to go out on a date with him, when he saw me coming home from his window. He couldn't wait to tell me his good news— he just had to tell someone...'

'So he dashed downstairs, grabbed a hold of some of your shopping—and gave you a kiss,' Barden finished for her. 'Jealousy,' he stated, that look of doubt gone, 'is a monster of an emotion.'

'Oh, Barden,' she sympathised softly. 'Er—just a... Didn't you say you'd called at my flat and I wasn't in?'

'You weren't—the first time.'

'You called twice?'

'Once I'd been able to ascertain that you weren't planning to be elsewhere for the weekend, I called back.'

'But you didn't stop and—?'

'What—with you and the dastardly Adrian exchanging kisses on the pavement?' He smiled.

'Oh, Barden, is that how it seemed?'

'Like I was so blindingly jealous I had to get out of there, lest I came över and threw him over the basement railings.'

'Ooh!' she exclaimed in awe.

'I got out of there, jealousy at my gut—what had been going on while I was away?'

'Nothing,' she answered.

'I know,' he said tenderly. 'Just as I know I'd no right to be jealous. I hadn't declared my love for you, or anything like that. But if what I'd witnessed was anything to go by I was *never* going to get the chance to tell you how I feel about you. Nor, I realised, as I began to calm down, was I going to have the chance to find out if the glimpses of your caring for me that—on dissecting your every nuance—I'd made myself believe I thought I'd seen were real. And I wasn't having that.'

'You weren't?'

'Sweet darling, I'd come home especially because I couldn't take not knowing any longer. I wasn't going back until I'd seen you alone and had the chance to talk to you.' He paused. 'It was then that I devised my devious plan.'

Emmie laughed; she had to. Who, loving him the way she did, could not? 'I love you,' she said, and Barden promptly delayed telling her of his devious plan by gathering her close and kissing her. For ageless loving moments they just stared lovingly at each other. 'Devious plan?' she reminded him dreamily.

Barden took time out to gently kiss her again, and then, collecting his thoughts, began to reveal, 'I was furious, jealous, sick—anything you care to name as I accelerated past your flat. But as my world started to right itself I knew I couldn't take any more—my emotions over you were crucifying me, dear love. I'd made myself believe you may have a little caring for me—but now...' Emmie gently kissed him, and he smiled, squeezed her to him, and continued. 'Nerves, by this time, were starting to set in—previously, I hadn't needed a reason to come and call on you, this time my vulnerability was raw. My first plan was to return to Keswick House and, if Mrs Whitford was willing, take her for an early lunch, and then, excuse ready-made, deliver her to your place.'

'You decided to take Aunt Hannah to lunch?'

'I had to do *something*.' He smiled. 'Though when I looked at my plan for snags one very large one was glaringly obvious. I was desperate for some private conversation with you—it would hardly be private with Mrs Whitford there.'

'So you went on to devious Plan B?'

He grinned. It was a joyous grin, and Emmie fell in love

with him all over again. 'I called at Keswick House and invited Mrs Whitford to have lunch here...'

'Here at Hazeldene?'

He kissed her. 'Correct,' he said, and, clearly liking the taste of her lips, he kissed her again before resuming, 'While Mrs Whitford was up in her room, getting her coat on, I took the opportunity to nip out to my car, ring my father and tell him how vitally important it was to me that he drove over to take an elderly lady for a tour around in one of his classic cars.'

'He—er—didn't mind?'

'He knows me—knows I wouldn't use the words "vitally important" unless I meant them,' Barden answered, going on to reveal, 'I had a few panicky moments when, after lunch, Mrs Whitford asked if we might get back because you would be calling for her soon. It's all right,' he quickly assured Emmie, 'she wasn't alarmed in any way, and quite happily accepted it when I told her that you would be picking her up from here, not Keswick House.'

'You were certain I'd come here for her?'

'Oh, sweet Emmie, you're so protective of the old dear. I was absolutely certain of it when I made sure she wrote this address in the "Out" book.'

'Rogue!'

'Desperately in love,' he corrected, and they smiled lovingly at each other as Barden ended, 'You needn't worry about her, you know. She was off like a shot the minute she first heard and then saw the Austin Healey—and my father will take excellent care of her. He was delighted with her interest in the car—they'll probably spend the whole time talking about motor engines and all things mechanical.'

They were silent, content for the moment holding each other. 'And, as deviously planned, I drove up just as you knew I would,' Emmie murmured.

'And I could hardly open the door for the importance of what I wanted to say to you—this chance I couldn't miss.'

'Has it been so very bad?'

'You've no idea,' he answered feelingly.

'Well, yes, I have, actually.' She grinned.

'It's been so emotion-tearing for you too?'

'You've had the ability to get to my emotions one way or another from the beginning.' She felt confident enough in his love to be able to confide in him.

'You told me you liked me once,' he remembered, 'Though I think we both agreed you were feeling a bit light-headed at the time.'

'That was when you came and brought me some linctus,' she recalled.

'And a few days later I find I'm totally enchanted by you when I invite myself to lunch.'

'You kissed me,' she murmured, and if she was dreaming she never wanted to wake up.

'And spent most of my time afterwards just thinking about you,' he owned.

'You took Karla Nesbitt out the other Friday,' Emmie reminded him sweetly.

He grinned. 'And spent most of that date, my jealous love, in dragging my thoughts back from *you*.'

'You say the nicest things,' she laughed.

Barden stared at her saucy mouth. 'Did I say you were enchanting? You're bewitching.' They kissed tenderly, then he was pulling back, and saying, that strain of jealousy still lurking, 'Are you still seeing the man we had to dash back from Stratford for you to see?' he asked.

'I don't remember…' she began, puzzled.

'No sooner am I coping with my annoyance that you seem quite happy to spend all day talking to Jack Bryant than you're telling me you're seeing someone later that night,' Barden reminded her.

Emmie remembered. 'Confession time: I—er—made him up,' she admitted.

'You didn't have a date?'

'I lied.' She smiled, and loved him when he smiled too, and just had to tell him, 'I knew, that night, when we were in my flat, that I was in love with you.'

Barden just sat and stared at her. 'You knew then?'

Emmie nodded. 'I'd just discovered how I felt about you—then suddenly we were kissing each other and—and…' Her voice faded.

'And I was in severe danger of losing my head when you said, "Don't", which brought me sharply to my senses.'

'You said it wasn't supposed to happen,' she recalled. 'And I knew then that already you were regretting that it had.'

'Oh, little love, I wanted to stay and make things right with you. But your lofty attitude afterwards made me realise that you'd prefer to be on your own. I was fairly shaken myself, if the truth be known.'

'Were you?'

'You were more deeply entrenched in my head than ever. But this would never do. I liked my life just as it was. Which was why I made the decision to keep everything between us only on a business footing. Only—' He broke off, that self-deprecating look there again.

'Only come Saturday you needed somewhere to rest your migrained head…'

'I'd been restless—unsettled all that day. I wasn't going to think about you any more—so I went to a party. But I wasn't in a partying mood, wasn't enjoying it, and left after a very short while. I hadn't planned to drive anywhere near to where you live. It was miles out of my way, if anything. But near to where you live was where I found myself when my head started to explode.'

'I'm glad you came to me.'

'So am I,' Barden said warmly. 'When my head started to clear, and I played everything back, I was sure you'd tenderly kissed the top of my head.'

'I—er—couldn't help it.'

'I'm glad. When I was scraping together every sign I could that you felt something for me—our mutual chemistry, a word here, a look there—I came back again and again to that kiss. I'd seen your tremendous kindness, your love and caring for Mrs Whitford—did that gentle, tender kiss mean you had a little caring for *me*?'

'You supposed it might?'

'I could only hope. After that Sunday morning you were more in my head than ever—and I, my darling, was starting to acknowledge that there was something very, very special about one Emily Lawson. Something that made it wonderful just to be near her. Then, by the middle of the next week, you didn't hesitate to put me in a black mood by daring to tell me you'd been out with some man called Simon!'

'I only went out with him the one time, and then mainly because I was jealous that you were taking Karla Nesbitt out,' Emmie confessed.

'Oh, love,' Barden murmured, and kissed her, and confessed in turn, 'I gave myself the sternest lecture that night.'

'The subject being?'

'That Emily Lawson was one beautiful woman and what did I expect—that she'd stay in nights?' Emmie began to wonder if her heart would ever stop racing. Oh, it was too wonderful just to be loved by Barden. 'That was the night I determined to get my act together. No more sulking. You had a perfect right to go out with anyone you wanted to. Only—by Friday I wanted that anyone to be me.'

'You did? That Friday before you flew to New York last Monday?'

'The same,' he agreed. 'Yet by that time I was close to being at my most vulnerable.'

Light dawned! 'You offered to take Aunt Hannah to the Motorcycle Museum!'

'Hoping you'd come with us.'

'You felt too vulnerable to ask me out direct!' Emmie gasped.

'Hell, Emmie, I've never been in love before! And anyhow, wasn't I still trying to convince myself I liked my life just as it was?'

'You're—wonderful!' She grinned, and was thoroughly kissed, so that when they broke apart she whispered, 'You were saying?' having absolutely no idea.

'I was saying how every minute apart from you was starting to become unbearable. I'm saying how bleak everything seemed last Sunday, when I would normally have been looking forward to the challenge of my two-week trip on Monday. All I could think of was you and how I wouldn't see you again for another fifteen days.'

That was exactly how *she* had been! She smiled at him, loving him. 'I smell another devious plot coming up.' Her smile became a grin.

Barden looked enchanted by her, kissed her nose, and owned, 'I could have come over to see you, of course, but how did I know the diabolical Simon wouldn't be with you—and how would I feel if he was? And might not the dastardly Adrian, with his penchant for dropping by at the most unexpected of times, drop by again? As I said—' he smiled '—I was feeling exceedingly vulnerable.'

'So instead you rang.'

'With the invention of some note-taking.'

Invention! 'You're wicked,' she berated him laughingly.

'I'll pay you back for that,' he promised, and she just had to beam at him. Life had never, ever been this good. Though as painful memory reawakened so her smile started to fade—as did some of the joy in her eyes, 'What?' Barden asked at once, his eyes full on her, not missing that something was not right. 'What are you thinking? What's wrong,

Emmie?' She didn't want to tell him—it seemed to put a blight on everything. 'Tell me!' he insisted—and she supposed it was better aired than stifled.

'That Sunday, when you phoned. Was it your intention from the start to try to seduce me?' she asked, and had her answer in his scandalised look.

That was before his vehement, 'Hell's bells, *no*! Is that what you thought—have been thinking?'

'Th-that phone call… You remember?' Oh, heavens, she was blushing again; she knew she was. 'When—'

'I know when,' he came in swiftly, to help her out. 'It was my uncle Tobin—my head was in such a mess after you'd bolted I didn't remember to ring him back until I was in the States. But what…?'

'He said…'

'What? I didn't think he said anything. I just thought you passed the phone to me and then realised where our lovemaking was leading—and panicked. But—' He broke off, and said gently then, 'Come on, Emmie, there are no secrets between us now. What did he say?'

He was right, she saw. She didn't want any secrets between them either. 'He said—and of course he thought it was you he was speaking to—he said for you to stop seducing your secretary and speak to him.'

Barden groaned. 'I'll kill him!' he threatened. 'Love him dearly though I do, I'll kill him!'

'Er—there's no need to do anything that drastic on my account.' Emmie felt then that she wanted only to make things better.

'He'll apologise. I'll tell him…'

'I'll die if you do. He doesn't know who I am, or the fact that it was me who lifted the receiver and heard what he said before I handed the phone over.'

'Oh, darling,' Barden mourned, and explained, 'I worked in Uncle Tobin's office for six weeks during my first student vacation. He's never let me live down the fact that I once made a callow play for his secretary. Oh, sweetheart, I'm sorry. I wish you'd said... Oh—what you must have thought...'

'I thought then that you'd set me up,' she admitted honestly.

'Come here,' he said gruffly, and held her close up to him while he explained, 'Little love, my sole reason for getting you to come here last Sunday was because I just *had* to see you. I hadn't the smallest intention for any of what happened to happen. My dear,' he went on, pulling back so he could see into her face, 'I'm fully aware of your inexperience—but, even while I hadn't accepted the true depth of my feelings, I thought too well of you to seduce you and then blithely fly off the next morning.' Emmie was convinced even before he followed on, 'I particularly tried to avoid igniting that chemistry that exists between us—only, as you may remember, with you so close I wasn't able to hold out for long.'

'It was mutual.' She met him halfway.

'You believe me?'

'Of course,' she answered, and they kissed tenderly.

Then he was leaning back to look into her face, and he scolded gently. 'Promise you'll never drive the way you did that night.'

'You followed me?'

'I had to deal with Karla first, though that didn't take long, and then I came after you. I backed off when—realising you knew I was following you—it looked to me as if your crazy driving would see you killing yourself in your efforts to shake me off.'

'It *was* you who rang when I got in?'

'You'd scared me half to death—I had to know you were home safe,' he confirmed. 'But my emotions were still raw; I couldn't speak to you then.'

'You left speaking to me until you were on the point of catching your plane the next day. You sounded so cool,' she remembered. 'Certainly as though you'd had a better night's sleep than I had.'

'Pretence,' he owned, and she smiled. 'There am I, wanting to speak to you nicely, and what do you do? You infuriate me by telling me you're not going to the office—that you're leaving!'

'Not for nothing,' she laughed, just so happy to be with him. 'You promptly dismissed me and we had a row.'

He smiled back. 'And I got on my plane, my mind in a furious turmoil—this woman has got me so I don't know where the devil I am. Then no sooner have we taken off than I'm realising this *isn't* where I want to be. I clearly remember thinking, You idiot—as it blindingly hit me—you idiot, you're in love with the woman!'

'Oh, how wonderful!' she sighed in delight.

'I'm glad you think so,' he growled. 'There am I, in a constant stew about you, wanting to phone you every five minutes—yet when I *do* give in to that mammoth urge you go all proud and stubborn on me, and have the utter gall to tell me you've found yourself work in someone else's office.'

'I've been working for a temping agency,' Emmie put in quickly. And was soundly kissed.

Then Barden was saying urgently, 'Emmie—Emmie, you're in my head night and day—I just can't leave without you.' And, while her heart picked up yet more speed, 'I love you, my dear heart, and want you with me,' he went on. 'Please, my love, say you'll come back with me.'

'To—New York?' she gasped, her heart fairly galloping now. 'B-but you're going tomorrow.'

'If you can't be ready in time we can catch Monday's Concorde—I can still make my eleven o'clock appointment.'

Emmie swallowed. 'I so wanted you to take me with you when I left the office on Friday. I couldn't bear not seeing you for—' She broke off, but had to quickly dampen the triumphant, joyous look that started to come to Barden's face. 'But I can't come,' she was forced to state.

'*Why?*' he wanted to know. 'Don't you love me enough?' he demanded. 'Emmie, I—'

'Aunt Hannah,' she interrupted. 'Oh, Barden, I do love you so. But I have to find a job. I can't just take time off. There's not only myself to think of. I need the security…'

'Haven't you been listening to a word I've been saying?' he demanded. 'I love you, Emmie. I adore you. My sweet darling, as my wife, you—and Aunt Hannah—will have all the security you will ever want or need.'

As his wife! She took a gasp of breath. 'Wife?' she gulped chokily.

'It goes with the territory,' Barden told her firmly. 'I've thought, eaten, slept, dreamt about you all this week, Emily Lawson,' he went on solemnly. 'I swear, now that I know you return my love, I cannot and will not take another week of it. You won't need to pack anything; you can shop for anything you need, anything you want, while I attend meetings. I know my parents will keep an eye on Mrs Whitford while we're away. We can leave their phone number for Keswick House to contact in the event she decides to break the rules. Though I've an idea my father would love to have an enthusiastic playmate he can show off his classic car collection to during the time we'll be away.' Barden shook her gently, 'But if you're in any way unhappy about any of that, then we'll take Mrs Whitford with us. Only please, please, my darling, say you'll come with me. Say you'll marry me.'

Emmie stared at him, her heart in her eyes. What could any girl say after such a speech, such a proposal? She swallowed, and looked at Barden lovingly. 'If it's not being too greedy,' she replied, 'may I say yes, to both?'

Helen Brooks lives in Northamptonshire and is married with three children. As she is a committed Christian, busy housewife and mother, her spare time is at a premium, but her hobbies include reading, swimming, gardening and walking her two energetic, inquisitive and very endearing young dogs. Her long-cherished aspiration to write became a reality when she put pen to paper on reaching the age of forty, and sent the result off to Mills & Boon®.

THE MISTRESS
CONTRACT
by
Helen Brooks

CHAPTER ONE

'ME?' SEPHY stared at Mrs Williams—the company secretary's assistant—in horror, her velvet-brown eyes opening wide as she said again, 'Me? Stand in for Mr Quentin's secretary? I don't think I could, Pat. I mean—'

'Of course you could,' Pat Williams interrupted briskly, her sharp voice, which matched her sharp face and thin, angular body, signalling that the matter was not open for discussion. 'You're as bright as a button, Seraphina, even if you do insist on hiding your light under a bushel most of the time, and after six years at Quentin Dynamics you know as much as me about the firm and its operating procedures. More, probably, after working for Mr Harper in Customer Support and Service for four years.'

Sephy smiled weakly. The Customer Support and Services department was, by its very nature, a fast-moving and hectic environment within Quentin Dynamics, and in her position as assistant to Mr Harper—who was small and plump and genial, but the sort of boss who arrived late, left early and had three-hour lunch breaks most days—she was used to dealing with the hundred and one panics that erupted daily on her own initiative. But Mr Harper and Customer Service was one thing; Conrad Quentin, the millionaire entrepreneur and tycoon founder of the firm, was quite another!

Sephy took a deep breath and said firmly, 'I really don't think it's a good idea, Pat. I'm sorry, but I'm sure there must be someone else more suitable? What about Jenny Brown, Mr Eddleston's secretary? Or Suzy Dodds? Or... or you?'

The other woman waved a dismissive bony hand. 'Those two girls would last ten minutes with Mr Quentin and you know it, and with the end of year accounts to pull together I can't desert Mr Meadows. No, you're ideal. You know the ins and outs of the business, you've got a level head on your shoulders, and you're used to dealing with awkward customers every day of the week so Mr Quentin won't throw you. We can get a good temp to fill in for you until Mr Quentin's secretary is back—'

'Can't Mr Quentin have the good temp?' Sephy interjected desperately.

'He'd eat her alive!' Pat's beady black eyes held Sephy's golden-brown ones. 'You know how impatient he is. He hasn't got time for someone who doesn't know the ropes, besides which he expects his secretary to practically live here, and most girls have got—' She stopped abruptly, suddenly aware she was being tactless as Sephy's small heart-shaped face flushed hotly.

'Most girls have got boyfriends or husbands or whatever,' Sephy finished flatly.

Sephy had never hidden the fact that she rarely dated and that her social diary wasn't exactly the most riveting reading, but it wasn't particularly warming to think that Pat Williams—along with everyone else, most probably—thought she had nothing better to do than work twenty-four hours a day.

'Well, yes,' Pat murmured uncomfortably.

'What about Marilyn?'

'Tried her first, lasted an hour.'

'Philippa?'

'Howled her eyes out in the ladies' cloakroom all lunchtime and has gone home with a migraine,' Pat said triumphantly. 'She's not used to men snapping and snarling at her like Mr Quentin did.'

Sephy thought of the beautiful ash-blonde who was the

marketing manager's secretary, and who had different men in flash, expensive sports cars waiting outside the building for her every night of the week and nodded. 'No, I can imagine,' she agreed drily. 'And you think I am, is that it?'

'Seraphina, *please*. Try it for this afternoon at least.' In spite of the 'please' it was more of an order than a request, and Sephy stared at the other woman exasperatedly.

Pat Williams was the only person she knew—apart from her mother—who insisted on giving her her full Christian name when she knew full well Sephy loathed it, but it went with the brusque, army-style manner of the company secretary's assistant, and the utilitarian haircut and severely practical clothes.

For her first two years at Quentin Dynamics, Sephy—along with the other secretaries and personnel of the hugely successful software firm that majored in specialist packages for different types of companies—had thoroughly disliked Pat Williams, but there had come a day when she and the other woman had been working late and she had found Pat in the ladies' cloakroom in tears.

All Pat's defences had been down, and when Sephy had discovered her history—an upbringing in a children's home where she'd met the husband she adored, only for him to develop multiple sclerosis just after they married, which now confined him to a wheelchair and made Pat the bread-winner—her friendship with the older woman had begun.

And it was that which made Sephy sigh loudly, narrow her eyes and nod her dark head resignedly. 'One afternoon,' she agreed quietly. 'But I can't see me lasting any better than the others, Pat. It's a well-known fact Madge Watkins is so devoted to him she puts up with anything, and she's been his secretary for decades! How can anyone step into her shoes?'

'She's been his secretary for thirteen years,' Pat corrected cheerfully, allowing herself a smile now Sephy had agreed to help her out of what had become a very tight spot. 'And I'm not asking you to step into her shoes; they wouldn't fit you.'

They both thought of the elderly spinster, who looked like a tiny shrivelled up prune but was excellent at her job, and absolutely ruthless when it came to ensuring that her esteemed boss's life ran like clockwork with lesser mortals kept very firmly in their place. 'How long is she expected to be in hospital?' Sephy asked flatly.

'Not sure.' Pat eyed her carefully. 'She was rushed in in the middle of the night with stomach pains and they're talking about doing an exploratory op today or tomorrow.'

Wonderful. Sephy sighed long and loudly and left it to Pat to inform Ted Harper that his secretary and right-hand man—or woman, in this case—had been commandeered for the foreseeable future. He wouldn't like it—he might have to start working for that sizeable salary he picked up each month—but he wouldn't argue. Everyone fell down and worshipped at the feet of the illustrious head of Quentin Dynamics, and it wouldn't occur to any of Conrad Quentin's staff to deny him anything, Sephy thought wryly.

Not that she had had anything to do with him, to be fair, but it was common knowledge that thirteen years ago, at the age of twenty-five, Conrad Quentin had had a meteoric rise in the business world, and his power and wealth were legendary. As was his taste for beautiful women. He was the original love 'em and leave 'em type, but, judging by the number of times his picture appeared in the paper with a different glittering female hanging adoringly on his arm at some spectacular function or other, one had to assume his attraction outshone his reputation.

Or perhaps the sort of women Conrad Quentin chose thought they were beautiful and desirable enough to tame the wolf? Sephy's clear brow wrinkled. Maybe they even relished the challenge? Whatever, in spite of his well-publicised affairs over the years, with some of the precious darlings of the jet-set, no one had managed to snare him yet.

Oh, what was she doing wasting time thinking about Mr Quentin's love-life? Sephy shook herself irritably and then quickly fixed her face in a purposely blank expression as Pat sailed out of Ted Harper's office and said cheerfully, 'Right, that's settled, then. I've told him I'll get a temp here for tomorrow morning and he can manage for one afternoon. Are you ready?'

For Conrad Quentin? *Absolutely not.* 'Yes, I'm ready,' Sephy said, with what she considered admirable calm in the circumstances, resisting the temptation to nip to the ladies' cloakroom. All the titivating in the world wouldn't make any difference to the medium height, gentle-eyed, dark-haired girl who would stare back at her from the long rectangular mirror above the three basins.

She wasn't plain, she knew that, but she was…non-descript, she admitted silently as she followed Pat out of the office and along the corridor towards the lift for the exalted top floor. Her honey-brown eyes, shoulder-length thick brown hair and small neat nose were all pleasant, but unremarkable, and to cap it all she had an abundance of freckles scattered across her smooth, creamy skin that made her look heaps younger than her twenty-six years.

'Here we are, then.' They had emerged from the lift and Pat was being deliberately hearty as she led Sephy past her own office and that of the company secretary and financial director. Conrad Quentin's vast suite took up all the rest of the top floor, and to say the opulence was intimidating was putting it mildly. 'Your home from home for the next little while.'

'I said an afternoon, Pat,' Sephy hissed quietly as the other woman opened the door in front of them. Sephy had visited the top floor a few times—rapid calls which had lasted as long as the delivery of files or whatever had necessitated—and she found the lavish surroundings somewhat surreal. 'He's bound to treat me the same as the rest.'

'And how, exactly, did I treat the rest, Miss…?'

Sephy heard Pat's sudden intake of breath, but all her senses were focused on the tall, dark man who had obviously been about to leave the room when they had opened the door. She had spoken to Conrad Quentin a few times in the six years she had been working at the firm—brief, polite words at the obligatory Christmas party and on the rare occasions their paths had crossed in the lift—but she had always been overcome with nerves at the prospect of saying the wrong thing and had escaped at the earliest opportunity. But now she certainly *had* said the wrong thing, and there was no retreat possible.

She stared desperately into the hard, chiselled face; the piercing blue of his eyes threw his tanned skin into even more prominence, picking up the ebony sheen in his jet-black hair, and she saw his straight black eyebrows were lifted in mockingly cruel enquiry.

And it did something to her, causing anger to slice through her body and tighten her stomach, and before she knew she had spoken she said, her voice tight and very controlled, 'You know that better than me, Mr Quentin,' and held his glance.

Pat looked as if she was going to faint at the side of her, and for the first time ever Sephy heard the company secretary's cool dragon of a secretary babbling as she said, 'This is Seraphina, Mr Quentin, from Customer Services. She's been with us six years and I thought she would be suitable for temporarily standing in for Miss Watkins. Of course, if you think—'

The man in front of them raised an authoritative hand

and immediately Pat's voice was cut off. 'You think I treat my staff unfairly, Seraphina?' he asked silkily.

All sorts of things were racing through Sephy's frantic mind. She couldn't believe she had spoken to Conrad Quentin like that, and her heart was pounding like a drum even as tiny pinpricks of sheer, unmitigated panic hit every nerve and sinew. This could be the end of her extremely well-paid and interesting job. And the end of her job could threaten the new flat she had just moved into, the flat it had taken so long to find. And if she left with a black mark over her, if he refused to allow Mr Harper to give her a good reference, how soon could she get other work?

Conrad Quentin was the ultimate in ruthlessness—everyone, *everyone* knew that—and people didn't talk back to him! People didn't even *breathe* without his say-so. She must have had a brainstorm; it was the only explanation. Maybe if she grovelled low enough he'd overlook the matter?

And then something in the icy sapphire gaze told her he knew exactly what she was thinking and that he was fully expecting her to abase herself.

In the split second it took for the decision to be made Sephy heard herself saying, 'If everything I have heard is true it would appear so, Mr Quentin, but not having worked for you personally I can't be positive, of course.' And she raised her small chin a notch higher as she waited for the storm to break over her head.

As he stared at her she was aware that the hard, masculine face—which just missed being handsome and instead held a magnetic attractiveness that was a thousand times more compelling than any pretty-boy good looks—was betraying nothing of what he was feeling. It was unnerving. Very unnerving. And she would dare bet her life he was fully aware of just that very thing.

'Then we had better rectify that small point so that you

can make a judgement based on fact rather than hearsay,' he said smoothly, inclining his head towards Pat as he added, 'Thank you, Pat. I'm sure Seraphina is capable of managing on her own.' The tone was not complimentary.

'Yes, of course. I was just going to show her where everything is…the filing cabinets and so on… But, yes, of course…' Pat had backed out of the doorway as she had spoken, her one glance at Sephy saying quite clearly, You rather than me, kid, but you asked for it! before she shut the door behind her, leaving Sephy standing in front of the brilliant and eminent head of Quentin Dynamics.

He was very tall. The observation came from nowhere and it didn't help Sephy's confidence. And big—muscle-type big—with a leanness that suggested regular workouts and a passion for fitness.

'So you have worked for Quentin Dynamics for six years?'

His voice was deep, with an edge of huskiness that took it out of the ordinary and into the unforgettable. Sephy took several steadying breaths until she was sure her voice was under control, and then she said quietly, 'Yes, that's right. That's one of the reasons Pat thought you would prefer me to a temp.'

'I don't use temps.'

The laser-blue eyes hadn't left hers for a moment, and Sephy was finding it incredibly difficult not to give in to the temptation to drop her gaze. 'Oh…' She didn't know what else to say.

'My secretary always aligns her holidays with mine and she is rarely ill,' he continued coolly. 'It doesn't fit in with my schedule.'

The sweeping pretension brought her thickly lashed eyes widening, before she saw the mocking glint in his own and said weakly, 'You're joking.'

'Many a true word is spoken in jest, Seraphina.'

They were standing in the outer office, part of which was kitted out as a small reception area. Deep easy seats were clustered around a couple of wood tables laden with glossy magazines, to the side of which were lush potted palms and a water chiller. Now he turned and walked past the sitting area to where his secretary's huge desk and chair stood, just in front of the interconnecting door to his office.

There was a row of superior filing cabinets in an alcove at the back of the desk, and he flicked one tanned wrist as he passed, saying, 'Acquaint yourself with those immediately. The more confidential files are kept in my office, along with data and documents relating to my other interests outside Quentin Dynamics. There are two sets of keys.' He turned in the doorway to his rooms and again the blue gaze raked her face with its cold perusal. 'I have one set and Miss Watkins has the other. Hopefully it will not be necessary to retrieve those from her; I am anticipating she will soon be back at her desk again.'

Not as much as she was, Sephy thought with a faint touch of hysteria. Suddenly Mr Harper and her battered little desk in Customer Services took on the poignancy of an oasis in the desert and she felt positively homesick.

Mr Harper might be work-shy and somewhat somnolent most of the time, and his personal hygiene was distinctly iffy on occasion, but he was rotund and genial and utterly devoted to his wife and children, and their ever-expanding family of grandchildren.

Conrad Quentin, on the other hand, was like a brilliant black star that kept all the lesser planets orbiting it in a perpetual state of fermenting unrest. It wasn't just the knowledge that he was a multimillionaire with a well-deserved reputation for ruthless arrogance, who demanded one hundred per cent commitment from his employees—it was *him*, the man himself. The harsh, flagrantly male features and muscular physique had a sensualness about them that was overwhelming.

His virile maleness was emphasised rather than concealed by the wildly expensive clothes he wore, and the unmistakable aura of wealth and power was so real she could taste it. He was everything she disliked in a man.

Still, she didn't have to like him, she reminded herself sharply, as she became aware he was waiting for her reply. She managed a careful, impersonal smile and said politely, 'I'm sure she will, Mr Quentin.' No, she didn't have to like him, and with any luck the resilient Madge, who was about four-foot-ten and looked as if a breath of wind would blow her away but must have the toughness of a pair of old boots to have lasted this long with her high-powered, vigorous boss, would be back at her desk within the week.

Not that she had much chance of lasting a week—half a day would be doing pretty good, Sephy thought ruefully.

He nodded abruptly, closing the interconnecting door as he said, 'Twenty minutes, Seraphina, and then I'd like you in here with the Breedon file, the Einhorn file and notebook and pencil.'

Pat, Pat, Pat... As the door closed Sephy leant limply against Madge's desk for a moment. How could you blackmail me with friendship into this position?

And then she straightened sharply as the door opened again and he poked his head round to say, 'Why haven't I seen you before if you've worked here for six years?' as though she had purposely been hiding in a cupboard all that time.

It was on the tip of her tongue to answer tartly, Because I'm not a model-type *femme fatale* with long blonde hair and the sort of figure that drives men wild—the type of woman Conrad Quentin usually went for if the newspaper pictures were to be believed—but a very ordinary, brown-haired, brown-eyed, slightly plump little nobody. But she felt that would be pushing her luck too far. Instead she gritted her teeth, forced a smile, and said quietly, 'You have seen me, Mr Quentin. We have spoken on at least two or three occasions.'

'Have we?' He frowned darkly. 'I don't remember.'

He clearly considered it her fault, and she was prompted to retort, with an asperity it was difficult to temper, 'There's no reason why you should, is there? You're a very busy man, after all.' He was often abroad on business, and Quentin Dynamics was only one of his many enterprises, all of which seemed to have the Midas touch, and it was to this Sephy referred as she added quickly, 'You can't know everyone who works for you, and the way you've expanded over the years…'

'I trust that is a reference to my business acumen and not my waistline?' And he smiled. Just a quick flash of white teeth as he closed the door again, but it was enough to leave her standing in stunned silence for some long moments. The difference it had made to his hard cold face, the way his piercing blue eyes had crinkled and mellowed and his uncompromising jawline softened, had been…well, devastating, she admitted unsteadily. And it bothered her more than anything else that had happened that day.

But she couldn't think of it now. She seized on the thought like a lifeline and took a deep, shuddering breath as she glanced towards the filing cabinets. She was here to stand in for the formidable Madge and she had to make some sort of reasonable stab at it. She had been used to looking after Mr Harper for four years and virtually carrying that office at times; she could do this. *She could.*

Twenty minutes later to the dot she knocked at the interconnecting door, the files and her notebook and pencil tucked under one arm.

She wished she had worn something newer and smarter than the plain white blouse and straight black skirt she had

pulled on that morning, but it was too late now. They were
serviceable enough, but distinctly utilitarian, and because
she had overslept she hadn't bothered to put her hair up,
as normal, or apply any eye make-up.

Oh, stop fussing! The admonition came just as she heard
the deep 'Come in' from inside the room. Conrad Quentin
wouldn't be looking at *her*, Sephy Vincent. He wanted an
efficient working machine, and as long as she met that cri-
terion all would be well.

She opened the door and walked briskly into the vast
expanse in front of her. The far wall of the room, in front
of which Conrad Quentin had his enormous desk and chair,
was all glass. Before she reached the chair he gestured at,
Sephy was conscious of a breathtaking view of half of
London coupled with a spacious luxury that made Mr
Harper's little office seem like a broom cupboard.

'Sit down, Seraphina.'

That was the fourth or fifth time; she'd have to say something. 'It's Sephy, actually,' she said steadily as she sat in
the plushly upholstered armless chair in front of the walnut
desk, crossing her legs and then forcing herself to look at
him. 'I never use my full name.'

'Why not?' He had been sitting bent over piles of papers
he'd been scrutinising, but now he raised his head and sat
back in the enormous leather chair, clasping his hands behind his head as he surveyed her through narrowed blue
eyes. 'What's wrong with it?'

The pose had brought powerful chest muscles into play
beneath the thin grey silk of the shirt he was wearing, and
at some time in the last twenty minutes he had loosened
his tie and undone the top buttons of his shirt, exposing the
shadow of dark body hair at the base of his throat.

Sephy cleared her dry throat. 'It doesn't suit me. Even
my mother had to agree she'd made a mistake, but I was

born on the twelfth of March, and on the calendar of saints Seraphina is the only woman for that day.'

He said nothing, merely shifted position slightly in the black chair, and now she was horrified to find herself beginning to waffle as she said, 'Mind, it could have been worse. There's a Gertrude and a Euphemia in the next few days, so perhaps I ought to be thankful for small mercies. But Seraphina suggests an ethereal, will-o'-the-wisp type creature, and I'm certainly not that.'

He leant forward again, the glittering sapphire gaze moving over her creamy skin, soft mouth and wide honey-brown eyes, and he stared at her a moment before he said, his tone expressionless, 'I think Seraphina suits you and I certainly don't intend to call you by such a ridiculous abbreviation as Sephy. It's the sort of name one would bestow on a pet poodle. Have you a second Christian name?'

'No.' It was something of a snap.

'Pity,' he said laconically.

She didn't believe this. How dared he ride roughshod over her wishes? she asked herself silently. She was searching her mind for an adequately curt response when he switched to sharp business mode, his eyes turning to the papers spread out over his desk as he said, his tone keen and focused, 'How familiar are you with the Einhorn project?'

As luck would have it she had been dealing with the problems associated with this particular package over the last weeks, and she had just spent ten of the last twenty minutes delving into the file to see if there were any confidential complications Customer Services hadn't been privy to. 'Quite familiar,' she answered smartly.

'Really?' He raised his dark head and the hard sapphire gaze homed in. 'Tell me what you know.'

She considered for a moment or two, trying to pull her thoughts into concise order, and then spoke quietly and fluently as she outlined what had been a disastrous endeavour from the start, due to a series of mistakes which Sephy felt could be laid fair and square at Quentin Dynamics' door.

He looked down at his desk as she began talking, a frown creasing his brow as he listened intently without glancing at her once. As she finished speaking the frown became a quizzical ruffle, and he raised his head and said, 'Brains *and* beauty! Well, well, well. Have I found myself a treasure, here?' And then, before she could respond in any way, 'So, you think we should take the full hit on this? Reimburse for engineering call-out charges as well as a free upgrade for the software?'

It probably wasn't very clever to tell him his company had made a sow's ear out of what should have been a silk purse within the first half an hour of working with him, but Sephy took a deep breath and said firmly, 'Yes, I do.'

'And Mr Ransome's report, that recommends we merely reduce the cost for the new software?'

Mr Ransome was trying to cover his own shortcomings with regard to the whole sorry mess, but Sephy didn't feel she could be that blunt.

She didn't answer immediately, and the blue eyes narrowed before she said quietly, 'He's wrong, in my opinion, and although the firm might save a good deal of money in the short term, I don't think it will do Quentin Dynamics' reputation any good in the long term.'

He gave her a long hard look. 'Right. And you think that is important?'

'Very.' Now it was her turn to hold his eyes. 'Don't you?'

He folded his arms over his chest, settling back in his seat again as he surveyed her thoughtfully. The white sunlight streaming in through the plate glass at the back of him was picking up what was almost a blue sheen in his jet-black hair, and Sephy was aware of the unusual thickness of the black lashes shading the vivid blue eyes as she looked back at him.

He had something. The thought popped into her consciousness with a nervous quiver. Male magnetism; a dark fascination; good old-fashioned sex appeal—call it what you will, it was there and it was powerful. Oh, boy, was it powerful!

'Yes, I do,' he said quietly. He stared at her a moment more and then snapped forward, speaking swiftly and softly as he outlined various procedures he wanted put into place. 'Internal memos to Customer Services, Marketing and Research,' he added shortly. 'You can see to those, I presume? And a letter to Einhorn stating what we have decided. And I want a complete breakdown from Accounts of all costs.'

'You want me to write the memos and the letter?' Sephy asked quickly as he paused for breath.

'Certainly.' The piercing gaze flashed upwards from the papers on the desk. 'That's not a problem, is it? I need my secretary to work on her own initiative most of the time, once I've made any overall decisions. I can't be bothered with trivialities.'

Sephy nodded somewhat dazedly. She could see Madge earnt every penny of her salary.

He continued to fire instructions and brief guidelines on a whole host of matters for some few minutes more, and by the time Sephy rose to walk back to Madge's desk she felt as though she had been run over by a steamroller.

She had enough work to last her two or three days and she had only been in there a matter of minutes, she told herself weakly as she plopped down on her chair. He was amazing. Intelligent—acutely intelligent—and with a razor-sharp grasp of what was at the heart of any matter that cut straight through incidentals and exposed the kernel in the nut.

And he scared her to death.

She worked solidly for the rest of the afternoon, her fingers flying over the keys of the word processor as the pile of papers for signature grew. Apart from telephone calls and a brief stop for coffee—delivered on a silver tray from the small canteen at the basement of the building by one of the staff and drunk at her desk—she didn't raise her head from the screen, and it came as something of a shock when she glanced at her wristwatch just after half past five.

She quickly gathered up all the correspondence awaiting signature and knocked at the interconnecting door, hearing the deep 'Come in' as butterflies began to flutter in her stomach.

He glanced up from his hand-held dictating machine as she entered, his expression preoccupied. He had been running his hand through his hair, if the ruffled black crop was anything to go by, and the tie had gone altogether now, along with a couple more buttons being undone, which exposed a V of tanned flesh and dark curling body hair.

The butterflies joined together in an explosive tarantella, and Sephy forced herself to concentrate very hard on a point just over his left shoulder as she smiled brightly and walked across to his desk. 'Correspondence for signature,' she squeaked, clearing her throat before adding, 'The post goes at six, so if you could look at them now, please? I didn't realise what the time was.'

He glanced at the gold Rolex on his wrist. 'Hell!'

'What's the matter?' Sephy asked guardedly.

'I've a dinner engagement at seven,' he muttered abstractedly. 'Look, ring her, would you? Explain about Madge, and that things are out of kilter here, and say I'll be half an hour late. She won't like it—' he grimaced slightly '—but don't stand any nonsense.'

'Ring who?'

'What?' He clearly expected her to be a mind-reader, as no doubt the faithful Madge was. 'Oh, Caroline de Menthe; the number's in here.'

He threw the obligatory little black book which he'd fetched out of a drawer across the desk.

'Right.' She took a deep breath and let it out evenly. She had heard of Caroline de Menthe. Everyone in the *world* had heard of the statuesque French model, who had the body of a goddess and the face of an angel and who was the toast of London and every other capital city besides. And she was his date. Of course she was. She was the latest prize on the circuit so she'd be bound to be, wouldn't she? Sephy thought with a shrewishness that surprised her.

Once back at her desk she thumbed through the book, trying to ignore the reams of female names, and then, once she had found Caroline de Menthe, dialled the London number—there were several international numbers under the same name. She spoke politely into the receiver when she got through to the Savoy switchboard.

It was a moment or two before Reception connected her, and then a sultry, heavily accented voice said lazily, 'Caroline de Menthe.'

'Good afternoon, Miss de Menthe,' Sephy said quickly. 'Mr Quentin has asked me to call you to say he is sorry but he'll be half an hour late this evening. His secretary has been taken ill and he is running a little behind schedule. He will pick you up at about half past seven if that is all right?'

'And you are what? An office girl?' The seductive sultriness was gone; the other woman's tone was distinctly vinegary now.

'I am standing in for Mr Quentin's secretary,' Sephy stated quietly, forcing herself not to react to the overt rudeness.

There was a moment's silence, and then the model said curtly, 'Tell Mr Quentin I will be waiting for him,' and the phone went dead.

Charming. Sephy stared at the receiver in her hand for a moment before slowly replacing it. Caroline de Menthe might be beautiful and famous and have the world at her feet, but she didn't have the manners of an alley cat. She glanced at the interconnecting door as she wrinkled her small nose. And that was the sort of woman he liked? Still, it was absolutely nothing to do with her. She was just his temporary secretary—*very* temporary.

The telephone rang, cutting off further deliberations, and when she realised it was the hospital asking for Mr Quentin she put the call through to him immediately.

It was a minute or two before the call ended and he buzzed her at once. She opened the door to see him sitting back in his chair with a stunned look on his dark face. 'It's cancer,' he said slowly. 'The poor old girl's got cancer.'

'Oh, no. Oh, I'm so sorry,' Sephy said helplessly. He looked poleaxed and positively grey, and she was amazed how much he obviously cared.

'They think it's operable and that she'll be okay in the long run, but it'll be a long job,' he said flatly, after taking a hard pull of air. And then he made Sephy jump a mile as he drove his fist down on to the desk with enough force to make the papers rise an inch or two. 'Damn stupid woman,' he ground out through clenched teeth. 'Why didn't she *say* something? The consultant said she must have been in pain for some weeks.'

'She probably thought it was viral, something like that,' Sephy pointed out sensibly. 'No one likes to think the worst.'

'Spare me the benefit of inane female logic,' he bit back with cutting coldness.

She swallowed hard. Okay, so he was obviously upset

about Madge, and she would ignore his rudeness this time, but if he thought she was going to be a doormat he'd got another think coming! She wouldn't take that from anyone.

'Hell!' It was an angry bark. 'This is going to hit her hard. Her job is her life, it's what makes her tick, and she's been with me from the start. She'll hate the idea of being laid low, and she's got no friends, just a sister somewhere or other.'

Sephy remained silent. This was awful for Madge, and difficult for him, but once bitten, twice shy. She was saying nothing.

'So...' He rose from the desk and turned to the window so his back was towards her. 'She's covered by the company's private health plan, but make sure she's in the best room available; any additional costs will be covered by me personally. And send her some flowers and chocolates and a selection of magazines. Is there anything else you, as another woman, would think she'd like?' he asked, turning to face her with characteristic abruptness.

She stared at him. 'A visit?' she suggested pointedly.

His eyes narrowed into blue slits and he was grimly silent for a full ten seconds before he said expressionlessly, 'I don't like hospitals,' as though that was the end of the matter.

'If she's as lacking in friends as you said she'd still like a visit,' Sephy said stolidly. 'She must be feeling very vulnerable tonight, and probably a bit frightened.'

She saw his square jaw move as his teeth clenched hard and then he sighed irritably, a scowl crossing his harsh attractive face. 'She's probably exhausted right now,' he snapped tightly. 'It doesn't *have* to be tonight, does it?'

Sephy thought of the ravishing Caroline de Menthe waiting at the Savoy and smiled sweetly. 'That's up to you, of course, but a little bit of reassurance at a time like this goes a long way,' she said with saccharine gentleness.

She gathered up the pile of correspondence, now duly signed, as she spoke, and then felt awful about the covert bitchiness when he said, his tone distracted, 'That's excellent work by the way, Seraphina. I trust you've no objection to standing in for Madge for the next few weeks?'

She hesitated for a moment, his big, broad-shouldered body and rugged face swimming into focus as she raised her head from the papers in her hands, and then, as he raised enquiring black eyebrows she forced herself to smile coolly. 'Of course not,' she lied with careful composure. 'If you think I'm up to the job, that is.'

'I don't think there is any doubt about that,' he returned drily, the deep-blue eyes which resembled a cold summer sea watching her intently. 'No doubt at all.'

And this time he didn't smile.

CHAPTER TWO

QUENTIN DYNAMICS occupied a smart, four-storey building in Islington and Sephy's new flat was just a ten-minute walk away, which was wonderful after years of battling on the train from Twickenham.

The late September evening was mellow and balmy as she trod the crowded London pavements, and the chairs and tables outside most of the pubs and cafés were full as Londoners enjoyed an alfresco drink in the Indian summer the country was enjoying.

Everyone seemed relaxed and easy now the working day was finished, but Sephy was conscious that she felt somewhat stunned as she walked along in the warm, traffic-scented air, and more tired than she had felt in a long, long time.

Mind you, that wasn't surprising, she reassured herself silently in the next moment. She always worked hard—as Mr Harper's secretary she was used to working on her own initiative and dealing with one panic after another most days—but being around Conrad Quentin was something else again! The man wasn't human—he was a machine that consumed facts and figures with spectacular single-mindedness and with a swiftness that was frightening.

No wonder he had risen so dramatically fast to the top of his field, she thought ruefully as she neared the row of shops over which her flat—and ten others—were situated. Other men might have his astute business sense and brilliance, but they were lacking the almost monomaniacal drive of the head of Quentin Dynamics.

Was he like that in all areas of his life? A sudden picture

of Caroline de Menthe was there on the screen on her mind, along with the long list of women's names in the little black book he had tossed to her. It was an answer in itself and it made Sephy go hot inside.

He would be an incredible lover; of course he would! He had lush beauties absolutely *panting* after him, and inevitably they were reduced to purring pussycats by the magnetism that surrounded him like a dark aura, if all the society photographs and office gossip were anything to go by.

He was king of the small kingdom he had created, an invincible being who had only to click his fingers to see his minions falling over themselves to please him. And he knew it.

She didn't know why it bothered her so much but it did. Sephy was frowning as she delved in her shoulder bag for her keys to unlock the outside door, behind which were stairs leading to the front door of her flat, and the frown deepened as she heard Jerry's voice call her name.

Jerry was the young owner of the menswear shop, and nice enough, even good-looking in a floppy-haired kind of way, but although Sephy liked him she knew she could never think of him in a romantic sense. He was too…boyish.

Jerry, on the other hand, seemed determined to pursue her, even after she had told him—politely but firmly—that there was no chance of a date. It made her feel uncomfortable, even guilty, when he was so likeable and friendly, as though she was smacking down a big amiable puppy with dirty feet who wanted to play.

She raised her eyes, her hand still in her bag, and turned her head to see Jerry just behind her, the very epitome of public school Britain in his immaculate flannels and well-pressed shirt.

'Just wanted to remind you about Maisie's party tonight,' he said earnestly. 'You hadn't forgotten?'

She had. Maisie occupied the flat two doors along, above her own boutique, and her psychedelic hair—dyed several vivid colours and gelled to stick up in dangerous-looking spikes—and enthusiastic body-piercing hid a very intelligent and shrewd mind. And Maisie's parties were legendary. The trouble was—Sephy's eyes narrowed just the slightest as her mind raced—Maisie and all of Jerry's other friends knew how he felt about her and, ever since she had moved into the flat, some eight weeks ago, had been trying to pair them off.

She had just opened her mouth to give voice to the weakest excuse of all—a blinding headache, which had every likelihood of being perfectly true the way her head was thumping after the hectic day—when a deep cold voice cut through the balmy evening air like a knife through butter.

'It would have been quicker to walk here with this damn traffic.'

'Mr Quentin!' She had whirled right round to face the road at the sound of his voice and her heart seemed to stop, and then race on like a greyhound.

Conrad Quentin was sitting at the wheel of a silver Mercedes, the driver's window down and his arm resting on the ledge as he surveyed her lazily from narrowed blue eyes in the fading light. The big beautiful car, the dark, brooding quality of its inhabitant and the utter surprise of it all robbed Sephy of all coherent thought, and it was a few moments before the mocking sapphire gaze told her she was looking at him with her mouth open.

She shut her lips so suddenly her teeth jarred, and then made a superhuman effort to pull herself together as she muttered in a soft aside to Jerry, 'It's my boss from work,' before walking quickly across the pavement to the side of the waiting vehicle.

'One set of keys.' He spoke before she could say anything. 'I noticed them on the floor as I was leaving and
thought they might be important?' he added quietly as he
handed her the keyring.

She stared at the keys for a moment before raising her
burning face to his cool perusal. Her flat keys, the keys to
her mother's house and car, as well as those for Mr
Harper's office and the filing cabinets. What must he be
thinking? she asked herself hotly. It wasn't exactly reassuring to think one's temporary secretary was in the habit
of mislaying such items. *Ex*-temporary secretary!

'I dropped my bag earlier.' It was a monotone, but all
she could manage. 'They must have fallen out.'

'Undoubtedly.' It was very dry.

'Tha…thank you.' Oh, don't stutter! Whatever else,
don't *stutter*, she told herself heatedly.

'My pleasure.' He eyed her sardonically.

'It was when the fax from Einhorn came through,' she
said quickly. 'I knew you were waiting for it and I knocked
my bag off the desk as I went to reach for it. I must have
missed the keys…' Her voice trailed away weakly. It could
have been *his* keys she'd dropped, the keys to his confidential papers and so on, if he had retrieved Madge's set.
Which he hadn't yet. And when he did, he was hardly likely
to give them to her now, was he? she belaboured herself
miserably. He must think she was a featherbrain! And she'd
never done anything like this with Mr Harper.

'No one is perfect, Seraphina.' And then he further surprised her when he added, the brilliant blue eyes holding
hers, 'It's a relief, actually. I was beginning to think I'd
have my work cut out to keep up with you.'

Her mouth was open again but she couldn't help it.

'So…' His dark husky voice was soft and low. 'Is that
the boyfriend?' The blue eyes looked past her and they
were mocking.

'What?' She was still recovering from being let off the hook.

'The guy who is glaring at me.' It was a slow, amused drawl. 'Is he your boyfriend?'

Belatedly she remembered Jerry, and as she turned her head, following the direction of Conrad Quentin's eyes, she saw Jerry was indeed glaring. 'No, no of course not,' she said distractedly. 'He's just a neighbour, a friend.'

The black eyebrows went a notch higher. 'Really?' It was cryptic.

'Yes, really,' she snapped back, before she remembered this was Conrad Quentin she was talking to. 'He…he owns the shop below my flat,' she said more circumspectly. 'That's all.' And then she added, as the vivid blue gaze became distinctly uncomfortable, 'Thank you so much for bringing the keys, and I'm sorry to have put you to so much trouble.'

'How sorry?' he asked smoothly.

'What?' It was becoming a habit, this 'what?', but then she might have known he wouldn't react like ninety-nine per cent of people would to her gracious little speech, she told herself silently.

'I said, how sorry?' he drawled lazily, the sapphire eyes as sharp as blue glass. 'Sorry enough to accompany me to the hospital tonight?'

She almost said 'The hospital?' before she managed to bite back the fatuous words and say instead, 'Why would you want me to do that, Mr Quentin?' with some modicum of composure.

'I told you, I don't like hospitals,' he said easily as he settled back in the leather seat. 'Besides, I'm sure Madge would feel more comfortable with another woman around.'

'I thought you had a date for tonight? I'm sure Miss de Menthe would be pleased to accompany you.' She hadn't meant to say it but it had just sort of popped out on its own.

'Caroline is not the sort of woman you take to the hospital to visit your aged secretary,' he said drily.

No, she'd just bet she wasn't! Sephy thought nastily. No doubt he had something else entirely in mind for the voluptuous model.

'But of course if you have other plans…'

She stared at him, her mind racing. If she stayed at home she would have to go to the party, and that would mean a night of further embarrassment with Jerry, because one thing was for sure—he'd made up his mind he wasn't going to take no for an answer. Which would have been nice and flattering if she'd even the slightest inkling of ever fancying him. As it was…

'When are you thinking of going?' she asked carefully, her voice low.

'Now seems as good a time as any.' And then he smiled slowly, a fascinatingly breath-stopping smile, as he added, 'Does that mean you are considering taking pity on me?'

Sephy stood as though glued to the hot pavement and swallowed twice before she managed to say, 'I'll have to go and change first. I'll be about five minutes?'

'Fine.' He glanced over her shoulder. 'The guy who isn't the boyfriend looks like he wants a word with you,' he drawled laconically before the sapphire gaze homed in again on her warm face.

'Yes, right…' She was backing away as she spoke, suddenly overwhelmed by what she had agreed to.

She must be mad, she told herself silently as she walked back to Jerry, who was waiting in the doorway of his shop, his pleasant, attractive face straight and his brown eyes fixed on her face. If it was a choice of an evening fending off Jerry as kindly as she could or choosing to spend an hour or so in Conrad Quentin's company there was no contest! The amiable puppy had it every time. But it was too late now.

'You told me your boss was small and fat and had eight grandchildren,' Jerry accused her as she reached his side.

'He is and he does,' Sephy said weakly. 'That's the owner of the business, Mr Quentin, and I'm standing in for his secretary for a while. There…there's an emergency and I've got to go with him.' She was terribly conscious of the parked car behind them.

'*Now?*' Jerry made no effort to lower his voice.

'I'm afraid so.' She nodded firmly and inserted the key in the lock as she added, 'So it looks like the party is off for me, Jerry. Make my apologies to Maisie, would you? Tell her I'll see her at the weekend. For a coffee or something.'

'How long do you think you will be?' He was nothing if not hopeful, his voice holding a pleading note which increased her guilt.

'Ages,' she answered briskly as the door swung wide. 'Bye, Jerry.' This was definitely a case of being cruel to be kind.

She ran quickly up the stairs to the flat, but once inside in the small neat hall she stopped still, staring at her reflection in the charming antique mirror her mother had bought her for a housewarming present.

Anxious honey-brown eyes stared back at her, and it was their expression she answered as she said, 'You might well be worried! As though working with him isn't bad enough you have to agree to go with him tonight.' He obviously wouldn't have dreamt asking the beautiful Caroline to do anything so mundane, but Sephy Vincent? Well, she was just part of the office machine, there to serve and obey. She grimaced at her reflection irritably.

What had he said? Oh, yes—Caroline de Menthe was

not the sort of woman you took to a hospital to visit your secretary. She—clearly—was. Which said it all, really.

The soft liquid eyes narrowed and hardened and her mouth became tight. Okay, so she wasn't an oil painting and she never would be, and she could do with losing a few pounds too, but no one had ever suggested she walk round with a paper bag over her head! And Jerry fancied her.

The last thought brought her back to earth with a bump. What was she doing feeling sorry for herself? she asked the dark-haired girl in the mirror with something akin to amazement in her face now. This wasn't like her. But then she hadn't felt like herself all afternoon if it came to it. It was him, Conrad Quentin. He was…disturbing. And he was also waiting outside, she reminded herself sharply, diving through to the bedroom in the same instant.

She threw off her crumpled work clothes and grabbed a pretty knee-length flowered skirt she had bought the week before, teaming it with a little white top and matching waist-length cardigan. She didn't have time to shower, she decided feverishly, but she quickly bundled her hair in a high knot on top of her head, teasing her fringe and several tendrils loose, and then applied a touch of eyeshadow and a layer of mascara to widen her eyes.

The whole procedure had taken no more than five minutes and she was out in the street again in six, to find him lying back indolently in the seat with his eyes shut and his hands behind his head as he listened to Frank Sinatra singing about doing it his way.

Very appropriate, she thought a trifle caustically. If only half the stories about Conrad Quentin were true he certainly lived his life by that principle.

His eyes opened as she reached the car and he straightened, glancing at his watch as he murmured, 'When you say five minutes you really mean five minutes, don't you?'

before leaning across and opening the passenger door for her to slide in.

'You find that surprising?' she asked unevenly as the closeness of him registered and all her senses went into hyperdrive.

'For a woman to say what she means?' He half turned in his seat, the brilliant blue gaze raking her hot face. 'More of a minor miracle,' he drawled cynically, one black eyebrow quirking mockingly as he started the engine.

Sephy would have liked to come back with a sharp, clever retort, but the truth of the matter was that she was floundering. She'd never ridden in a Mercedes before for a start, and the big beautiful car was truly gorgeous, but it was the man at the wheel who was really taking her breath away.

The office—with plenty of air space, not to mention desks, chairs and all the other paraphernalia—was one thing; the close confines of the car were quite another. They emphasised his dominating masculinity a hundredfold, and underlined the dark, dangerous quality of his attractiveness enough to have her sitting as rigid as a piece of wood.

She tried telling herself she was stupid and pathetic and ridiculous, but with the faint smell of his aftershave teasing her senses and his body warmth all about her it didn't do any good. This was Conrad Quentin—*Conrad Quentin*—and she still couldn't quite believe the whole afternoon had happened, or that she was actually sitting here with him like this.

She felt a momentary thrill that she didn't understand and that was entirely inappropriate in the circumstances, and reminded herself—sharply now—that she had to keep her wits about her after the episode of the keys if he wasn't going to think she was utterly dense. She was a useful office item as far as he was concerned—like the fax or the computer—and he expected cool, efficient service.

He was a very exacting employer, and it was well known
that he suffered fools badly—in fact he didn't suffer them
at all! And that was fair enough, she told herself silently,
when you considered he paid top salaries with manifold
perks like private health insurance and so on.

He was the original work hard and play hard business
tycoon, and until today she had never so much as exchanged more than half a dozen words with him, so it
wasn't surprising she was feeling a bit…tense. Well, more
than a bit, she admitted ruefully.

And then, as though he had read her mind, she was conscious of the hard profile turning her way for an instant
before he said softly, 'Relax, Seraphina. I'm not going to
eat you.'

Her head shot round, but he was looking straight ahead
at the road again and the imperturbable face was expressionless.

It took her a second or two, but then she was able to say,
her voice verging on the icy, 'I don't know what you mean,
Mr Quentin,' even as she knew her face was burning with
hot colour.

'The suggestion that you accompany me to the hospital
was purely spontaneous,' he said mildly, without looking
at her again. 'I'm not about to leap on you and have my
wicked way, if that's what's worrying you.'

'Nothing is worrying me,' she bit back immediately, horrified beyond measure, 'and I wouldn't dream of thinking
you intended…that you would even think of—' She
stopped abruptly, aware that she was about to burst into
flames, and took a deep breath before she said, 'I'm quite
sure you are not that sort of man, Mr Quentin.'

There was a moment of blank silence, when Sephy felt
the temperature drop about thirty degrees, and then he said,
his dark voice silky-soft, 'I do like women, Miss Vincent.'

This was getting worse! 'I know you do,' she said

quickly. 'Of course I know that; everyone does. I just meant—' She wasn't improving matters, she realised suddenly, as she risked a sidelong glance at the cold rugged face.

'Please, do continue.' It was curt and clipped. '"Everyone" takes an interest in my love life, do they?'

Oh, blow it! He was the one prancing about with a different woman each week! What did he expect for goodness' sake? 'I was just trying to say I know you like women, that's all,' Sephy said primly, her face burning with a mixture of embarrassment and disquiet.

'Right. So my sexual persuasion is not in question.' There was liquid ice in his deep voice. 'That taken as read, why would it be so unlikely that I might have ulterior motives in asking you to spend the evening with me?'

The evening? They were going to visit poor Madge Watkins, that was all! Afterwards she would realise she could have answered in a host of ways to defuse what had become an electric moment: he was not the sort of man to mix business and pleasure would have been a good one; she was aware he was dating someone at the moment could have been another. What she did say, the words tumbling out of her mouth, was, 'There has to be some sort of a spark between a man and a woman, doesn't there? And I'm not your type.'

'My *type*?' If she had accused him of a gross obscenity he couldn't have sounded more offended. There was another chilling pause, and then he said, 'What, exactly, do you consider my "type", Miss Vincent?' as he viciously cut up a harmless, peaceable family saloon that had been sailing along minding its own business.

She couldn't make it any worse. She might as well be honest, Sephy told herself silently as the two 'Miss Vincents' after all the 'Seraphinas' of the day registered like the kiss of death on her career. 'Women like Miss de Menthe, I suppose,' she said shakily.

'Meaning?' he queried testily.

He didn't intend to make this easy. 'Beautiful, successful, rich…' Spoilt, selfish, bitchy…

The grooves that splayed out from either side of his nose to his mouth deepened, as though she had actually voiced the last three words, but he remained silent, although it was a silence that vibrated with painful tension. Finally, he said coldly, 'So, we've ascertained my type. What is your type, Seraphina?'

At least the Seraphina was back, although she didn't know if that was a good or a bad thing, Sephy thought feverishly as she clasped her hands together so tightly the knuckles showed white. And her *type*? That was funny if he did but know it. In the age of the Pill and condoms being bought as casually as bunches of flowers, she must be the only girl in the whole of London whose sexual experience was minimal to say the least. But that was the last thing she could say to a man of the world like Conrad Quentin. He'd laugh his head off.

The thought brought the door in her mind behind which she kept the caustic memories of the past slightly ajar, and as the image of David intruded for a second her stomach turned over. And then she had slammed it shut again, her mouth tightening as she willed the humiliation and pain to die.

She forced herself to shrug easily and kept her voice light as she said, 'I guess I'm not fussy on looks; dark or fair, tall or short, it doesn't matter as long as the guy is a nice person.'

'A nice person?' he returned mockingly, with a lift of one dark eyebrow, his large capable hands firmly on the wheel as he executed a manoeuvre that Sephy knew wasn't exactly legal, and which caused a medley of car horns to blare behind them as the Mercedes dived off into a side-street to avoid the traffic jam which had been ahead. 'And how would you define a nice person?'

A man who could accept that one-night stands and casual sex weren't obligatory on the first date? Someone who could understand that some women—or certainly this one at least—needed to be in love before they would allow full intimacy, and who was prepared to think with his head and hopefully his heart rather than that other vital organ some inches lower. Someone who cared about her just a little more than their own ego, who didn't mind that she hadn't got a perfect thirty-six, twenty-four, thirty-six figure, with fluffy blonde hair and big blue eyes, someone…someone from her dreams.

Sephy twisted in the seat, knowing she had to say something, and then managed, 'A man who is kind and funny and gentle, I suppose,' and then cringed inside as he snorted mockingly.

'And that's it?' he asked scathingly. 'You don't want a man, Seraphina. Your average cocker spaniel would do just as well. And the lovelorn guy back at your flat, does he fit all the criteria?' he added before she could react to the acidic sarcasm.

'Jerry?' she asked with a stiffness that should have warned him.

'Is that his name?' He couldn't have sounded more derisory if she'd said Donald Duck. 'Well, it's clear Jerry's got it bad, and he looked a fine, upstanding pillar of the establishment and *impossibly* kind and gentle, or am I wrong?'

She didn't often get angry, but around this man she seemed to be little else, and now the words were on her tongue without her even having to think about them. 'I wasn't aware that my job description necessitated talking about my friends,' she said with savage coldness, 'but if it does you had better accept my resignation here and now, Mr Quentin.'

There was absolute silence for a screaming moment, but as Sephy glared at him the cool profile was magnificently indifferent. He'd make a fantastic poker player, she thought irrelevantly. No wonder he was so formidable in business.

'The name's Conrad.'

'What?' If he had taken all his clothes off and danced stark naked on the Mercedes' beautiful leather seats she couldn't have been more taken aback.

'I said, the name is Conrad,' he said evenly, without taking his eyes from the view beyond the car's bonnet. 'If we are going to be working together for some weeks I can't be doing with Mr Quentin this and Mr Quentin that; it's irritating in the extreme.'

She wanted—she did so *want*—to be able to match him for cool aplomb and control, but it was a lost cause, she acknowledged weakly as she sank back in her seat without saying another word. Game, set and match to him, the insensitive, cold-blooded, arrogant so-and-so.

CHAPTER THREE

THEY stopped on the way to buy flowers and chocolates for Madge—the flowers taking up the whole of the back seat of the car and the box of chocolates large enough to feed a hundred little old ladies for a week—and it was just after half past seven when the Mercedes nosed its way into the immaculate car park of the small, select private hospital on the outskirts of Harlow.

The dusky shadowed twilight carried the scent of the crisply cut lawns which surrounded the gracious building, and as Sephy nervously accompanied Conrad up the wide, horseshoe-shaped stone steps to the front door, her arms laden with flowers, the surrealness of it all was making her light-headed.

If anyone had told her that morning she would be spending part of the evening in the company of the exalted head of Quentin Dynamics she would have laughed in their face, but here she was. And here he was. All six foot plus of him.

She darted a glance from under her eyelashes at the tall, dark figure next to her and her heart gave a little jump. He exuded maleness. It was there in every line of the lean powerful body and hard chiselled face, and as her female hormones seemed horribly determined to react—with a life all of their own—to his own particular brand of virile masculinity it didn't make for easy companionship.

Once they were inside the building the attractive, red-haired receptionist nearly fell over herself to escort them to Madge's room, which—as Conrad had decreed—was the best in the place.

But Sephy didn't notice the ankle-deep carpeting, exclusive and beautifully co-ordinated furnishings or the magnificent view from the large bay window over the lawns and trees surrounding the hospital. All her attention was taken up with the fragile, pathetic little figure huddled in the bed.

At a little over four foot ten Madge Watkins had always been tiny, but she seemed to have shrunk down to nothing since the day before and the effect was shocking.

Her grey hair looked limp and scanty, her skin was a pasty white colour, and the expression in her faded blue eyes stated quite clearly she was terrified. Sephy's heart went out to her.

So, apparently, did Conrad's.

The aggressive and ruthless tycoon of working hours and the mocking, contemptuous escort of the last forty-five minutes or so metamorphosed into someone Sephy didn't recognise. He was quiet and tender with his elderly secretary, dumping the chocolates and the rest of the flowers he was carrying on a chair, before taking the shrivelled thin figure in his arms and holding her close for long moments without speaking.

Madge's face was wet by the time he settled her back against her pillows, but then he sat by her side, talking soothingly and positively after he had drawn Sephy forward to make her greetings. After a while it dawned on Sephy that Conrad and his secretary had a very special relationship—more like mother and son than boss and employee. And it stunned her. Totally.

The receptionist brought them all tea and cakes at just after eight o'clock, and by the time they left, at ten to nine, Madge was smiling and conversing quite naturally, the look of stark dread gone from her eyes and her face animated.

'You needn't come again, lad.'

Once Madge had relaxed and understood Conrad had no

intention of standing on ceremony in front of Sephy, she had referred to her brilliant boss as 'lad' a few times, and Sephy had realised that the special circumstances were allowing her to see the way they were normally when they were alone. Before this night she had never heard Madge give him anything but his full title, and even at the Christmas dances and such the elderly woman had always been extremely stiff and proper.

'Of course I'm coming again, woman!' His voice was rough but his face was something else as he glanced at the small figure in the bed, and Sephy was surprised at the jolt her heart gave.

'No, really, lad. I know how you hate these places,' Madge said earnestly.

And then she stopped speaking as Conrad laid his hand over her scrawny ones and said very softly, 'I said I'll be back, Madge. Now, then, no more of that. And you're not rushing home to that empty house before you're able to look after yourself either. You're going to get better, the doctor's assured me about that, but it'll take time and you'll have to be patient for once in your life.'

'There's the pot calling the kettle,' Madge said weakly, her eyes swimming with tears again as his concern and love touched her.

It touched Sephy too, but in her case the overwhelming feeling was one of confusion and agitation and the knowledge that it had been a mistake—a big, big mistake—to come here with him like this. As the cold, ruthless, cynical potentate Conrad Quentin was someone she disliked, as the ladykiller and rake he was someone she despised, and as her temporary boss he was someone she respected, for his incredibly intelligent mind and the rapier-sharp acumen that was mind-blowing, at the same time as feeling an aversion for such cold, obsessional single-mindedness.

But tonight… How did she think about him tonight? she

asked herself nervously as she watched him make his good-byes to Madge. But, no, he was her boss—just her boss—and come tomorrow morning things would be back on a more formal footing and she would forget how she was feeling right now—she *would*; of course she would! She, of all people, knew that men like him—wildly attractive, charismatic brutes of men—were shallow and egocentric and could charm the birds out of the trees when they liked.

They had just reached the door when Madge's voice, urgent and high, brought them turning to face her again. 'Angus! I forgot about Angus. I can't believe I could forget him. He's had no dinner, Conrad.'

'He could live on his fat for years, Madge, so don't put on sackcloth and ashes,' Conrad said drily, and in answer to Sephy's enquiring face he added, 'Madge's cat,' by way of explanation.

'He'll be wondering where I am—'

'Don't worry.' Conrad cut short Madge's tremulous voice, his own resigned. 'I'll pick him up on the way home and he can board with me for a while until you're home again. Daniella loves cats, as you know—even Angus. She'll look after him.'

Daniella? Who was Daniella? And then a prim voice in her head admonished, It's nothing to do with you who Daniella is.

It was dark outside, the air a wonderful scented mixture of grass and woodsmoke and hot summer days after the sterile warmth of the hospital, and Sephy raised her head as she took several deep gulps of the intoxicating mixture.

'Thanks, Sephy.' His voice was unusually soft.

Surprised into looking at him, she became aware he was watching her closely from narrowed blue eyes, his hands thrust deep in his pockets and the brooding quality she had noticed about him more than once very evident.

'Sephy?' She stared at him, suddenly acutely shy without knowing why. 'You said you didn't intend to call me that.'

'It seems the least I can do after you've helped me out so ungrudgingly this evening,' he said with quiet sincerity.

It made her previous thoughts about him uncharitable, to say the least, and she could feel herself blushing as she said, 'That's all right; it killed two birds with one stone, actually.'

'Yes?' He glanced down enquiringly as they began to walk.

'I'd been invited to a party that I didn't want to go to but it would have been difficult to get out of it without a valid excuse,' she explained quietly.

'And there was me thinking you had succumbed to my irresistible charm.'

It was cool and light, but somehow she got the impression he wasn't as amused as his smile would have liked her to believe, and something he had said earlier in the day—'many a true word is spoken in jest'—came back to her. The male ego again. She mentally nodded at the thought. The male sex in general really did seem to believe they had been put on the earth to receive due homage.

'Anyway, party or no, the least I can do is to feed you before I take you back,' he said smoothly, for all the world as though she was a little lost orphan he had found wandering about the streets of London. 'Come on, we'll stop off for a bite to eat on the way home. I know I'm starving.'

She stared at him uncertainly, searching for the right words to refuse his invitation without appearing rude. Dinner with Conrad Quentin? She wouldn't be able to eat a thing, she told herself feverishly as she stopped dead in her tracks. 'But…'

'Yes?' He glanced down at her again and his eyes were cool.

'What about Miss de Menthe?' she said quickly. 'I thought you were seeing her tonight?'

'Cancelled,' he said cryptically.

'And there's Madge's cat.' Thank goodness for Madge's cat.

'So there is.' His gaze was distinctly cold now, and when she still didn't move he made a quiet sound of annoyance and took her arm in one firm hand, guiding her along the winding path between bowling-green-smooth stretches of grass and into the car park.

His flesh was warm through the thin cotton of her cardigan, and it wasn't the swiftness with which he was urging her along that made her suddenly short of breath. He was so big, so male, so much of everything if the truth be known. And knowing what he was like, all the women he had had, made her feel gauche and inadequate and totally out of her depth. He smelt absolutely wonderful. The unwelcome intrusion of the thought did nothing to calm the wild flutters of panic that were turning her stomach upside down.

He opened the car door for her when they reached the Mercedes, and as he leant over her slightly it took every ounce of her will-power to slide into the confines of the car with a small polite nod of her head, as though she was totally oblivious to his male warmth.

And then, as he walked lazily round the bonnet of the car, she took herself severely in hand. Conrad Quentin was one of those men who had everything—wealth, success and an alarming amount of sex appeal—and she'd better get it clear in her head now that she wasn't going to let him intimidate her, consciously or unconsciously. If she was going to continue standing in for Madge, that was. Which she rather thought she was, crazy though that made her. Anyway, she had given him her word at the office earlier, so that was that. She couldn't back out now.

'You're frowning.'

She glanced up to see a pair of very piercing blue eyes surveying her through the open driver's door, and then, as she flushed hotly, he slid into the seat and started the engine with a flick of his hand.

Sephy waited for him to follow up on his terse statement, but when they had gone a mile or two and he still hadn't spoken she swallowed drily, and then said quietly, 'Mr Quentin—'

'Conrad,' he interrupted pleasantly.

She tried to ignore the long lean legs stretched out under the steering wheel and the delicious faint odour of what must be wildly expensive aftershave, and took another surreptitious swallow before she managed, 'Conrad, there really is no need to buy me dinner. I'm sure you must be terribly busy, and I've masses of things to do when I get home—'

'Don't you want to have dinner with me, Sephy?' he interrupted again, the even tone fooling her not at all.

She hesitated just a second too long before she said, 'It's not that. Of course it's not that I don't *want* to.'

'No?' It was very dry. 'Well, we won't labour the point. I take it you have no objection in calling in Madge's place on the way back and picking up the terrible Angus? It is *en route*, so it makes sense.'

She wanted to ask, Why the *terrible* Angus? but said instead, 'Yes, of course. That's fine,' her voice tight and stiff.

'And it might be easier to drop him off at my house before I take you home; he doesn't like travelling and it'll be less stressful,' he continued smoothly. 'We don't want to distress him.'

Put like that, she could hardly do anything else but agree. She had no idea where he lived, but somehow she didn't feel she could ask him either. She just hoped it wasn't *too* far from Madge's.

Madge's house turned out to be a small and awe-inspiringly neat semi in Epping, with a paved front garden methodically interspersed with miniature shrubs. The interior of the building smelt of mothballs and furniture polish and was as spick and span as the front garden. It was *exactly* Madge—which made Angus all the more of a shock.

The cat was an enormous battle-scarred ginger tom, with a shredded right ear, a twisted tail that looked distinctly the worse for wear and a blemished nose that bore evidence of numerous fights. He was the very antithesis of what Sephy had expected.

He was waiting for them in Madge's gleaming compact little kitchen when Conrad opened the door from the hall, which had been firmly closed, and it was clear he was confined to that room of the house during the working day from the massive cat flap in the back door, which gave him access to the rear garden, and the big, warm comfortable basket in one corner of the kitchen, next to which were two saucers. Two *empty* saucers—a fact which the cat immediately brought to their attention by his plaintive miaows.

'Oh, he must be starving, poor thing.'

Sephy was all concern as the enormous feline wound hopefully round her legs, but as she glanced anxiously at Conrad she saw him shake his head mockingly, and his voice was amused as he said, 'He'd have you wrapped round one paw the same as he has Madge. If ever a cat could look after itself this one can, I assure you. Angus always has his eye to the main chance and he keeps everyone dancing to his tune.'

It takes one to recognise one.

For an awful moment Sephy thought she had actually spoken the words out loud, but when Conrad's face didn't change and he merely gathered up the cat basket and the saucers she breathed out a silent sigh of relief. She'd said more than enough already.

'See if you can find a tin of cat food for tonight while I take these out to the car. Although once I get him home I dare say Daniella will be feeding him salmon and steak.' Conrad shook his head again at the huge cat, who eyed him unblinkingly out of serene emerald eyes. 'He boarded with us last year while Madge had a couple of weeks' holiday with her sister, and he didn't taste cat food once.'

'Daniella?' Sephy queried carefully as he passed her with the basket. She didn't think it unreasonable to ask now.

'My housekeeper,' he tossed easily over his shoulder.

His housekeeper. As the kitchen door closed behind him Sephy stood staring into space as she pictured a nice, plump, middle-aged little body, and then, as she heard Conrad returning, quickly opened a cupboard or two for the supply of cat food.

Angus submitted perfectly happily to being carried out to the car, his two huge front paws resting on Conrad's chest as he gazed solemnly at Sephy over Conrad's shoulder when she followed them out. Once in the Mercedes, however, the calm composure faltered a bit as he crouched on the back seat and began to growl as Conrad started the engine. A low, heated and rather nasty growl.

'Ignore him.' Conrad appeared quite unconcerned. 'He'll keep that up until we reach home, but as long as he isn't confined that's all he'll do. He just hates being shut in.'

'How do you know that?' Sephy asked nervously. The animal was half domestic cat, half lion, and she didn't fancy having those vicious claws and teeth in the back of her neck.

'Because I made the mistake of putting him in a cat carrier Madge had provided the last time,' Conrad said evenly, his face expressionless. 'It's called learning the hard way.'

'Bad idea?'

'You could say that.' It was clear the subject wasn't a favourite one. 'He'd ripped it apart and escaped before we were halfway home, and he leapt about the car like a demoniac maniac before he decided to take his revenge by scenting every corner.'

'Oh, I see.' The mental picture of her suave, cool, imperturbable boss being put in his place so completely by a cat was sweet, and although she managed to keep her face straight there was a gurgle of laughter in her voice as she said, 'He's a big cat.'

'With a big bladder.' The blue eyes raked her face for one moment. 'I had the car cleaned three times before I got rid of the odour, and even then the smell wafted back on hot days.'

She glanced round at Angus, who was sitting quite quietly apart from the low, threatening growl in the back of his throat, and as honey-brown eyes met brilliant green she could have sworn the cat winked at her. She smiled at him, she couldn't help it, and then turned back in her seat again, her eyes scanning the hard male profile at the side of her as she did so. The amusement left her features abruptly.

Somehow she was more entangled in Conrad Quentin's life after a few hours than she was in Mr Harper's after working for him for a few years. She didn't quite know how it had happened, but something was telling her it was unwise at best, and at worst it was downright dangerous. He had something, a drawing power, a magnetism, and how was she going to feel when Madge was back at work and she was unceremoniously dumped back into Customer Services? But that was stupid—she'd feel relieved. Of course she would.

'My house is on the outskirts of Edgware.' His voice, calm and controlled and even as always, cut in on her racing thoughts. 'And I do appreciate you helping me out like this, Sephy.'

The charm was out in full force, she thought with un- usual cynicism, but then as she was complying with that determined, hard male will perhaps it wasn't surprising. He was a man who didn't like to be crossed, even in the small- est of things. 'No problem. No problem at all,' she said lightly, glancing out of the side window at the dark, shad- owed road along which they were travelling. 'Like I said, this has done me a favour in a way.'

'Ah, yes, the party.' There was a granite quality to his voice for a moment, and then it cleared as he said silkily, 'This might surprise you but I don't usually have to try and persuade a woman to spend time in my company, not since I made my first million anyway. And I can't remember one refusing dinner before.'

She said nothing, simply because she couldn't think of anything which would defuse what had suddenly become an electric moment.

'This Jerry—do you intend to put the poor man out of his misery and go out with him, or is there someone else on the horizon?' he asked conversationally, so conversa- tionally she felt she couldn't really ask him to mind his own business, as she would have liked to do and as she felt he deserved.

'No to both,' she answered shortly, hoping he would take the hint.

He didn't. 'So you're fancy-free and single?' he drawled easily. 'Enjoying the odd date but without any ties or com- mitments?' He didn't look at her as he spoke, his eyes on the windscreen.

'There hasn't been an ''odd date'' for quite some time.' She aimed to make her voice faintly amused, as though she wasn't as taut as piano wire inside. 'But, yes, I suppose you could put it like that.' Not that my private life is anything to do with you.

He nodded slowly. 'Are you a career girl?' he asked evenly.

Bearing in mind who he was, she could really only answer in one way, but it had the added advantage of being the truth when she said, 'Yes, I am, if being a career girl means I want to do well in my job and get somewhere.'

'And you enjoy being independent and autonomous.' This time it was a statement, and Sephy stiffened slightly. He saw too much, this man, and she didn't like where the conversation was going.

She forced herself to take a deep calming breath before she shrugged and said airily, 'Doesn't everyone at some stage?'

'No, I don't think so,' he challenged smoothly.

'Well, most of my friends think that way.' Her voice was too defensive, and she recognised it even before he spoke.

'I'm sorry, I seem to have touched a nerve,' he said, in a voice which suggested he wasn't sorry at all.

Arrogant swine! She gritted her teeth and stared straight ahead.

The rest of the journey was conducted in a silence in which Conrad seemed to feel extremely comfortable but which Sephy found unpleasant and disturbing to say the least. It didn't help that he was completely oblivious to her and she was aware of every tiny movement he made—his strong capable hands on the wheel, his big powerful body, the way his trousers pulled tight over lean thighs…

Sexual attraction. The words were stark but Sephy faced them bravely, aware she had been putting off the moment all day. Okay, so she was sexually attracted to him and she hadn't felt this way in years, not since… Her thought process hesitated, and then she followed through. Not since David.

David Bainbridge. The cliché of tall, dark and handsome. He had been the ultimate prize in the small village community near Banbury where she had been born, and the summer after she had finished her A levels and he had been home on holiday from university had been a thrilling one.

His father was something big in the City, and from the age of seventeen David had driven his own red sports car with a different girl in tow for every day of the week. Sephy had always been in awe of him, and consequently excruciatingly shy in his presence whenever the young people of the villages thereabouts got together. Her shyness had expressed itself in a cool aloofness that had earned her the nickname 'Ice Maiden' amongst the lads, although she hadn't known about that at the time.

She had been a short fat toddler and a short fat child, and even at eighteen a vestige of puppy fat had remained. That, combined with her abundance of freckles and the ugly brace she had had to wear on her teeth, had made her self-esteem zero, but she had hidden her lack of confidence under a reserved, touch-me-not exterior that protected the vulnerable girl underneath.

And then that summer David had appeared interested in her. He had returned from university with a beautiful blonde who had stayed two weeks and then disappeared to visit her family in Sweden, and from almost the day Annika had left David had begun seeking her out at the local dances, picnics, visits to the pub and so on. He had been quite open about it.

She hadn't been able to believe it at first, and then she had floated in a bubble of wonder and excitement as she had waited for him to ask her for a date, a real date, without any of the rest of the crowd along. She had dreamt about the moment for nights on end.

And then he had asked, one evening when a gang of them had been sipping ice-cold beer in the garden of the village pub. David had taken her aside and told her he was crazy about her, that he couldn't understand how he'd never noticed her before, that he really wanted them to get to know each other better.

'Come for a quiet meal at my place?' he suggested softly, his arms round her waist and his ebony eyes looking into her dazed brown ones. 'The parents are away so we'll have the house to ourselves. We can get a video and just chill out with a pizza and a bottle of wine. Please, Sephy?'

And he kissed her, drawing her into him as his hands moved seductively over her body before wandering under the loose thin cotton top she had on and cradling her breasts, his thumbs rubbing and tweaking their hard points until she thought she'd melt right at his feet.

It was her first kiss, her first tentative sexual encounter, and it blew her mind. She had worshipped him from afar all her life and suddenly the impossible, the *inconceivable* was happening. He'd fallen for her. *Her*...

She was the girl he drove home in his flash red sports car that night, and as they waved goodbye to the others she felt as though she was in a wonderful, blissful dream.

And then the dream turned into a nightmare.

It was her friend Glenis who told her. Glenis came round the next morning, sympathetic and commiserating but with an edge to her pity that told Sephy the other girl was perhaps secretly relishing the drama too, to say that Robbie— Glenis's boyfriend—had told her on the quiet that David was taking Sephy out for a bet.

'A bet?' Sephy looked into Glenis's round eyes, owl-like behind their thick glasses. 'I don't understand.'

Glenis wriggled a bit, but she still took a delight in telling her. 'One of the lads, I don't know who, bet David that he couldn't get the "Ice-Maiden"—that's you—into bed on a first date,' Glenis said conspiratorially. 'And David said he could. His parents are away in America for a few weeks so he told the lads he'd do it at his house, and they could hide in a spare bedroom and then he'd call them in to prove it when he'd finished. I'm sorry, Sephy, but I couldn't let you walk into that, could I? I had to tell you. I couldn't believe it at first, but it is true, honest.'

She thanked Glenis somehow, and once the other girl had gone picked up the telephone with numb fingers and called David's home. She didn't think about what to say, she just asked him. And he didn't even try to pretend once he knew he had been rumbled. That hurt as much as anything else. He was offhand and contemptuous and amused, and it was he who put the phone down on her.

She wanted to die for a time, dragging herself through each day and putting up a front whenever she was with the others until her nerves were as raw and lacerated as her heart. And at the bottom of her, whatever she tried to tell herself through the long sleepless nights when she tossed and turned until she thought she'd go mad, she knew David would have won his bet if she had gone to his home that night. She had been his for the taking and he had known it. Known she was crazy about him, that she adored him.

And then the holidays finished and David and some of the others went back to university. Months passed and she had the brace off and learnt to make the best of her naturally thick silky hair and smooth creamy skin; several hours at the gym each week toned her body and improved her shape. She took a college course in business management and secretarial skills, and, armed with that and her excellent A levels, left the womb-like village life and her mother's small, pretty cottage and headed for London at the age of twenty.

But somehow, deep inside, she was still that small, hurt, shy teenager who had had the ground swept from under her feet and had been left vulnerable and exposed, and she had never fully realised it until this moment. She had carved a new life for herself, even dated occasionally—never the same man twice and always allowing nothing more than a goodnight kiss, although most of them had seemed to think ending up in bed was a good idea—and she'd become adept and composed at handling all of life's ups and downs. And yet sexually and emotionally she had frozen that morning in front of Glenis, and it could have been yesterday so securely had the ice held.

And then this morning she had been drawn into Conrad Quentin's fiery orbit and now the ice was melting. She was attracted to him. She didn't want to be, but she didn't seem able to control the feeling. And he was just another David at heart. Oh, he was undoubtedly wealthier, more powerful, more magnetic and fascinating, but basically he was a ruthless womaniser who worked hard and played hard and lived his life by his own set of rules.

Was she one of those women she'd read about? she asked herself searchingly. Women with a built-in self-destruct button who were always drawn to men who would use and abuse them; men who were charming and hypnotic but with a flaw that made them cruelly self-absorbed and narcissistic?

But, no, any woman would be attracted to Conrad Quentin; he was extremely fanciable, she reassured herself in the next moment. This was just a lust thing, however you wanted to dress it up, an animal awareness, something base and carnal, and as such quite easily controlled once it had been recognised.

And as she was as far out of his league of beautiful, famous models and starlets and the like as the man in the moon, it really didn't matter too much one way or the other anyway. Conrad Quentin would never bother with someone like her—why, she'd worked for Quentin Dynamics for six years and he hadn't even known she'd existed until fate had put her right under his nose!

Sephy had been lost in her dark thoughts and oblivious to the miles the powerful car had eaten up, so now, as a deep, husky voice at the side of her said quietly, 'Here we are. Angus will soon be in Daniella's tender care,' she raised her head in startled surprise to see the car was pulling up in front of a nine-foot-high security wall with massive gates set in it, which Conrad opened smoothly with remote control from the car.

Once through the gates, the car moved slowly along a curved, pebble-covered driveway which opened on to a wide sweep in front of a very gracious, large, red-roofed house. Immaculate bowling-green-flat lawns surrounded the mansion on three sides, with a border of mature trees and bushes hiding the wall from view, and at their approach security lights lit up the grounds as bright as day.

It was all very epicurean and controlled—just like Conrad Quentin—and the beautifully tended gardens and rich scents coming from the warm vegetation suggested they were in the middle of the country somewhere, rather than the city. A lavish, opulent, fertile oasis in the middle of a desert of high-rise buildings and the madness of the rat-race, Sephy thought enviously. How the other half lived!

Conrad had left the car and walked round to open her door whilst she had been gaping at the view, and now, as his warm hand cupped her elbow once she was standing on the drive, he said, 'Come in and have a drink while you're here.'

'Angus...' She gestured somewhat vacantly towards the parked Mercedes' back seat, only to turn her head again and see one very dignified, massive ginger tom padding ahead of them towards the house, his tail straight up in the air and every line of his body indicating he wanted it made plain he was doing Conrad the most enormous favour by consenting to be his guest.

'He knows the way,' Conrad said wryly. 'I told you, you needn't concern yourself about him. He's streetwise.'

It wasn't the cat that was worrying her, Sephy thought with a touch of silent hysteria as she allowed herself to be ushered through the huge double front doors and into a truly baronial hall that would have swallowed her little flat whole. She had a fleetingly brief impression of dark gleaming wood, bowls of flowers and undeniably fine paintings before she found herself entering what was clearly the drawing room. Just as she sank down on the silk-covered chaise longue Conrad indicated, a slender, dark-haired and exquisitely lovely young woman followed them into the room. The girl was holding Angus in her arms and the big cat was purring loudly.

'He is telling me he wants his dinner,' the woman said laughingly in a bright, heavily accented voice, glancing at Conrad as she spoke. Then she turned to Sephy and added, 'You must be Sephy, yes? I am Daniella and I am pleasured to meet you,' adjusting Angus in her arms so she could shake Sephy's hand.

'You are *pleased* to meet her,' Conrad corrected softly with an indulgent smile. 'And I brought a tin of cat food from Madge's, incidentally, until you can get some tomorrow.'

'Cat food?' Daniella wrinkled her small perfect nose in utter distaste, turning to Sephy as though for moral support when she said, 'Angus the cat, he no like the food from tins.'

'Not when he can dine on best salmon,' Conrad agreed drily.

'Oh, you! You have the—how do you say it?—the bark that is worse than the bite?' Daniella's voice was warm and loving, and the glance she gave Conrad caused Sephy's eyes to open wide for an instant.

Housekeeper, my foot, she thought balefully. This defi-

nitely was no employer/employee relationship, but then she
shouldn't really be surprised, should she? It was the nature
of the animal after all. But didn't Daniella mind when he
paraded women like the lovely Caroline de Menthe in front
of her? Obviously not.

'I go now and see to the dinner.'

Daniella was smiling at her, and Sephy could do no more
than smile back before she said, 'I'm sure Angus will appreciate that.'

'*Si, si.* I think so too.' And then, as the cat wriggled in
her arms, Daniella said, 'Oh, you cat, you are the impatient
one,' before she nodded and smiled at them both again.
She left the room saying, 'Ten minutes, Conrad? *Si?*'

'Ten minutes will be fine, Daniella. That will give us a
chance to have a drink first,' he said with suspicious satisfaction.

'First?' As the door closed behind the young Italian
woman Sephy forced herself to speak quietly and calmly,
even though her heart was pounding. Something was afoot,
she could sense it. 'What does ''first'' mean?'

'Before something or someone else?' Conrad suggested
helpfully as he walked over to a large cocktail cabinet set
at the side of a huge bay window and gestured at the bottles
that were revealed as he opened the polished wood doors.
'What would you like to drink? Wine? Martini? Or perhaps
a gin and tonic?'

'I didn't mean I wanted a dictionary definition,' Sephy
said steadily as she met the brilliant blue eyes without
flinching. 'And I don't want a drink, thank you.'

He looked at her quietly for a moment. 'Why so wary
and guarded, Sephy?' he asked softly. 'Whatever have you
heard about me that's so terrible it's scared you to death?'

Sephy's face was brilliant and her voice was sharp with
embarrassment as she said, 'I'm not scared! Of course I'm

not scared. That's…that's a perfectly ridiculous thing to say.'

'Then you've no objection to staying for dinner?'

She stared at him, her soft golden-brown eyes enormous. Why was it that every conversation with this man was like a minefield? He was manipulative and devious, and he never missed a chance to go for the jugular. It might make him a force to be reckoned with in the business world, but on a personal level she found his high-handedness distinctly offensive. And nerve-racking.

And then, as a thought occurred to her, she said tightly, 'Just now, when Daniella said about seeing to the dinner, she wasn't just talking about Angus's dinner, was she?'

His eyes narrowed just the slightest at her tone but his voice was cool and unconcerned. 'No, she wasn't,' he agreed easily. 'You seemed reluctant to go out for something to eat so I phoned Daniella when I was outside Madge's and asked her to prepare something here for us. But first a drink to clear the palate.'

She might have known! She opened her mouth to object but he was already saying, as he poured two glasses of white wine, 'You have been great tonight, Sephy, and dinner seemed like the least I could do. Added to which, I am, quite frankly, starving. I forgot to eat lunch and breakfast seems like a year ago. Once we have eaten I'll take you straight home, okay?'

He walked across the room and handed her an enormous glass of sparkling white wine with the lazy smile she had seen once or twice, and although she felt as though she had been railroaded Sephy took it with a polite nod of thanks. This was a *fait accompli*. She could do nothing about it so she might as well accept it with good grace. Besides which, being fed and watered was hardly something to complain about. At least it wouldn't be with anyone else!

'Thank you.' She managed to sound courteous without

being deferential. 'But I hope it hasn't put Daniella to a lot of trouble to have to prepare a meal so unexpectedly.'

'She's half-Italian; she loves cooking whatever the time of day,' he said smoothly. 'It's in the genes.'

It might well be, but she just bet he hadn't employed the lovely Italian girl for her culinary skills, Sephy thought with an acid bitterness that shocked her. She'd have to watch herself round this man, she warned herself silently. She was getting crabby and it didn't suit her. She had always prided herself on her sense of humour and tolerant flexibility, and both seemed to have deserted her since she had walked into Conrad Quentin's office.

He sat down opposite her, and although there was a good three feet of space between them her heart started to thunder as he casually crossed one leg over his knee and settled himself more comfortably in the seat. He had discarded his suit jacket as they had walked in the room, slinging it down in a chair, and now, as he placed his wine glass on a small occasional table at the side of him and leant back with his hands clasped behind his head, she caught the dark shadow of body hair beneath the thin silk of his shirt and her mouth went dry. His masculinity was bold and blatant, and all the more threatening for its casual unconsciousness.

He wouldn't know what it was to have to try and pursue a woman, she thought wryly. All he'd have to do was crook his little finger and they would fall into his hands like ripe peaches. Look at Daniella; she was stunning. And there was Caroline de Menthe champing at the bit, and probably others besides for all she knew. They obviously didn't mind that they didn't have the monopoly on his heart or his body; free spirits one and all.

'You're frowning again.'

Her eyes shot to meet his and she saw he was studying her with an air of controlled irritation.

This time she refused to blush and her chin went up a notch as she said coolly, 'I'm sorry.'

'No, you're not,' he said silkily. And then he suddenly leant forward, his elbows resting on his knees as he looked straight into her startled eyes and said softly, 'You disapprove of me, don't you, my stern little secretary with the golden eyes? Who do you get your colouring from? Your father or your mother?'

His voice was smoky, and she rather suspected it was amusement she could hear in its husky depths. The realisation she was being laughed at made her tone brittle when she said, 'Neither, actually. My father was a blue-eyed blond, and my mother's a redhead with hazel eyes.'

'Was?' The amusement was gone and his tone was gentle.

'My father died when I was a baby,' she said shortly.

'I'm sorry.' He actually sounded as though he was. 'And did your mother marry again?'

'No.' She'd never been sure if she was pleased or disappointed about that. It had meant she had had her mother all to herself—she had been their first child—and consequently the two of them were best friends as well as mother and daughter, but she hadn't come into contact with many males during her formative years and it made her a sitting target for someone like David.

'Your mother must have struggled to raise you on your own?' It was another probing question, but spoken as it was, in a quiet, almost tender tone, it didn't occur to her not to answer.

'I suppose so, certainly at first, although our house was paid for on my father's death and he'd had the foresight to take out insurance policies and so on. Once I was at school my mother went to work again—she's a nurse—and she has worked ever since. She likes it. She's risen to the top of her profession now,' she added quietly. 'And no one deserves success more than she does.'

'You're proud of her,' he murmured softly. 'You obviously love her very much.'

'Yes, I do.' She had flushed again and her voice was somewhat defensive. There had been something in his tone she couldn't place, but whatever it was, she didn't like it. 'But it's not unusual to love one's parents, is it?' she added reasonably.

'I wouldn't know. I never had any.' He had risen abruptly as he spoke, and now he held out a hand and said coolly, 'Let me get you another drink.'

She hadn't noticed she had almost drained the glass, but the frantic little sips she had taken in between speaking had all added up, and now she passed him the glass silently, her mind racing. What had he meant, he hadn't had any? Leaving aside the biological necessity, most children who lost their parents were fostered or adopted, surely? If he *had* lost his, that was.

She hesitated, gnawing on the soft underside of her bottom lip, but in view of his pertinent enquiries she felt emboldened to say, as he walked back across the room with her glass, now refilled, 'What do you mean, you never had any?'

For a moment, as she took the proffered glass, she thought from the look on his face he was going to tell her to mind her own business, but instead he expelled a quiet breath and said, his voice cold and expressionless, 'I've always disagreed with the accepted definition of parent. It's clarified as "one who has begotten or borne offspring, father or mother", did you know that? But parenting means much more than that if it's done properly.'

She stared at him, and he stared back at her from vivid blue eyes that were as cold as ice, then moved to lean against the ornate mantelpiece a few feet away. After folding his arms across his chest, he said, his voice taking on an almost bored, flat tone, 'I was born to two human beings, that's all. They had already produced another child, a girl, ten years before, and she had been a mistake too.'

He stopped, as though waiting for her to make some comment, and when she didn't he continued, 'My sister escaped at the age of eighteen by running away, far away, and getting married. And then she returned five years later, to make her peace with our parents, and in a cruel twist of fate which I've never understood she was killed, along with them, when the car they were travelling in from the airport crashed. I was thirteen years old.'

'I'm sorry.' She didn't know what else to say.

He smiled mirthlessly. 'It was a one-day wonder in the newspapers—"Tragic family ripped apart in horror crash" was how it was portrayed—but we were never a family in even the remotest sense of the word. Still, it probably sold a few more papers.'

'What happened to you?' Sephy asked softly. 'Who looked after you?'

'I was at boarding school when it happened and I stayed on, so it was only the holidays when I was passed round the relatives,' he said flatly. 'Looking back, I put them through it. I wasn't nice to be around. I was full of anger and resentment and I let it show. Once I was eighteen and I could claim what was left of my parents' estate after the school, the lawyers, and of course my dear relations had had their pickings for their dubious protection, I took off to see a bit of the world. Bummed around once the money was gone; got into trouble a few times; the usual.'

There was nothing usual about this man, Sephy told herself silently. If nothing else that much was certain.

'And then I woke up one day in some seedy hotel room in Brazil and realised I'd had enough.' A muscle clenched in his hard jaw. 'I couldn't remember anything of the night before and I found I didn't recognise the lady.' The last was very dry. 'So I came back to England and became a respectable member of the establishment…once I'd made my first million, of course. Doors open and memories are very forgiving once you've made your first million.'

'You're very cynical,' she said quietly.

'I'm very practical,' he countered evenly. 'I know that filthy lucre buys anything and anyone; everything has its price.'

She was utterly shocked at the bald statement and her face reflected this, but the sapphire eyes were cool and unconcerned as they gazed back at her.

'That's not true.' She knew that she wouldn't even make a mark on that tough hide of his but she just couldn't let such a remark go by without challenging it. 'I know there *are* people who would sell their soul, but there are plenty more who wouldn't, who live their lives without compromising their own personal standards.'

He looked hard into her troubled eyes, her flushed face and indignant voice bringing a mocking smile to his clean sculpted mouth. 'What a baby you are,' he murmured softly. 'Either that or you walk round with your eyes shut most of the time.'

The cool ridicule caught her on the raw. 'I am neither blind nor a baby,' she snapped back tightly, 'and I'm perfectly entitled to have a different opinion to you without you trying to make me feel a fool. You aren't always right, you know.'

His eyes were midnight-blue now, and unblinking, and he wasn't smiling any longer. Sephy remembered too late that no one—no one—argued with Conrad Quentin and got away with it, especially not such a lowly creature as a secretary. She swallowed deeply and waited for the explosion.

'So you're not a baby,' he said silkily, after a silence

that seemed endless. 'You are a fully grown woman with a mind of her own.'

Sephy opened her mouth to agree and then closed it again. From the look on his face this wasn't a good time for further sparring. She watched him warily as he walked across to stand in front of her, her honey-brown eyes opening wide as he stretched out one strong hand and pulled her to her feet.

The top of her head just reached his big, broad shoulders and every cell in her body was reacting to his dangerous proximity as his powerfully muscled chest beneath the thin silk of his shirt came frighteningly close. He kept his hold on her fragile wrist with one hand, his other snaking round her waist and pulling her in to him so the scent and warmth of him was all about her.

'You have the air of an ingenue,' he murmured, as she raised her face to look at him, 'and you're as scented and soft as any true innocent. But by your own admission you are an independent career girl with her sights set on the top of the ladder, so you can't be all you seem, can you? It takes a tough cookie to survive in this arena we call the business world. Do you think you've got what it takes, Sephy, to fight your way to the summit?'

The hand which had been holding her wrist slid under her small chin as he forced her head further back so he could look deep into her eyes and his voice was uncompromisingly grim.

Sephy wanted to wrench herself out of his grasp and verbally floor him with a cuttingly cold put-down, but for the life of her she couldn't move or speak. The magnetic quality of his dark attractiveness was enhanced tenfold, a hundredfold, by his nearness. He had loosened his tie at some point during their conversation and also undone a couple of the top buttons of his shirt—a habit of his, she now acknowledged—and consequently, with the tie askew, she could see silky dark hairs below his collarbone.

Was he hairy all over? It was a ridiculously inappropriate thought in the circumstances, but she found she couldn't concentrate on anything but what his body was doing to hers by its closeness.

'No, you're not what you seem,' he said contemplatively, as though he was thinking out loud. 'Take your hair; I thought it was dark brown at first, but there are myriad colours in it when the light catches it and it turns to spun silk.' The hand left her small chin to wander into the nape of her neck where his fingers stroked her soft skin thoughtfully. 'And your eyes, liquid gold…'

She was standing perfectly still now, frozen in his light grasp and not daring to breathe as his husky voice continued, 'And then there's those freckles. What hard-bitten career woman has freckles these days, for goodness' sake? Freckles belong on young, carefree children, playing in the sun through long summer days when the corn is high and the nights are endless.'

'I…' She had to move, to say something to break the spell he was casting over her. 'My mother has freckles.'

'Ah, yes, the redhead.' He nodded as the slanted blue gaze locked with soft gold. 'And that would explain the colours in your hair; you're a redhead under that façade of prim brunette.' He made it sound wicked, indecent even, as though he had discovered she was wearing titillating erotic underwear in an effort to seduce him, and she found herself blushing scarlet.

'And this.' He touched her burning cheeks with a light, mocking finger. 'I thought it'd gone out of fashion years ago, along with men giving up their seats on buses for the weaker sex and protecting the fair lady of their choice by walking on the outside.' He smiled lazily, his eyes narrowing still more as the tip of her red tongue appeared, to moisten lips that were suddenly dry. 'And then you had to come along,' he added softly. 'My stern little secretary.'

'Your stern little *temporary* secretary,' she corrected shakily, knowing she had to defuse the tensely vibrating atmosphere before— Before what? she asked herself silently. Before he kissed her? But he wouldn't do that, not Conrad Quentin. Would he?

She was gazing at him, mesmerised, and she was sure the dark tanned face was coming nearer, the piercing blue of his eyes holding hers with a power that was unbreakable, and then…

'The dinner, it is ready!' Daniella's voice called out just a second before the beautiful Italian opened the drawing room door. But, although Sephy jerked in his hold, and pushed away from him, hotly embarrassed, Conrad's hold tightened for a moment or two before he let her go—certainly long enough for Daniella to be aware of their position.

'Shall we?'

He was every inch the cool suave host and charming dinner companion as he gestured for Sephy to follow Daniella to the dining room, and as Sephy glanced at the other woman she saw nothing but a sweet smile on her face. Nevertheless, she had never felt so acutely uncomfortable in her life as she walked out of the room, and she vowed, with every step, that at some point in the next hour or so she would find some way of telling Conrad Quentin that the arrangement was off. She was returning to the innocuous sanctuary of Customer Services forthwith, and if he didn't like it— Well, she'd cross that bridge when she came to it!

The bitter experience of her youth had taught her that some people were quite capable of playing cruel and dangerous games with no thought of anyone else but themselves, and she rather thought Conrad Quentin fell into that category.

He was the sort of man who would totally dominate any relationship he embarked on; everything about him proclaimed it. There would be no sharing with him, no compromise, no meeting point, and she just didn't want to be around someone like that.

Of course he hadn't been about to kiss her, she reassured herself silently. That had been her wild imagination, that was all. He did that—made her think crazy thoughts—and she didn't know why. Which was another good reason for not working for him.

But he was a womaniser. That *wasn't* her imagination. And a dyed-in-the-wool bachelor with a woman for every day of the week and even one at home!

But if he thought he might be getting one at the office too he could think again!

CHAPTER FOUR

As it happened the chance to tell Conrad she wanted to return to Mr Harper came and went a few times during the excellent meal which Daniella served them, but every time Sephy opened her mouth to grasp it she lost her nerve.

This was partly due to the perturbation she was feeling as she sat opposite Conrad at the magnificent dining table in a room that matched the drawing room for opulence. But the fact that Daniella was forever popping in and out, and also that Conrad had metamorphosed into engaging, butter-wouldn't-melt-in-his-mouth host, didn't help either.

However, once she had spooned the last remnants of a quite wonderful lemon soufflé into her mouth, and a smiling Daniella had taken their order for coffee, Sephy steeled herself for the inevitable. She would be short and concise and firm, she told herself silently, and she wouldn't be persuaded to deviate from her decision, even if he threatened her with dismissal. She couldn't handle this—she couldn't handle *him*—it was another world from the one she was used to. If this was what was entailed in being the secretary to a high-flying tycoon she'd settle for dumpy little Mr Harper any day.

'Mr Quentin—'

Black brows frowned at her and she hastily qualified, 'Conrad. I need to say something.'

'Fire away.' He settled back more easily into the large antique carving chair and she forced her eyes not to flinch from the searching scrutiny of the laser-sharp gaze. She couldn't afford to show any weakness in front of this man—she already knew him well enough to know that!

There had been a telephone ringing somewhere in the house a few moments before, and now, as Sephy opened her mouth to speak, there was a tap at the dining room door which was the prelude to Daniella entering a second later.

'It is Mr Walton,' she said quickly. 'He say it very important he speak with you. He sound upset, very upset.'

'Walton?' Conrad's brow wrinkled as Daniella handed him the telephone, and he glanced at Sephy, saying briefly, 'Excuse me a moment, would you? Walton's the manager of a company I've set up recently in the States and there's been a few teething troubles which I thought were sorted,' before he spoke a few succinct words into the receiver.

There was silence for a moment or two, and from Conrad's darkening face Sephy assumed the news was not good. The jovial, charming, amusing dinner companion had vanished, and in his place was the cold hard man who was a legend in his own lifetime in business circles.

'Don't do anything until I get there.' It was a terse bark, and Sephy inwardly flinched for the hapless Mr Walton. Then, as the phone was slammed down with a great deal more force than was necessary and he raised his head, she stiffened. 'It looks like I'm on the next plane,' he said mildly, with a complete change of tone as he looked straight at Daniella. 'Arrange it, would you? There should be something later tonight or early morning. I need to get out there and see what's going on for myself.'

'Tonight?' It was Sephy who squeaked the word, and now the diamond-hard eyes focused on her, but she could see he was already concentrating on the problem in the States and was only with her in body. He had gone into work mode.

'You'll hold the fort.' It was a statement not a question. 'You've work for a couple of days, haven't you?'

Sephy nodded dazedly.

'And I'll fax any instructions, as well as communicating

by phone, of course. You've got Madge's keys now, so you have access to everything you need.'

She nodded again; it was all she could manage. She had heard of living life in the fast lane but Conrad's lifestyle was something else. Grand Prix speed.

'Could you ask Enrico to take Sephy home, Daniella, before you make that phone call?' he asked smoothly, and then, as the housekeeper scurried from the room, he smiled at Sephy and said softly, 'I'm sorry for such an abrupt ending to our meal.'

'Who's Enrico?' she asked bewildered. She had thought he and Daniella lived here alone.

And then, in the instant the smile became shark-like, she realised he had known what she had been thinking all along. 'Enrico is Daniella's husband,' he said easily as his lids dropped lazily, hiding his expression for a moment. 'He is training to be a chef and had the chance to work in a big London restaurant, so it seemed opportune for the pair of them to live with me for a time. Daniella insists on looking after things, which isn't necessary, of course. She is my niece after all.' And the lids raised as mocking blue eyes took in her confusion with a relish that wasn't lost on Sephy.

His niece! He had known what she was thinking and all the time he had been playing a game with her. But if Daniella was his niece that meant she was his dead sister's child.

As if in answer to her thoughts, he said silkily, 'When Janette left England she ran away with her lover, Daniella's Italian father, and they married once they were in Italy. When Daniella was born some years later her birth prompted my sister to seek out my parents, to see if some sort of relationship could possibly be established. She wasn't sure of her reception and so they decided—her husband and herself—that she would come alone. That decision probably saved the lives of Daniella's father and Daniella, but meant my niece had only one parent to bring her up. And a host of Italian relatives, of course,' he added with a wry smile.

Sephy took a much-needed gulp of the last of her wine, draining the glass before she said, 'So you do have some family you're close to?'

'Close to?' He considered the words as he rose from his chair, his big masculine body moving with surprisingly lithe grace as he walked over to the window and stood with his back to her, staring out into the dark vista beyond the lighted room.

He said nothing for a moment or two, and then he turned, his eyes hooded and distant as he said, 'I don't think I'm capable of being close to anyone, Sephy. I simply don't know how. The Jesuits used to say, ''Give us a child until he is seven and we'll have him for life'', and I can agree with the philosophy. I lived a solitary existence as a child before I was packed off to boarding school when I was seven years old, like my sister before me, and frankly I wouldn't be where I am now if that had been different, so perhaps it was a blessing in disguise.'

'No.' The word left her lips without her volition, brought up from the very depths of her being. 'You can't really believe that,' she protested painfully. 'Not deep inside.'

'Why?' he asked coolly. 'Why should that be so difficult to accept? Because it happens to be different to what you believe?'

'No, no, it's not that. It's just...' Her voice trailed away as she searched for words to make him *see*. 'You're missing out on so much if you don't ever let yourself fall in love and be loved,' she said earnestly. And then she stopped, shocked to the core at what she had said. Here she was preaching at Conrad and what had she been doing for the last eight years? she asked herself silently. Talk about the pot calling the kettle black!

'Missing out?' he echoed mockingly, a cutting edge to the sarcasm. 'Missing out on betrayal, heartache, divorce, alimony payments? Because that's what inevitably happens once this myth called love—which is nothing more than natural animal attraction, incidentally—fades and dies. Or perhaps I'm missing out on staying with someone who drives me mad, and who I, in turn, probably drive mad, for the sake of offspring who eventually will go off and live their own lives and not care a jot about me? Believe me, Sephy, if that's what I'm missing out on it suits me just fine.'

Sephy did not know how to answer, but she was appalled at the cynicism he had revealed, and Conrad, perhaps sensing this, smiled indulgently as he walked over to her and lifted her shocked, tragic face up to meet his eyes. 'Such a baby,' he murmured very softly, and then, as he continued staring into the drowning, liquid gold of her thickly lashed eyes his expression changed.

His head lowered, his probing lips taking her tremulous, soft mouth in a kiss that was meant to be light and teasing but which swiftly turned into something fiery the second their mouths touched, something incredibly sweet and wild.

Dimly Sephy realised she was kissing him back, but, locked in his arms as she was, with the smell and feel of this big harsh magnetic man all about her, all coherent thought seemed to have fled. For another second the kiss deepened, and then Conrad made a low guttural sound of protest, lifting his head and letting go of her as he stepped back a pace.

It was him who had stopped. It was *him*. That was the one and only thought in her head initially as she faced him, her colour coming and going in a face that was chalk-white.

And then he sighed heavily, his eyes raking her face as

he said softly, 'Don't look like that, Sephy. In spite of all the signs to the contrary I'm not about to leap on you and ravish you on the carpet, and please believe me when I say I have never taken advantage of my position to act in such a way before.'

He made a movement to put out his hand to her, but when she flinched he withdrew it immediately, his mouth tightening.

Why had he kissed her? She stared at him as she desperately tried to pull herself together. She believed him when he said he didn't make a habit of seducing his employees. In fact it was a well-known fact that he had never so much as given any of the girls a Christmas kiss, in spite of the way some of the more confident of his female employees had thrown themselves at him.

And then he seemed to answer the question himself, making her even more ashamed and humiliated by her reaction to his lips when he said, 'You just looked so…lost for a moment. Hell!' He raked back a lock of black hair from his forehead with an impatient hand. 'That's no excuse; I know that.'

'It…it's all right.' She had transferred her gaze to somewhere just over his left shoulder and it helped. He was too dark and dangerous, too attractive, with his shirt half undone and his hair ruffled, for her to be able to speak and look at him at the same time. *Lost.* He had thought she looked lost. It was the final blow to her fragile self-esteem. He hadn't been prompted by desire or even the tiniest shot of lust—he had felt sorry for her. And what had she done? Practically eaten him! After all she'd said about rarely dating and so on, he'd think she was sex-starved.

The thought caused her face to become brilliant, but it put steel in her backbone and enabled her to draw herself up straight and say, with a composure that was born purely of fierce pride, 'It really is all right. Let's forget it, shall we? It's late and it's been an exhausting day. Please, you go and do whatever you need to do to get ready to leave for the airport. I'll wait for Enrico here.'

As though on cue, Daniella tapped on the dining room door in the next instant, this time entering with a small, plump, slightly balding man who was the very antithesis of the stunningly beautiful Italian woman, but whose smile was sweet and manner gentle as he introduced himself.

Sephy was aware she was working on automatic as she smiled and conversed with Conrad and the others in the minute or so before she left the room, but then, thankfully, she was outside in the cool mellow air.

Once ensconced in the car, she raised a brief hand of farewell to Conrad and Daniella, who were standing in the lighted doorway, and then sank back limply against the seat once the powerful car had nosed its way out of the drive. She listened to Enrico enthusing about England, his work, and how *grateful* he and Daniella had been when Conrad had offered them a home once they had decided to come to England. By the time they reached Islington her nerves were stretched to breaking point.

The night was throbbing with the sounds of Maisie's party, but she managed to reach the flat and fall into the hall without anyone seeing her. She leant against the front door for some long minutes, her eyes tightly shut and her face beginning to burn again as she let herself relive those few moments in Conrad's arms, and then she walked through to the bathroom and ran herself a steaming hot bath.

She lay in the bubbly scented water until it was cool and she cried on and off the whole time, but when, eventually, she padded through to the bedroom to dry her hair she felt better for the release of emotion. It was a kiss, that was all it had been, and nothing to get upset about, she reassured herself for the umpteenth time. In this day and age a kiss meant absolutely nothing! He wasn't remotely attracted to her and that was fine—a hundred per cent fine; she couldn't have remained working for him if he was. Not someone like Conrad Quentin.

His image on the screen of her mind brought her heart thumping and her stomach churning again, and she shook herself irritably, angry at her reaction. Okay, so he was an attractive and charismatic kind of guy, with the added bonus of power and wealth and goodness knows what; it wasn't at all surprising she'd been knocked off guard tonight, she concluded firmly. That was how she had to look at this.

She reiterated the thought over and over again, and then walked through to the small fitted kitchen where she made herself a strong cup of black coffee.

Conrad Quentin had every aphrodisiac in the book going for him, and she was only human; in fact she should perhaps consider it a blessing that she could feel the way she had when he kissed her after all the years of fancying no one. She'd thought more than once that David had made her frigid, and if nothing else that theory had been well and truly smashed!

He had made it abundantly plain he had no intention of repeating the exercise—she didn't like the little twinge her heart gave at this point and hastily went on—and so she could work the few weeks before Madge returned secure in the knowledge that it couldn't do her career any harm at all. There was no problem, there really wasn't, and she mustn't create one.

And the way he had been before dinner? a little voice in her head questioned. He had held her then, and said her hair was like spun silk and her eyes liquid gold...

Enough. It was harsh and final. He hadn't meant anything by it—his reaction to her when she had kissed him back had proved that—and she had been gauche and naive to panic and want to scuttle back to the safety of Mr Harper and Customer Services like a frightened rabbit.

Thank goodness she hadn't said anything during the meal about returning to her old job. She breathed in the rich fragrance of coffee beans as her eyes narrowed. He would have thought she was mad! She couldn't have given any logical reason for such a decision. *No, she could do this.* She could work for Conrad Quentin until Madge was better; she owed herself this chance to prove she was up there with the best of them.

She nodded at the thought, picked up the coffee mug and went to bed.

The next few days proved to be an anticlimax.

The emergency in the States developed into more of a crisis than Conrad had first expected, and apart from one or two terse phone calls—one of which requested that Sephy visit Madge at the hospital with reassurances as to Angus's welfare—he didn't contact the England office.

Sephy had finished the work he had given her by the second day, and the third morning found her in the unusual position of searching out things to do. It was a useful breathing space in which to familiarise herself with current files, procedures, problems and the like, and the couple of visits she'd made to the hospital helped in that regard too.

Madge seemed to have taken a liking to her, and, far from being defensive and wary—as Sephy had half expected the elderly spinster might be in view of her fierce hold on both her boss and her job—she had proved to be a mine of information about matters great and small. Sephy discovered a wicked sense of humour under the austere outer shell, and also a wry, slightly cynical way of looking at things that helped Sephy to understand why Madge's partnership with her young, dynamic boss was such a successful one. They were really very much alike.

The weekend was taken up with painting the flat's sitting room. When Sephy had moved into her new dwelling place some weeks before she had loved the decor, apart from this particular room which had been a dingy shade of green. By the time Monday morning dawned she was eating her breakfast at the little table by the sitting room window surrounded by sunshine-yellow, her new curtains of warm ochre cotton and carpet of a pale buttery hue toning in perfectly, causing her to glance round several times in satisfied perusal of her hard work.

The flat was costing an arm and a leg, and she wouldn't be able to afford anything more than paint after the extravagance of the new curtains and carpet for months and months, but it was worth it. Situated above the shops as they were, the row of flats looked out over rooftops and a wide expanse of light-washed sky, and after years of managing in a tiny rundown bedsit Sephy felt she had come home.

Life was good and it was going to get better. That was in the nature of a declaration, and she wasn't quite sure why she had to emphasise it in her mind, but later, as she walked into her office and saw the interconnecting door open and Conrad already seated at his desk, she repeated the silent vow.

'Good morning.' He glanced up briefly from the papers on his desk, the vivid sapphire gaze taking in her upswept hair and the smart dusky-red suit she was wearing before returning to the open file in front of him.

'Good morning.' The all-encompassing glance had thrown her slightly, but her voice was cool and steady even as her face turned the same shade as her suit.

'Order us some coffee, would you? And then bring in your notebook and pen. It's going to be a busy morning.' His voice was preoccupied and he didn't look up again.

It set the tone for the next few weeks.

Conrad was an exacting employer, who expected his secretary to work long into the night when circumstances demanded it. He never tired—at least Sephy never saw any signs of it—and his mind was as razor-sharp at the end of a gruelling day as first thing in the morning.

Even on the days she left the offices at roughly the normal time she was too exhausted to do more than fix herself a quick sandwich at home before falling into bed, and the weekends were simply rounds of sleep, and more sleep, with the week's washing being squeezed in somewhere along with a quick clean of the flat.

But even before she received her first pay-cheque in the role of Conrad's temporary secretary—which was treble the amount she received in Customer Services and made her sit down very suddenly as she stared in disbelief at the row of figures—she relished the job. It was exciting and stimulating and she couldn't wait to get to work in the morning.

All the years of covering for Mr Harper had stood her in good stead—she thrived on challenge and wasn't afraid of responsibility or using her own initiative; all essential in her role as Madge's replacement.

Conrad never once alluded to the night he had taken her to his home—he probably had never thought of it again, she told herself drily. Instead he simply used her as his right-hand man—more of a personal assistant than a secretary—and was always perfectly correct and businesslike, to the point where she couldn't remember him so much as touching her. When he looked at her he probably saw a small compact computer on legs! Which was perfect, ideal, *splendid*! It was; it *really* was, she told herself when she wasn't too tired to think. She was another Madge Watkins to him, which was…splendid.

On the sixth weekend her mother arrived unexpectedly on her doorstep, worried by the amount of times she had phoned an empty flat, only to learn later Sephy had been working late. The two of them spent a day sightseeing and acting like tourists, before staying up half the night drinking cheap red wine and talking about everything under the sun. Everything except Conrad Quentin. For some reason—and Sephy couldn't explain it, even to herself—she couldn't bring herself to discuss her boss.

And it was on the Monday morning following her mother's visit that it happened.

The day had begun like every other working day over the last six weeks except that—the November morning being a stormy one, with dark skies and heavy rain—she had accepted the offer of a lift to work from Jerry, who was on his way to see his solicitor in Woolwich. They had collided on the doorstep just as Sephy was leaving for work, umbrella in hand, and she had been grateful to slide into Jerry's old but very presentable BMW.

The ten-minute walk took just as long by car in the rush hour, but at least she was in the dry and travelling in comfort. She hadn't seen anything of Jerry—she hadn't seen anything of anybody!—since she had been standing in for Madge, although she had slipped along to Maisie the first weekend after the party and explained her new position. And it was Jerry, his manner somewhat diffident, who broached the matter of her absence from the social get-togethers.

'There's a bunch of us going to the theatre next week, but I suppose you won't be able to make it with the new job and all?' he said quietly, the windscreen wipers swishing frantically at the torrential flow.

Sephy hesitated. If she was being absolutely truthful she probably could—there had been several occasions over the last weeks when she could have joined in what the others were doing, especially at the weekends, but the job had been an opportune excuse to distance herself from Jerry's affections. And she *had* been exhausted most nights, she told herself firmly to assuage the pang of guilt. 'I might,' she said carefully, 'but there's always the chance of some crisis or other.'

'The thing is, Sephy...' His voice trailed away and she was aware of him taking a deep breath before he went on, his voice resolute, 'I need to ask you something.'

'Yes?' She prayed he wasn't going to ask her out again.

'I think I know the answer, you've made it pretty clear in the nicest way possible of course, but...' The car had just reached the top of the road wherein Quentin Dynamics was situated, and Jerry negotiated the BMW past parked cars on either side before nipping into a parking space right outside the front doors of the building. 'Is there any hope at all for me?' he asked with sudden and surprising directness as he cut the engine and turned in his seat to face her. 'With you, I mean?'

She had been expecting something of the sort, but it didn't stop the flood of colour washing over her face as she stared back into his nice, good-looking face. 'Jerry, I like you, very much, as a friend,' she managed unevenly, wishing she was more adept at this sort of thing. 'But as anything more... No. I'm sorry.'

'It's all right.' He smiled at her, his puppy-dog eyes as friendly as ever, which made Sephy feel worse. 'I needed to know, that's all. You see, Maisie and I are hitting it off rather well, but I had to make sure with you first. But if there's no chance...' He shrugged and she saw he was keeping the smile in place with some effort. 'I've nothing to lose, have I? And Maisie is a lovely girl. She's had a rough deal in life, actually, rotten childhood by all accounts, and behind all the hair and rings and things she's quite insecure and sensitive.'

Jerry and *Maisie*? The easy-going, public school, correct Englishman and the outlandish, wild, flamboyant Maisie? But why not? Sephy thought in the next instant. Opposites attract, and there *was* something very vulnerable about Maisie when she thought about it. Yes, she could see it working. He would look after Maisie, and she would bring out the fun-loving side of Jerry that was lurking under the surface. They were two very intelligent, ambitious individuals with more in common than was apparent at first. Yes, it could be a terrific partnership, given the chance.

'I think you and Maisie are perfect for each other,' Sephy said warmly, 'I really do. She needs someone like you, Jerry, a *real* person and a gentleman to boot.'

'Thank you.' And now his smile wasn't strained any more as he said, 'Can I kiss you, as a friend?'

'Sure.' She smiled at him, her eyes warm.

She leant forward and their lips touched briefly as he hugged her tight for one moment before they settled back in their seats, and Jerry was just saying, a touch of laughter in his voice, 'And you can be bridesmaid, eh?' when there was a sharp tap on the passenger window, which nearly caused Sephy to jump into Jerry's lap in fright.

Conrad Quentin was glaring at them—that was the only word she could use, Sephy thought with a touch of silent hysteria—as she surveyed the cold, harsh face of her boss through the glass.

'What the...?'

As Jerry began to speak, his tone the angriest she had ever heard it, Sephy put one hand over his and said quickly, 'It's all right, really, Jerry, I'll sort it. Thanks for the lift, but just go now, would you?'

'Are you sure?' he asked doubtfully, and then, as Conrad had the audacity to smack on the glass again, with enough power to make it shake, Sephy saw Jerry's face change and quickly opened the car door. She had heard it said the quietest ones were the worst when they got going, and Jerry looked as though he was about to do murder.

'I'll see you tonight,' she said hurriedly, before she

slammed the door shut and walked straight past the tall, dark figure at the side of the car, intent only on keeping the two men apart.

She was already in the foyer of the building when Conrad caught up with her, and she could see he was furious with the type of white-hot rage that could explode at any moment. Nevertheless, he didn't say a word as he joined her in the lift, and neither did she, and it was like that that they travelled up to the top floor and entered the outer office.

But before the door had even had time to close, Sephy had whirled to face him. 'How dare you? How *dare* you behave like that?' she said furiously as their eyes locked. She hadn't lost her temper in years, but suddenly all her mother's spirited red-headed genes took over with a vengeance, and although she knew—somewhere in the depths of her—that it was goodbye to her job, to the nice fat salary that paid the bills, no power on earth could have stopped her.

'How dare *I*?' he ground out, anger making the blue of his eyes steely. He was wearing a heavy black overcoat, which increased the overall impression of dark strength and power, and the moments in the rain had caused his short black hair, a lock of which had fallen across his tanned forehead, to curl slightly. It was the only hint of softness in an otherwise formidable countenance. 'You expect me to allow my secretary to sit necking in full view of the rest of the staff?' he bit out savagely.

'Necking?' She ignored the tense set of his jaw and the splintered bolts of blue shooting from his eyes. 'I wasn't necking! I exchanged a peck of a kiss, nothing more, and I don't have to explain to you anyway,' she added vehemently. 'I work for you, that's all, and as it's only—' she consulted the pretty lacy wristwatch that had been a twenty-first birthday present from her mother '—twenty to nine, I'm not even officially doing that at the moment.'

'Wrong.' He eyed her grimly, his mouth taut. 'As my personal secretary there are certain standards you adhere to at all times.'

Standards? He dared to lecture her about standards—moral standards—when he had had more women than she'd had hot dinners? she thought venomously. He had been waiting for her to slip from grace in some way; she just knew it! She had caught him, several times over the last weeks, surveying her coldly from icy-blue eyes as though she was a bug under a microscope.

She didn't measure up to his precious Madge, obviously, but the covert scrutiny had only had the effect of making her work her socks off to prove herself, so he had nothing to grumble about. If nothing else she had given value for money and he knew it! He knew it all right.

Sephy drew herself up to her full five feet six inches and took a deep breath before she said, her voice withering, 'Then perhaps it's better if I resign as your secretary?'

'Taking the easy way out?'

The easy way out! The contempt in his voice caused her to want to do or say something to hurt him, really hurt him, and it shocked her to the core. She had never in all her life wanted to harm another human being, not even David, and now here she was, in real danger of losing control. The thought checked her, enabling her to say tightly, 'I won't be spoken to like that, Mr Quentin.'

'If you're trying to make this worse with the ''Mr Quentin'' tactic then you are succeeding,' he snapped harshly.

How had she ever got herself into this position? The thought was there in the midst of the awfulness of the moment. Six or seven weeks ago she had been jogging along quite happily, secure in the knowledge she had found the home of her dreams, which she could—just—pay for, and that her life at work and home was tranquil. Admittedly there had been Jerry to deal with, but in comparison to Conrad... Well, there was no comparison.

Conrad Quentin seemed to think he could ride roughshod over all and sundry and get away with it—mainly because he did! But enough was enough. He might be heart-thumpingly attractive, with that certain undefinable some-thing, but she was determined to show him how wrong he had been to jump to such an erroneous conclusion regard-ing Jerry. Then, having explained, she would walk out of here with some dignity, if nothing else.

'I'm not trying to make anything worse,' she snapped back sharply now, 'but you are the most provoking—' She stopped abruptly. 'I've worked for you until I've dropped over the last few weeks,' she continued stiffly, after one swift glance at his rigidly cold face that was granite-hard, 'and I am the last person in the world to take the easy way out. If I'd been going to do that I'd have left the day after I started working for you.' You impossible man, she added silently.

'I'm not questioning your efficiency at work, or your aptitude,' he stated harshly, and then, as he raked back the errant lock of hair from his forehead—something he was apt to do when he was disturbed, she'd noticed in the last weeks—Sephy had the most alarming desire to burst into tears.

She clenched her teeth against the weakness, refusing to acknowledge the trembling in her limbs the confrontation had produced, and prayed for enough composure to be able to say what was needed before she walked out. 'I thought I had made it plain weeks ago that Jerry and I are just friends,' she said tightly. 'He gave me a lift to work be-cause of the rain, that's all, and he'd just told me he was seeing someone else, as it happens. I…I congratulated him and we exchanged a friendly hug.'

'A friendly hug.' It was expressionless, but nevertheless it had the effect of catching her on the raw. 'And the kiss? Was that friendly too?'

'I don't lie, Conrad.' It was the last straw, the very last straw. The colour had flooded back into her face and her eyes glittered with outrage. 'And I don't appreciate being made to look ridiculous in front of my friends either. Your behaviour, not mine, was outrageous, but, like I said, you can have my resignation right now.'

'In the six weeks since we've been working together you have resigned twice, once on the first day,' he said evenly, after a long pause when Sephy continued to stare back at him, refusing to drop her eyes or in any way appear deferential. 'What do you suppose that suggests?'

'I've no idea.' His tone was suddenly too smooth and she didn't trust him. He was looking at her in that strange way again, which caused further flutters in her stomach. 'But if I had to take a guess I'd say it might be that it shows you'd have been better off with Marilyn or Philippa or one of the other secretaries?'

'Marilyn or Philippa?' The names were said with deep disgust as his eyes narrowed into laser keenness. 'I think not. You suit me, Sephy. You suit me very well.'

His tack *had* changed. She swallowed hard, finding herself suddenly at a loss. She had seen it before—this mercurial ability to totally change direction in the midst of a heated discussion. He used the ploy often in business, usually with devastating consequences to his opponents, leaving them confused at best and at his mercy at worst. But she was *not* confused, she reassured herself silently, and neither was she at Conrad Quentin's mercy!

'Would it be very crass of me to say it wouldn't appear so from this morning's episode?' she asked doggedly with flat directness, calling on all her resources and looking him in the eye.

'No, not crass, merely misguided,' he answered smilingly, good humour apparently perfectly restored. 'I'm never bored with you, Sephy, and that's quite a compliment if you did but know it. I bore easily. Madge never bores me either,' he added softly.

'Oh, good.' It was deeply sarcastic, and she wasn't quite sure why she felt so affronted, but the urge to knock the satisfied arrogant smile from his dark face was strong. 'I'm glad Madge and I have our uses,' she said scathingly.

He gave a soft laugh and she could tell he was really genuinely amused. That made her madder.

'No man in his right mind would compare some of your uses with Madge's,' he said silkily, his eyes taking on a smoky hue as they wandered over the thick silk of her hair for a moment. 'And Madge has certainly never been responsible for challenging one concept I have always held dear.'

'Which is?' She hadn't really wanted to ask but she needed to know the answer.

'Never to mix business with pleasure,' he answered smoothly, before turning and walking into his office and shutting the door.

CHAPTER FIVE

THE two months until Madge returned to work were difficult ones for Sephy. Not that Conrad was anything less than the perfect boss—polite, detached, fair and supportive—but all the time she was on edge.

It was as though the incident on the morning Jerry had given her a lift to work had opened a Pandora's box of emotions, and she could never quite get the lid on it again.

She went over and over his last words to her on that caustic occasion until she thought she'd go mad, and finally came to the conclusion that he *couldn't* have meant what she had—foolishly—thought he was suggesting. He didn't seriously fancy her; she would know if he did, she told herself firmly, several days after the episode had happened. He had merely been giving her a brief, placatory compliment because he had known—even before she did—she'd taken umbrage at being viewed in the same way as the elderly spinster.

No, he didn't *fancy* her—the comment had been a sop to her feminine pride, that was all, she finally decided, and as his cool attitude confirmed the conclusion without any shadow of a doubt that should have been the end of the matter. But somehow, since that fateful day, all her senses seemed to be tuned to breaking point if he was anywhere in the vicinity, and he ruthlessly invaded her head every night with such erotic dreams that she blushed to think about them in the cold harsh light of morning.

As the Christmas party approached she secretly degenerated into a bag of nerves whilst telling herself that whereas everyone else might let their hair down and flirt outrageously Conrad had never been known to as much as dabble in a spot of chatting up. And then, two days before Christmas Eve, twenty-four hours before the party, he called her very early to tell her he was leaving within the hour for Germany, to finalise a deal they had been setting up for weeks with a leading electronics firm who had finally—and very suddenly—capitulated to Conrad's terms.

And that was that. She went into work later that morning to find a Christmas card, with a mind-blowingly generous Christmas box in the form of a cheque tucked inside, on her desk. The card read, 'Have a great Christmas, Sephy, and please accept the cheque with many thanks for helping out. C.'

'C'. She stared at the scrawled initial for some time. He hadn't even bothered to write his name. And 'helping out' couldn't have made it plainer she was a very transitory figure in his life. Which she had known all the time, of course. *Of course.* She was a sensible, mature woman, wasn't she?

She hired a car and drove to Banbury to spend Christmas with her mother, and the two of them indulged in a truly traditional Christmas Eve by decorating the little cottage and trimming the tree as they drank hot mulled wine and ate too many mince-pies.

They woke up to snow on Christmas Day—great white flakes that settled immediately and turned the village into a chocolate-box wonderland—and after a service in the thirteenth-century parish church trudged home to a roaring log fire, turkey and plum pudding, followed by the Queen's speech.

Friends from the hospital where her mother worked called round for tea in the afternoon and stayed all evening, and they were invited out on Boxing Day to a party at one of the consultants' homes, which went on into the early hours.

The holiday flew by in a festive haze of eating, drinking and making merry, and Sephy enjoyed herself—she really did—so why was it, she asked herself during the drive back to London, that all the time a tall, dark, blue-eyed spectre had been broodingly present on the edge of her consciousness?

And then the New Year swept in, at one of Maisie's wildly sensational parties; a wet, damp spell removed the last trace of the holiday spirit, and the first three weeks of January were gone in a hectic spell at the office which had her working twelve- and fourteen-hour days and even through all one weekend.

So she ought to have been glad—delighted, even—when, on the last Monday in January, Conrad stopped by her desk on the way into his office and said, his voice crisp and businesslike, 'Good news by the way, Sephy. Madge has had the all-clear and is returning to work next week. I've said you'll take the day off on Friday and spend it at her home, acquainting her with anything you think is important and bringing her up to date on the bigger events of the last three months.'

They looked at each other for a second, her honey-brown eyes wide with shock and his crystal-clear blue gaze as cold and deep as an arctic sea. Good news. She was going and it was good news?

'Yes, yes, of course.' His utter detachment enabled her to draw on her pride and answer as coolly as he had spoken. 'I'll clear out my things on Thursday afternoon.'

For a second his eyes narrowed, a flare of something she couldn't understand at the back of them. Then the hard male head nodded abruptly and he passed her without another word, although she thought his door was shut on something of a bang before she assured herself she must be mistaken.

Just like that! No thank you, no word of appreciation,

she thought grimly. The man was a machine, a mass of steel components made into the likeness of a human being. She had never known anyone who could keep themselves so aloof on a personal level as Conrad. And yet the evening of that first day she had worked for him— She caught hold of the thought sternly. She had made a vow to herself to put that out of her mind and she'd succeeded…most of the time.

It didn't matter that the long days she had worked for Conrad, often until well into the night when all the other staff had gone home, leaving just the two of them in their luxurious eyrie high at the top of the building, had meant she had got to know every little mannerism and characteristic of this powerful, magnetic man. She knew what the downward quirk of his firm bottom lip meant—trouble for someone! And the way he raised one black eyebrow ever so slightly just before he went in for the kill on a business deal. And…oh, hundreds of things. But just because they had virtually lived in each other's pockets for several months, that didn't mean she was any nearer to breaking into that formidable, essentially private part of him than anyone else was.

She stared at her word processor in horror. Where had that thought come from? she asked herself silently. The last thing, the very last thing she needed in her life was any sort of complication with someone like Conrad Quentin. Not that he would dream of looking at her twice, of course.

She let her mind play over the article in one of the more glossy periodicals that had surfaced recently, which had been reporting on some lavish première or other. The photograph of Conrad had been a good one, and the exquisite blonde hanging like a limpet on his arm had looked extremely pleased with herself. As well she might, Sephy thought sourly.

Sephy had derived a moment's comfort from the fact that

the woman was not Caroline de Menthe—only because she didn't think Caroline was right for him, she had assured herself immediately—but the more she had examined the blonde's face and figure the quicker the brief consolation had faded. The girl was gorgeous, truly gorgeous, and was obviously the latest string to Conrad's well-used and energetic bow.

She had just packed the last of her personal items in the small cardboard box she had brought into the office on Thursday evening when Conrad strode into the office.

He had been out all day, and as Sephy glanced up when the door opened she felt the momentary thrill that always attacked her when she wasn't fully prepared to see him. He walked across the room with a nod of acknowledgement to her quick hallo, his broad, powerful body radiating leashed strength and purpose.

She stood waiting for some command or other—he had that look about him which suggested something was afoot—but as he stopped just in front of her their glances held, and she couldn't read a thing in the steady blue gaze. It had obviously been raining outside, diamond drops of water glittered in the short black hair and his overcoat looked damp, and she found herself saying, 'I thought James had driven you in the Mercedes?' James was Conrad's chauffeur, who also was in charge of the company car park in the basement of the building.

Conrad shrugged, his fixed regard unwavering. 'He did. I got him to drop me off a couple of blocks away; I had something to collect.'

'Oh.' She lowered her lids, her thick lashes masking the confusion she was feeling. She was right, something *was* afoot, but for the life of her she couldn't work out what it was. But he was tense, even covertly excited. She sensed it.

'Sephy?' His voice was very soft and deep, and now, as she raised her eyes again, his compelling gaze held hers in a vice-like grip clothed with velvet. 'This is for you.'

She glanced at the jeweller's box in his hands—the name on the satin lid causing her eyes to open wide for a moment. It was well-known, and the sort of establishment which encouraged clients who never had to ask the price of an item into its hushed confines.

'Me?' It was a squeak and she made no effort to take the package. He hadn't really bought her something, had he?

'To say thank you for being everything I could have asked for over the last months while Madge was away,' he said, with a warm charm that made him a different man from the reserved, cold being of the last months. Dangerously different.

She stared at him, totally out of her depth, and then, as the dark face began to frown, hastily stretched out her hand with a quick, 'Thank you—thank you very much. But you really shouldn't have bought me anything. I've only been doing my job after all, and you've paid me handsomely as it is. It wasn't necessary to— Oh!' The last was a soft gasp of disbelief as she raised the lid of the box and saw the superb gold choker and matching earrings it held. The choker was made up of delicate gold stars with tiny amber stones set in exquisite detail, their beauty riveting, and the earrings were elegant and dainty in their own right. They would have cost a small fortune.

'To match your eyes,' he said softly, his tone bringing her head jerking up to meet his watchful gaze.

'I… I can't… I mean…' Her mouth had suddenly gone dry and her tongue was cleaving to the roof of her mouth. 'This is too expensive; I can't possibly accept it. You must see that?' What on earth had possessed him to do this?

'I see nothing of the sort,' he answered promptly. 'Do you like it?'

'Of course I like it. How could anyone not like it?' she said shakily. 'But that's not the point.'

'I had it specially made for you, *that's* the point.' He was eyeing her with something akin to amusement now, and his voice was still warm and possessed of something that made her skin tingle. She was seeing the man those other women saw—the beautiful women he loved and petted and cosseted—and he was sheer dynamite. And *definitely* incredibly dangerous. 'If you don't accept it I shan't give it to anyone else.'

'You could take it back to the shop,' she suggested tremblingly. He'd have to, because she wasn't accepting it.

'I could, but I wouldn't.' There was a trace of impatience colouring the smooth tones now.

'I can't accept this, I'm sorry.' Her voice was firmer now, and there was no doubt she meant what she said. 'It's very kind of you, and I do appreciate the thought, but it is far too expensive. It…it just wouldn't be right.'

It was his turn to stare at her in disbelief. He didn't say anything for a moment, merely stepping backwards a step or two until he was leaning against the interconnecting wall of the office with his arms folded over his chest and his narrowed eyes fixed on her hot face. His words confirmed his incredulous expression when he murmured, half to himself, 'You are one on your own, Seraphina Vincent, do you know that? I have never had a woman turn down such a gift before.'

And of course he would have given many women presents. It shouldn't have hurt but it did, and it panicked her, the smudge of freckles across her nose standing out in protest as hot colour came and went in her face. 'I'm sorry,' she repeated stiffly.

He cut off her voice as he said, 'And why wouldn't it

be right anyway? What does the price of a gift matter? It should be the motive behind it which counts.'

Exactly, and suddenly—though it might be terribly presumptuous on her part—she wasn't at all sure of his motives! But she couldn't say that—she was going to look the biggest fool on earth if she was wrong, and she had to be wrong. She had to. Conrad had beautiful women throwing themselves at him all the time; he wasn't going to bother with her.

'You're my boss,' she said with unintentional primness, her soft mouth trying to be stern and assertive as she called on all her wilting self-confidence.

'Not any more,' he said, with a satisfaction that started her heart thumping again. 'Why did you think I waited until today to show my appreciation?'

Help! 'You're the boss of the company anyway,' she said quickly, 'whether I work in this office or downstairs for Mr Harper.'

'True, but Customer Services is far removed enough for it not to be a problem.'

It. He wasn't talking just about the necklace and earrings. There was suddenly no doubt in Sephy's mind. *He was propositioning her.*

'You're like a drug, Sephy, one of the insidious kind that is supposed to be non-addictive,' he said softly, moving off the wall and coming to stand in front of her again, but this time at the side of her so that the desk wasn't between them. He made no attempt to touch her as he continued, 'Gentle and harmless and ordinary enough on the outside, but then, when it hits the bloodstream…'

Her utter amazement must have shown in her face, but she really couldn't believe this was the cold, controlled, autocratic figure who had been so distant over the last months. She had thought she had come to know him, just a little, but she didn't know a thing about him, she realised now. And that was scary.

She took a deep wavering breath as she fought to get a handle on the situation. Was he saying he wanted an affair with her? Was that it? A casual fling? But of course it would be that with Conrad Quentin. He had already told her on that first night in his home that he didn't go in for anything else.

She looked at him, so tall and powerful, radiating a dark virility that was more than a little exciting, and the hot little quiver that had trickled down her spine more times than she would like to admit in the last weeks made its presence known again. It was crazy, stupid—he was a carbon copy of David in all the things that mattered—but she was more attracted to this man than any other she had ever met or seen.

'What…what are you saying, exactly?' she asked at last, still nervously clutching the elegant box in her hands.

'I want you, Sephy. I want you very badly,' he said, as expressionlessly as if he was reading a train timetable. 'Is that clear enough? I would like to start seeing you—out of work.'

'Why me? You can't,' she protested shakily. 'You can't mean it.' But suddenly she had no doubt that he did.

'Why not?' he asked quietly, his eyes never leaving her face for a second. 'What's so hard to believe about it?'

'Because…' She didn't know how to put it. 'I'm not…not like Caroline de Menthe and all your other women,' she said somewhat helplessly. 'They are beautiful and glamorous and they know how to… They fit in with you,' she added weakly.

'We've done the bit about your type and mine,' he said, with a slight edge to his voice that suggested the conversation still rankled, 'and I agree with you in essence. But…'

He allowed his voice to trail away silkily as his eyes spoke their own message.

'But?' she asked when the silence became screamingly loud.

'But it doesn't explain why I still want you,' he said very softly. 'You've got under my skin in a way I can't explain, with your great golden eyes and touch-me-not façade.'

It was as if he was accusing her of something, and her voice was indignant when she said, 'It's not a façade!'

His mouth twisted. 'Two minutes—one minute—in my arms and you'd be begging me to make love to you,' he said with a raw bluntness that was challenging. 'You know it and I know it. There has been something between us from the first minute you walked into this office, and that night at my home I found myself doing something I'd never done before. Seducing one of my staff. I knew what I was doing and yet I didn't seem able to help myself, and I didn't like that, Sephy.'

Hence the ice-man from that time onwards. Suddenly it all fitted. How he would have disliked that momentary lack of control.

'When I kissed you we ignited. Admit it.' His deep voice brooked no argument. 'You wanted me as much as I wanted you but the timing was all wrong. So, I was prepared to wait.' His head tilted slightly and the sapphire gaze became piercing. 'And you've been like a cat on a hot tin roof any time I'm anywhere near you, so don't bother to deny it.'

The arrogance was overwhelming, and for a moment she was eighteen again, in the midst of a long hot summer that had turned into a living nightmare, and it was David's face stamped over Conrad's. The illusion vanished as quickly as it had come but it gave her the strength to say quietly, 'You are talking about a cheap affair, aren't you?'

'No, I am not.' He shook his head firmly. 'It wouldn't be cheap and it wouldn't be casual. I like you, Sephy, and more than that I respect you as a person. I've got to know you over the last months and I think we would be good together for as long as it lasts. How long that would be I've no idea, but it wouldn't be a brief fling. However, I can't lie to you. The things I said that night still hold.'

'You were warning me then, weren't you?' She stared at him, her brain racing. 'You were actually stating the rules of play without me realising, getting things ready for when you were prepared to make your move, and that would only be—' she took a hard deep breath as further revelation hit '—when Madge was ready to come back and you didn't need me at work any more.'

The nerve of him! The utter, absolute, cold-blooded nerve of the man! He wasn't human; he couldn't be.

'It wasn't like that,' he said quickly, but she had caught the flash of disconcertion, even astonishment, in the blue eyes, and she knew her words had hit home.

'Yes, it was,' she said with painful flatness. 'You told me that night at your home that money can buy anything and anyone, and you thought you could buy me when you considered the time was appropriate.'

No wonder he had been so angry that morning when Jerry had given her a lift to work; he had envisaged his neat programme of events being interfered with! The thought did nothing to calm her mounting rage.

'No doubt you saw me as a challenge,' she continued, as more and more things fell into place. Just as David had done all those years ago. The Ice Maiden. It had been her cruel teenage nickname that had prompted the other boys to egg David on; with Conrad it was his monstrous ego. She had dared to defy him and dispute his firmly held theories and convictions so he had to prove to her and himself that he was right. He didn't really want her; why would he, with all the stunning beauties he had at his beck and call?

'A challenge?' He considered the word for a second as she still faced him bravely, her chin lifted proudly and her eyes masking the deep hurt she was feeling. 'Yes, I guess there is an element of that in the feeling I have for you, but that's natural, isn't it? The caveman throwback, the primeval instinct to prevail and conquer in the face of adversity, to seek that which demands its worth is recognised?'

'You thought I was playing hard to get.' Her voice was tight as she placed the box on the desk with careful deliberation. 'That's it without all the soft soap. Well, I'm sorry, Conrad, but I'm not about to prostitute myself for that—' she flicked her hand at the box '—or anything else, so forget it.'

'Prostitute yourself?'

The charm was gone, along with the cool, faintly amused expression his face had been wearing moments before, and now Sephy felt a dart of fear as she surveyed the furiously angry man in front of her. His fists were jammed into the pockets of his overcoat as though to stop them reaching out for her neck, and his jaw was set hard, muscles working under his chiselled cheekbones. There was no doubt at all she had made her point.

'What else would you call it?' she managed faintly. A relationship on his terms was a sterile dead-end; he had *told* her that. It could never progress past the physical intimacy into true caring and loving, into wanting the best for one's partner, into tender friendship and putting another's happiness before your own. As he had said that evening months ago, he simply didn't know how. More to the point, he didn't *want* to know how. He had his empire; he had his women; his world was just as he liked it.

He glared at her, his narrowed eyes flickering with cold blue fire, and then without any warning he reached out and pulled her into his arms with enough force to jerk her head backwards. 'Perhaps we've said enough,' he rasped angrily. 'Maybe it's better if I show you.'

Sephy struggled in the instant before he bent his head and took her mouth but it was useless; she might as well be fighting the Rock of Gibraltar for all the difference it made. She was captured by his arms, his lips, his tongue; the sharp lemony flavour of his aftershave combined with the power and strength of him, reminding her of all the long days and evenings when she had been closeted in this suite of rooms fighting her awareness of him as a man.

He gave her no chance to protest, launching an experienced attack on her senses that took all logical argument clean out of her head and filled it with the magic of his closeness.

His hand cupped her head and forced her into a deeper, passionate acceptance of his lips and tongue, the exquisite sensitivity he was causing making her moan softly, low in her throat, before she could stop herself. She was dazed and shaking but enchanted, incapable of any struggle now, her body melting against him as he crushed her closer into the lean hard shape of him.

His lips scoured a hot sweet path down the line of her silky throat, causing her to quiver in response, before moving to take her mouth again as his hands roamed up and down her body, bringing shivers of delight wherever they touched.

'You can't deny this, Sephy,' he murmured huskily, 'and you know it. You want me every bit as much as I want you, and it's nothing to do with proving anything, damn it. I left that stage behind years ago.'

She sighed against his mouth, unaware that her arms had slowly drifted up to his neck, only knowing that she was melting right into him, every curve, every arch of her femininity finding its home against the virile male body pressed against hers. There was a heat in the base of her stomach that was pulsing with her heartbeat and it was intoxicating, wild, luscious.

'You taste delicious and honey-sweet,' he whispered softly as his mouth continued to plant burning kisses in between each word. 'The things I want to do to you… Hell, you can't deny us, Sephy. You know that at the heart of you. It would be so good between us. We've both known it from day one.'

She was barely aware of what he was saying; it was only his deep husky tone which was registering on the whirling light behind her closed eyelids. She felt weightless and curiously heavy at the same time with the growing ache inside her, so when the office telephone began to ring at the side of them—harsh and shrill and cutting as it bit into the bubble that surrounded her—she actually stumbled, and would have fallen but for his arms swiftly reaching out to steady her as she jerked away.

She stared wildly at him for a moment, unable to gather her scattered senses at her rude awakening from the world of colour and light his lovemaking had taken her into, and then, as she began to fumble frantically with her clothing, realising the state of her dishevelment, she saw Conrad pick up the telephone with a steady hand and speak coolly into the receiver.

He could do that! He could behave like that, when she was a melting, aching mess, she thought numbly. It was the ultimate humiliation. This hadn't affected him at all, not in his heart.

It was a moment or two before he put down the receiver and turned to look at her, and by then she was working on a feeling of outrage to cover her shame at her own complicity, at what she had allowed. 'So, that was showing me,' she stated as flatly as her pounding heart would allow. 'Do you feel better now you've got that out of your system?'

'Ah, I get it. Attack is the best defence, eh?' His voice

held a nasty edge of irony and his attitude was not reassuring.

'I'm not attacking,' she lied quickly through lips that still bore the imprint of his mouth. 'I was merely asking if your demonstration is finished. Because I would really like to go home now.'

'For crying out loud!' The words were a low growl and then she saw him breathe deeply as he mastered the brief lack of control. 'Sephy, in case you didn't know, that was no demonstration,' he mocked softly. 'I kissed you because I wanted to; I've been wanting to for months, damn it. In fact that's the least of what I want to do to you.'

'Just because you want it it doesn't mean it has to happen.' It was a flat, bald statement and she faced him squarely as she said it. 'I can't lease out my body, Conrad. I'm not made like that.'

'If that phone hadn't rung—'

'But it did,' she interrupted with painful determination. Her eyes dropped for a moment, and then as she raised them she went on, 'You are very good at what you do, Conrad—in all aspects of your life. And I can't deny that I…that I am attracted to you physically.'

She wasn't used to speaking about such things and she knew her cheeks were burning.

'But?' he said with lethal control.

'But it isn't enough. Not for me,' she stumbled on. He was going to think she was callow and unsophisticated and pathetic; he'd probably have a good laugh at her expense in a moment and put the final nail in her coffin.

'You want the till-death-us-do-part bit?' he asked incredulously. But he didn't laugh; for that she was eternally grateful. The way she was feeling it would have finished her.

'I don't know what I want,' she answered with a frankness that was disarming, 'but I do know it's not what you are offering. I… Something happened when I was younger and it made me…go into myself, shut down on emotions and men and the whole love thing. Meeting you has made me realise I can't go on like that any more, so that's something.'

'I am so glad.' It was deeply sarcastic and carried a strong note of smarting male ego.

'I want the sort of relationship my mother had with my father,' she said suddenly, his mordant cynicism loosening her tongue. 'They were ecstatically happy together and when he died…well, she didn't want anyone else. She has always said she was lucky enough to have more happiness in a few short years than most people experience in a lifetime, and their relationship made her strong enough to face the years alone rather than take second-best. I want that sort of love or nothing at all.'

'You call that love?' he asked shortly. 'I call it distinctly unhealthy.'

'Exactly.' She passed a tired hand across her face. 'That's what I mean; you see things so differently from me there's no meeting point. You must be able to see that.'

'You call what we just shared no meeting point?'

She had seen this side of him so often over the last months—the razor-sharp mind taking advantage of every unguarded word, every tiny weakness of his opponent—so it shouldn't have surprised her. She drew in a long silent breath before she said, her voice very calm now, 'You could get that and a darn sight more from any one of your women, Conrad. You don't really need me at all. All cats are grey in the dark, isn't that what they say?'

She saw his eyes narrow and sharpen on her face, his hard countenance darkening, but she still found the courage to say everything that needed to be said. 'You imagine you want me because I'm different to your usual diet of beautiful society women who are happy to play musical beds.

For once you feel you have had to play the hunter and it's amused the ''primeval—''' here she couldn't stop a note of bitterness colouring her voice for a second before she took another deep steadying breath and went on—'part of you. That's all. You don't care about me as a person, not really.'

'Cut the amateur psychoanalysis,' he grated coldly.

'I bet you even had the restaurant booked tonight, didn't you?' she went on, as though he hadn't spoken. 'First the gift, then the wining and dining, followed by— Well, we both know what you intended it be followed by, don't we, Conrad?'

She was right. She had known it even before she saw her words confirmed in the furious blue eyes. And the pity of it was *he* was right in one respect—she did want him as much as he wanted her, more in fact, because he had lots of women and she only wanted him.

Everything in her had been fighting against his magnetic attraction from day one, but when he had held her, touched her, she had known that she didn't want him to stop, not ever. He could have had her today, right here on the office carpet, where anyone could have walked in and found them. She had been his for the taking. And they said history didn't repeat itself!

A muscle was working in his jaw and she felt pinned to the spot by the brilliant sapphire gaze as she waited for him to respond to the accusation. But when his voice came the content of the words was more shocking than anything she had expected, even from someone as well versed in the cut and thrust of human warfare as Conrad. 'So, I take it I cancel the restaurant?' he drawled with cruel indifference, and then he turned, walking into his office like he had done so many times in the last months and shutting the door on her.

CHAPTER SIX

IF ANYONE had ever told Sephy that Madge Watkins was an angel in disguise she would have laughed in their face.

However, from the moment Sephy walked into Madge's squeaky clean house the next morning that was exactly what Madge became. The elderly spinster took one look at Sephy's wan, bleached face and pink-rimmed eyes—the results of a sleepless night and many tears—and metamorphosed into a maternal cherub.

Whilst her tiny hands busied themselves in making a pot of tea and several rounds of toast—Sephy having admitted she'd had no breakfast before she left—Madge skilfully drew out the full story of what had transpired, and when Sephy broke down in the telling she offered a lavender-scented shoulder for the younger woman to cry on.

Once ensconced in Madge's neat and cosy sitting room in front of a blazing coal fire—Angus on her lap and a cup of tea and a plateful of toast on a little table at the side of her comfy armchair—Sephy felt a little better. Harsh, icy rain was lashing against the windowpanes and the morning was as dark as if dusk was falling, but here inside Madge's home there was a semblance of peace. And she desperately needed that.

Angus had been delighted to see her, and kept up a low, steady rumbling of pleasure once he had established himself on her lap. The warmth of the big cat's furry body and the way he snuggled into her brought a measure of comfort to Sephy's bruised heart. There was something very therapeutic about Angus.

Madge talked of inconsequentialities until the teapot had

been drained and the toast reduced to a few crumbs, and then she came straight to the point. 'You did absolutely right to refuse him, Sephy,' she said firmly, as though the conversation in the kitchen had happened the moment before instead of fifteen minutes ago. 'And I don't say that because I'm an old-fashioned, fuddy-duddy killjoy either,' she added briskly. 'I know what people think of me; old, dried-up spinster who doesn't know what it's all about. But I've had my moments, m'dear, I can tell you.'

Sephy became aware she was sitting with her mouth agape and shut it quickly, but she couldn't have been more surprised if Angus had suddenly woken up and started talking.

'No, the reason I say you are right is because you think too much of him to enter into what must be—because of Conrad's nature—an essentially disastrous affair.'

'What?' Sephy's senses suddenly became heightened to breaking point. Madge's snug little room—with the small, black-leaded grate and red, glowing fire; the mantelshelf with its wooden candle-holders and stout ticking clock; the well-stuffed three-piece suite and elaborately patterned rug in front of the fire—took on a clarity that made the moment timeless.

'You think too much of him, dear.' Madge's voice was very gentle now as she stared into the shocked golden-brown eyes in front of her. 'I've seen it every time you've visited me.'

'No, no…it's…it's not like that,' Sephy stammered before she came to an abrupt halt. It *was* like that. Some time in the last months she had fallen for Conrad Quentin big time. Oh, admit it, a voice in her head challenged scornfully. Say the word! You love him. In spite of all you know about him, you *love* him. Perhaps it had been inevitable from the start, working with him all the hours under the sun and virtually living in his pocket. He was too mesmerising a man, too fascinating and charismatic, for it to have been any different.

Madge sighed, her shrewd but not unkind button eyes tight on Sephy's face as she watched the realisation dawn. 'It's better to face up to it now,' she said quietly. 'He's broken a good few hearts in his time, believe me. Oh, not that he intended to,' she added quickly, as though Sephy had suggested that very thing. 'No, he's always careful to be scrupulously honest about what he can and can't give, but some of the women—especially the more beautiful ones—have thought they could change him, you see. But it just didn't happen.'

A tide of hot colour washed over Sephy's strained face. 'I've never thought that, Madge,' she said through the tightness in her throat. 'I didn't even know he was thinking like he was until last night. I mean, me…' Her voice trailed away.

Madge gave a sudden snort that caused Angus to raise a startled head from Sephy's lap. 'Why not you?' she asked briskly. 'Don't undervalue yourself, Sephy. You've got more of what makes a real woman in your little finger than women like Caroline de Menthe have got in the whole of their bodies.' Madge stopped abruptly, a strange look passing over her face as she stared into Sephy's huge liquid eyes, their thick lashes accentuating the amber tint. 'Who knows?' she said very softly, as if to herself. 'Stranger things have happened. Every man has his own Waterloo.'

'What?' Sephy hadn't been able to catch what Madge had said.

'Nothing.' Madge shook herself, planting her feet firmly on the floor as she raised herself from the chair. 'Right, I'm going to put two baked potatoes and some pork chops in the oven to cook for our lunch, and then we'll get down to those.' She indicated the pile of files Sephy had brought with her. 'And don't worry, m'dear,' she added softly, stopping by Sephy's chair and stroking one smooth cheek for a second. 'You carry on being yourself.'

'Yes, I will.' Sephy stared at her, somewhat bewildered but feeling comforted. There was much more to this little woman than met the eye!

It was gone half past eight before Sephy stood up to leave the benign confines of Madge's small home, and then only after a delicious tea of hot toasted muffins and home-made strawberry jam.

For most of the long winter afternoon the two women had just sat in front of the fire and chatted about all sorts of things, and it wasn't until Sephy was driving home in the taxi—which Conrad had previously insisted she take both ways and charge to the company—that she realised Madge had confided far more about Conrad than she'd appreciated at the time.

The stark, utilitarian existence he had been forced to endure at boarding school from the age of seven, which had aimed at a rigid, army-like discipline; his difficult teenage years when he had fought against authority at school and rebelled at being shipped from pillar to post among his relatives in the holidays; the pain he still felt about his sister's untimely death, and much more besides.

'He's carved a name for himself. Quite literally carved it, with his blood, sweat and tears,' Madge had said pensively, adding with a wry smile, 'No, forget the tears. He told me once, oh, years ago now, that he can't remember the last time he cried—it wasn't encouraged, either at home or at the school, to show emotion, you see. If he'd been mine it would have been different.'

'You look on him as a son, don't you?' Sephy had said gently, and the elderly woman had nodded slowly.

'I was fifty years old when Conrad engaged me as his secretary over a host of young things with degrees and what have you,' Madge had said softly. 'I'd been made redundant, and it seemed like everyone had written me off because of my age, and then Conrad gave me a chance. He said he believed in me, in my experience and wisdom over material qualifications. One minute I was an old has-been everyone was treating with contempt, the next... Yes, I look upon him as my lad. I can't help it.'

He had been wonderful to Madge, the little woman had related incident after incident to prove it, so why couldn't he extend the milk of human kindness to the rest of the human race? Sephy asked herself as she looked out of the taxi's steaming window into the gray sleety rain outside. There had been times this afternoon when she had found herself envying the lonely, solitary little old woman, and if that didn't make her the saddest person in London she didn't know what did! A self-mocking, mordacious smile brushed her soft lips.

Anyway, the most unlikely affair in the whole of history was over before it had even begun! She had to put this behind her, concentrate on her job and perhaps even consider moving companies to further her career. The boost the last few months had made to her CV wasn't to be sneezed at, and besides—her mouth drooped unknowingly as street after sleet-drenched street flashed by outside—she couldn't continue working at Quentin Dynamics now.

Conrad had talked about her getting under his skin, but he had done something much more ruthless. He had taken her heart, stolen it under the guise of familiarity and comradeship and everything else working together so closely had embodied. She hadn't *wanted* to fall in love with him but it had happened nevertheless. And now she could understand what had made him the way he was, could feel compassion and tenderness and a thousand other emotions besides, it made him much more dangerous if he did but know it. She couldn't risk any contact with him. That was it in a nutshell.

By the time the taxi drew up outside Jerry's menswear shop the situation had clarified as coldly as the icy weather outside. Which made it all the more devastating when—the second the taxi drew away and she hurried towards the flat entrance, her head down against the stinging torrent—a deep, dark, husky voice spoke her name.

She swung round just in time to see Conrad's big, lean body moving towards her, the Mercedes parked on the opposite side of the road, and she froze. She just froze.

'Hello, Sephy.' It was cool, cold even, but the sensual impact of those stunning blue eyes was undiminished. 'I expected you home long before this,' he said as he reached her side.

She could have said any one of a number of things to defuse—or at least steer—the conversation, all of which came to her with hindsight, but instead she found herself staring at him with huge shocked eyes as the driving sleet enveloped them in an icy blanket. And still she couldn't speak.

'Where have you been?' His voice was impassive but his gaze was intent on her reaction. 'It's late.'

'You know.' And then, as his face didn't change, 'I've been to Madge's, of course. That's what you ordered, isn't it?' she said with a sudden burst of anger.

'Right.' He looked at her for a long moment which seemed endless and then he moved closer, to tower over her. 'You've been there all day?' he said calmly. 'Until now?'

'We had lunch.' She was trying to pull herself together and sound matter-of-fact but he just looked so *gorgeous*. 'And then tea. And we talked some.'

'Lunch and tea.' He was surprised, she knew it, and, knowing Madge's reputation for keeping all her subordinates ruthlessly in their place, it perhaps wasn't surprising.

'And she's invited me for Sunday lunch,' Sephy couldn't

resist adding, as a little demon of pride urged, Show him, show him you aren't like all the rest as far as his esteemed Madge is concerned at least!

'Has she?' He nodded slowly. 'Well, well, well. That's quite an honour if you did but know it. Madge is a tough old bird; she's had to be with the sort of knocks life's dished out in her direction.'

Sephy gazed at him uncertainly. She had to guard herself against him; she *had* to. If he sensed any weakness in her, any irresolution, he would pounce. The more she got to know about this man the more she realised the very words he had just said about Madge applied to him. Deep inside somewhere, hidden under layers and layers of steel cladding, was an emotionally scarred individual who was as vulnerable and scared of being rejected as the next person. But if she allowed her love to override her common sense it would be nothing short of emotional suicide.

She didn't know what it would take for someone to break through the hurt of thirty-eight years—some sort of a miracle, probably—or even if anyone *could*, but she would have to be a pretty special woman, that was for sure. Caroline de Menthe and all his other beauties rolled into one and then some.

She, herself, didn't have a clue how to reach him and wouldn't stand a chance of surviving a relationship with him. David Bainbridge had been a spoilt, selfish brat of a boy. The person she had thought she loved had never existed except in her girlish imagination. Conrad Quentin was a man, an emotionally damaged, hard, ruthless man, and even knowing all that she loved him.

He was momentarily attracted to her because he found her different. She had stood up to him to start with, and then refused to jump into bed with him when he had expected it. She was a novelty, a curiosity; her self-confessed lack of interest in the male species had probably been something of a challenge to him to begin with. Men were like that. But he would tire of her immediately she became his.

Sephy took a deep breath and said quietly, 'Why are you here, Conrad? I thought we had said all there was to say yesterday at the office. I don't want to argue with you again.'

'Can we talk inside?' He raised his hand to her hair, which was now wringing wet. 'We're both getting soaked out here.'

She felt her stomach turn over but managed to say, fairly steadily, 'I don't think that's a good idea,' as she jerked away from his touch. 'I think it's better if you go, don't you?'

Now his strong hands cupped her damp face and the blue eyes were relentless. 'I want to talk to you, Sephy, and you know me well enough by now to know that I don't take no for an answer. We can have this conversation in my car, at my house, in your flat, a pub, wherever. But have it we will, and I refuse to let you get pneumonia because of a childish determination to prove a point.'

His arrogance provided a welcome shot of adrenalin that put some force in her hands as she pushed him away, and fire in her eyes. 'You think you've always got to win, don't you? Always get your own way?' she hissed furiously.

'Exactly.' And he had the nerve to smile mockingly. 'So, that accepted, defiance is useless. Now, where is it to be?'

'It is to be nowhere,' she spat, with a disregard for grammar and lucidity. 'Just leave me alone, will you?'

And it might have been all right, he might have gone, if Jerry hadn't chosen that precise moment to call to her from the doorway of his shop. 'Sephy? Everything all right?'

Sephy groaned inwardly even before she saw Conrad's face stiffen and his eyes become pinpoints of blue ice as he turned slightly to face the shop. 'What the hell is it to do with you?' he asked with lethal control.

Considering that Conrad was considerably broader and a few inches taller than the other man, and right at this moment seemed even more so with the rage that had tightened his powerful body and darkened his features, Sephy thought Jerry was incredibly brave when he said, without a quiver, 'I'm Sephy's friend, so it's everything to do with me if she's being hassled.'

'Hassled?'

Conrad had actually taken a step towards the figure in the doorway when Sephy grabbed his arm, her voice urgent as she looked across at Jerry and said, 'It's fine, really. Conrad's come to discuss a problem at work.' *Why had Jerry had to work late tonight?*

'The hell Conrad has!' Conrad said grimly. 'I've come here to see Sephy, and the whys and wherefores are between the two of us, okay? Clear enough for you?'

'Sephy?'

Jerry's nice brown eyes focused on her face, and she found herself nodding somewhat frantically, like one of those toy dogs with bobbing heads in the backs of cars. 'It's all right, Jerry. It really is all right. Please, you go in. I mean it.'

She could feel the bunched muscles under her hand as she hung on to Conrad's arm and she knew it wouldn't take much for the situation to spiral way out of control.

'We're…we're just going to go for a drive,' she improvised rapidly. 'Conrad has come to pick me up.'

'Followed by dinner,' Conrad added silkily. 'Right, Sephy?'

He didn't miss a trick! Sephy forced a smile as she kept her gaze on Jerry, sensing the younger man was still concerned. 'And to get something to eat,' she agreed as steadily as she could. 'Please, you go in. You'll get frozen out here.'

'Well, if you're sure…' Jerry muttered unhappily.

'She's sure.' It was icy-cold and dismissive, and in the next instant Sephy found herself being steered towards the waiting Mercedes.

She had assumed Conrad was driving himself, as he did when the mood took him, so it was something of a shock as she neared the car to see the impassive figure of James in the driving seat. Oh, great! Just great! He probably hadn't heard anything but he must have gathered plenty from the little scene outside the window, Sephy thought tightly. It didn't take much for rumours to start at work and she'd lay good money on what the next one would be!

Conrad opened the door for her and she slid into the rear of the car with as much dignity as her dripping state would allow. He followed a second later, and she forced herself not to stiffen or react in any way as his dark bulk seemed to fill the Mercedes.

'Back to the office, James.' His voice was expressionless, uninterested even. 'And then you can go; I'll get a taxi home. Pick me up in the morning at…' He considered for a second. 'Nine. Okay?'

'Yes, Mr Quentin.'

Very nicely done. Sephy kept her eyes on the back of James's immaculate neck as she sat stiffly at Conrad's side. To all intents and purposes he had picked her up to go back to the office to work; his consideration of her reputation was priceless in the circumstances!

She didn't know whether to feel angry or touched that Conrad had bothered to try and protect her good name, but in view of all he had said regarding his openly predatory designs she decided on the former. Hypocrite! She repeated the word a few times for good measure, feeding her outrage.

He thought he had manoeuvred things all his own way, as usual, but she was blowed if she was going to be relegated to that section of his mind labelled 'crumpet', along with all the others. If nothing else he would remember Sephy Vincent as the one who wouldn't play ball when he snapped those impossibly arrogant fingers.

She sat quietly at his side as the powerful car cut its way through the late-evening traffic, and Conrad made no effort to break the silence. She was hotly aware of him; the big black overcoat on the perimeter of her vision, the intoxicating sensual smell of his aftershave, the animal warmth of his big body in the limited confines of the car. But she forced herself to stare out of the side window as though his presence didn't disturb her at all. He didn't have the monopoly on cool remoteness!

James stopped outside the main entrance of Quentin Dynamics, and after Conrad had thanked the chauffeur and told him to stay in the car he walked round himself to open her door.

'Thank you.' She exited with her head held high and her eyes straight ahead, although the rat's tails hanging round her face spoilt the effect somewhat.

The building was all but deserted when they entered it, just a few cleaners going about their business in the empty offices, and as Conrad began to walk towards the lift Sephy stopped him in his tracks as she said, 'You don't need to call a taxi for where we're going to eat; it's only a few minutes' walk away.'

He stopped, turning very slowly to face her, and piercing blue eyes narrowed. 'Meaning?'

'Meaning this is my treat,' she said brightly, wondering if he knew how devastating he looked when he adopted that forbidding, sexy, masculine expression.

'Your...?' He stared at her as though she'd spoken in Chinese.

'Treat, yes.' And put that in your pipe and smoke it. 'If I remember rightly you gave me dinner at your home the last time, so it's only right I treat you now. There's a great little Italian place that Jerry found—' She stopped abruptly as the blue gaze became laser-bright. 'Where a bunch of us go to eat quite regularly. It's clean, the prices are reasonable and the cannelloni *ripieni* is out of this world.' It was also extremely basic, and not at all the place a multimillionaire would ever be found dead in.

'And it's your treat,' he said very flatly.

It was sticking in his craw, and much as she loved him Sephy relished the fact. She nodded briskly as she said, 'Take it or leave it.'

'Oh, I take it. I most certainly take it,' he drawled lazily, something in his eyes making a tiny shudder of sensation curl through every vein and sinew and remind her that she was playing with fire. And fire had a way of getting out of control too fast.

'Good.' She gulped silently. 'It's halfway between here and the flat, so it's only a five-minute walk.'

He glanced over her shoulder, surveying the weather, which had worsened—if that was possible—in the last few minutes, and then let his eyes run over her wet hair, which was drying in tiny curls around her face where it had become loosened from the knot at the back of her head. She didn't flinch at his mocking perusal.

'I'm sure Reception won't miss this.' He bent over the beautifully stained wood desk that ran in a large semicircle at one side of the lobby and extracted a huge courtesy umbrella from its hiding place. 'There's room enough for two under here.'

The words were innocuous enough; it was the tone of his husky voice that made her shiver.

She was ashamed of the weakness, she really was, but Sephy found herself wishing the walk to the restaurant could have lasted for ever. It was the sort of stuff dreams were made of.

As they stepped out of the centrally heated warmth of the foyer into the harsh, driving sleet Conrad folded her securely into his side, one arm round her shoulders and the other holding the massive umbrella protectively over her so that they were enclosed in their own intimate world.

Her head slid just under his square chin, as though it had been made to fit there, and the angle at which he was holding her forced her arm round his waist so that her stomach was pressed against his hard thigh and the smell and feel of him was all around her.

'Mmm, this was a good idea of yours after all.' His voice was deep and husky as they stood just outside the building, careless of the harassed commuters hurrying past them, anxious to catch buses and trains. 'I never realised what I was missing using the car all these years.'

One of his other women would have made some light, teasing, amusing reply, no doubt, but held against his powerful male body as she was, with trickles of heat making her limbs fluid, Sephy thought she was doing pretty well just to remain upright.

He didn't love her, and his interest was predacious to say the least, but her body seemed determined to ignore all the frantic warnings her brain was giving it and thrill to his closeness. Her breasts were heavy and full, there was a warm throbbing ache deep inside her and her blood was singing through her veins in a way that made her feel more gloriously alive than she had in years.

'Five minutes, did you say?' He whispered the words into her hair, lowering his head slightly, and she felt herself go weak at the knees. 'How about we go the long way?'

'I...I don't know a long way,' she said feebly.

'Pity.'

He lowered his head further, his eyes moving over her

flushed cheeks and bright eyes, and then he smiled, very slowly, his gaze warm on her face. 'Eyes like warm honey. Eyes a man could lose himself in,' he murmured softly. 'I've never seen such eyes before. And your skin is real peaches and cream.'

'We…we ought to start walking.' If they didn't she would melt into a little pool at his feet and he would have to scoop her up off the pavement.

'You're beautiful, Sephy, and you really don't know it, do you?' he continued in a low voice. 'I've watched you over the last months—hell, I've done nothing else but watch you all day and take umpteen cold showers all night—and you're genuinely oblivious to how you effect the male sex.'

She stared at him in utter surprise, the eyes of which he had spoken open wide and her mouth slightly agape. He couldn't seriously be talking about her, could he? Was he mad?

She couldn't let him guess what this was doing to her. She drew on all her reserves and managed to say, her voice faintly teasing, 'Cold showers? With Caroline and all those other gorgeous women available? I think not.'

The stunning blue eyes were very steady as he said, 'My position makes it necessary to have companions at various functions and whatever, but since the first day you have worked for me that's all they have been. I have never yet taken one woman to bed for mere sexual release when my mind and my body has been occupied with someone else. Even I have certain principles.'

'You weren't occupied with me,' she protested shakily.

'Oh, yes, I was, Sephy,' he said softly, a strange half-smile on his lips. 'More than you'll ever know.'

This powerful, magnetic, ruthless tycoon, who could in-spire fear and trembling in the most hard-boiled business associates and have women falling at his feet in seconds, had been waiting for her? It was unbelievable, and yet in all the months she had known him she had never heard him lie.

'You accused me of playing musical beds and that assumption is based on gossip and hearsay,' he continued quietly. 'Whilst it wasn't particularly flattering to think you considered me that crass, I could understand where it had come from. I've had women, Sephy, lots of women, from the time I ventured out into the big bad world, but if I'd slept with all the females accredited to me I'd deserve a medal for sheer endurance. I can actually take a woman out for the pleasure of her company and nothing else.'

She stared up into the dark lean face, totally unaware of anything but him.

'I'm rich and I'm powerful and those attributes carry their own penalties,' Conrad said evenly. 'There's always some reporter somewhere who's anxious to fill a column, and if they can get under your skin a bit, rile you, then all the better. Human nature is the same the whole world over, and the have-nots will always take a hit at the ones who have made it, even if they've sweated blood to get there.'

'And have you sweated blood?' she asked softly.

They looked at each other for a second and then he shrugged dismissively. 'There were a few rough times in the beginning, but I can't complain,' he said, in such a way she knew the brief glimpse into the psyche of this complicated and disturbing man was over. He allowed her so far and then no more, and it was tantalising.

'So…' He pulled her closer in to him as he lowered the massive umbrella a fraction and kissed her swiftly before straightening again. 'I'm in your hands,' he said silkily, his eyes lazy.

'My hands?' Brief as the kiss had been, it had caused feelings akin to little flames flickering through her.

'The way to the restaurant?' he mocked softly. 'Remember?'

'Oh, yes, of course.' She tried to pull herself together but it wasn't easy, locked against him as she was. And he knew, he *knew* how he was affecting her, she told herself silently, but just at the moment she couldn't work up the annoyance his arrogance should have demanded. Not with him holding her like this.

Time lost all meaning on the short walk to Giorgio's. She had never felt so cherished, so protected, so deliciously feminine in her life before, and even though she knew it was an illusion—at least the cherishing part—it didn't stop her from feeling as though she'd entered heaven on earth.

The little restaurant was almost full when Conrad opened the door and she stepped into the warm, aromatic interior— Giorgio was beginning to benefit from a well-deserved reputation and inevitably Friday nights were always popular— but when Giorgio saw her he at once came bustling to their side, his round face beaming.

'We haven't booked,' Sephy said quickly, before he asked, 'but I wondered if you'd got a table for two, Giorgio?'

'For you, my beautiful lady, anything,' Giorgio enthused in his heavy accent, before turning to Conrad and saying, 'This lovely lady, she is beautiful, *si*? I tell her all the time.'

'Very beautiful,' Conrad agreed, 'and I tell her too.'

'This is good, verrry good.' The smile became beatific. 'You give me your coats and I take you to my verrry best table, *si*?'

Once they were seated in the far corner of the restaurant, and Giorgio had given them a somewhat dog-eared menu along with further effusive compliments for Sephy, she leant forward and said very quietly, 'He calls all the women beautiful; he's Italian.'

'I'm English, and I agree with him in this instance.'

She stared at him, wondering if he knew how incongruous his designer suit and handmade shoes looked in the
spartan confines of Giorgio's scruffy little restaurant. He
didn't appear to, in fact he seemed perfectly relaxed and at
home, but then Conrad never gave anything away. An
enigma, that was what he was. A unique, twenty-four-carat
enigma, with blue eyes and a smile to die for.

When the food came it was as good as Sephy had promised, and the raspberry-flavoured dry red wine Conrad had
insisted on ordering and paying for was excellent, although
wildly expensive.

'I didn't know he had wines like this,' Sephy gulped in
surprise after her first taste. 'But then we always go for the
cheap plonk, I'm afraid. Giorgio must despair at times.'

'We?' Conrad queried smoothly.

'There's a gang of us who normally come once or twice
a week.'

'Right.' Narrowed blue eyes surveyed her thoughtfully
for a moment. 'Well, let me tell you your Giorgio knows
his wines,' Conrad said pleasantly. 'This place is quite a
little find.'

Was he being patronising? Sephy asked herself silently,
before she admitted she was being unfair. He was enjoying
himself, it was patently obvious, and it wasn't exactly what
she had expected. It wasn't very uplifting to admit she was
capable of such mean-mindedness but she had to acknowledge she had hoped, deep inside, that he would display
some disdain or superciliousness—anything—to bring to
light a deficit in his character. She needed something to
dislike him for, and snobbishness was as good as anything
else.

She looked at him as he sat back in his chair, sipping
his wine and gazing around the small restaurant, and her
heart lurched and then raced on like an express train. She
could still hardly believe she was here with him like this,

or that yesterday evening had happened. Her and Conrad? It was surreal, impossible.

'What's the matter?' As the piercing eyes fastened on her face she realised, too late, that he had been aware of her scrutiny.

'The matter? Why does anything have to be the matter?' she parried quickly, knowing she was blushing a bright red.

There was a significant little silence as he gave her a long, meaningful look. 'Because you are you,' he said drily, 'and I'm learning fast. What have I done wrong this time?'

'Don't be silly. You haven't done anything wrong.'

She was immensely glad that Giorgio chose that particular moment to come bustling up to remove their empty plates and give them the dessert menu. He didn't often wait on customers, his two daughters were employed in that role, but he seemed to have taken a liking to Conrad—or more probably a liking to his obvious wealth, Sephy thought a trifle cynically. Giorgio was a businessman first and foremost.

'Wow.' Conrad glanced at the handwritten menu before looking at Sephy, his eyes smiling. 'Can I choose anything I like?' he asked humbly, his eyes gently mocking her.

'Of course.' Her voice was stiff; she couldn't help it.

'Then I'll have a double portion of the tiramisu,' Conrad said with open unrepentant greed, 'and, as I'm not driving, a liqueur coffee to follow. French, I think.'

'Ah, this is good. A man who knows what he likes,' Giorgio gushed at their side.

And then Sephy went a brilliant pink as Conrad said softly, his eyes fixed on her flushed face, 'Oh, I know what I like, but not everything is as easy to get as the tiramisu.'

'Yes, well, I'll have the caramel orange, please,' Sephy cut in quickly, her voice something of a snap as she lowered her eyes to the menu in her hands. 'And just coffee with cream, Giorgio.'

For the rest of the meal Conrad put himself out to be amusing and charming, and Sephy thought he had forgotten their previous conversation, but then, having paid the bill among more ebullient profusion from Giorgio, they stepped into the dark, cold world beyond the restaurant doors. It had stopped sleeting but the winter night was freezing, the sky covered by dense cloud, and they had only gone a few steps towards the flat when Conrad turned her to face him. He looked down at her, his blue eyes narrowed and thoughtful.

'I want to know,' he said softly.

'Know?' She stared up at him, genuinely at a loss.

'What you were thinking of in there before Giorgio came up with the dessert menu,' he said evenly. 'Were you comparing me with him? With this guy who broke your heart?'

'I've never said anyone broke my heart,' Sephy protested hotly. She didn't want to do this, and especially not right now.

'Who was he, Sephy?' His voice was harsher now, tight even. 'This "something" that happened to you when you were younger that you spoke of? Did he abuse you, was that it? Or was it a love affair that ended badly? Did you live with him?' he pressed further.

Sephy was stunned. 'What? No, of course I didn't live with him,' she said unthinkingly, before coming to an abrupt halt.

'In this day and age there is no "of course" about it,' he said tersely.

'There is for me.' She tried to remove herself from his grasp but his grip on her forearms tightened. 'It was nothing like that.'

'So, tell me.' His eyes were holding hers, their blue blinding.

'There's nothing to tell,' she said defensively. And there wasn't, not really. 'He, David, was just a boy I knew in the place where I grew up. I thought he liked me, he didn't, so that was that. It happens all the time in one way or another. End of story.'

He let go of one of her arms, but only so he could cup her small jaw. 'The hell it is,' he said softly. 'He hurt you badly, didn't he, this David. Put you off the male sex for a long time?'

She shrugged, showing him her pure sweet profile as she looked away. 'It happens,' she said stiffly. 'It's history now anyway.'

'How old were you?'

'Eighteen.' Oh, God, please make him stop asking these probing questions, she prayed silently. She couldn't tell him all of it; she would rather die. A broken love affair was one thing; there was at least some street cred in that. But what had happened to her was just debasing and humiliating and horrible. And he was a man who had had hundreds of women; his experience was vast and his mind was blasé and sophisticated. He would find it laughable that she had allowed it to happen in the first place, and be incredulous that it had continued to affect her up to this present time. What would he say if he knew she had *never* had a steady boyfriend, just the odd date now and again?

'Eighteen.' Anger thickened his voice and he swore, a raw profanity that shocked Sephy into lowering her thick lashes and jerking away. She couldn't talk about this any more.

'Please, Conrad…' She took a silent pull of the icy air and forced her voice to be steady. 'I don't want to talk about this, okay?'

'Okay.' He reached out and pulled her roughly into his arms, his voice controlled again. 'I'm sorry he hurt the young eighteen-year-old Sephy,' he said quietly, his voice deep and sincere, and with a note in it that brought her head up to meet his eyes. He touched her mouth tenderly with one finger as he added, 'But if he hadn't, you might have settled for boring domesticity instead of turning into the career woman you are now, and then we wouldn't have met.'

Career woman. She felt a sharp stab as guilt pierced her conscience. All this, to him chasing her and everything that had happened, was because she had misled him from the start. She wasn't a career woman. Not in the way he assumed anyway—the way all his other women were. Boring domesticity—she would give the rest of her life for a day of boring domesticity with him. And he would run a mile if he knew that! This was all suddenly very muddled.

She knew he was going to kiss her and she had never wanted anything so much in her life. Nevertheless she stiffened, attempting to pull away, but then she was crushed against him in the dark shadows of the badly lit street and his lips moved against hers, dominating and hungry.

And immediately, without any warning, she felt the desire rise up in her with such desperate need that she sagged against him slightly as his whole body seemed to enclose her.

He was too good at this; that was the trouble. The warning thought was there, but it did nothing to help. He was too tender, too sensual, too strong, too powerful to resist, and dangerous. Frighteningly dangerous. Excitingly and thrillingly dangerous.

Her head had fallen back as she'd instinctively allowed him even greater access to the sweet confines of her mouth, and he swiftly drained her response, taking everything, until she was limp and trembling against him.

'Come on.' His breathing was ragged and not quite steady when he at last lifted his head and released her. 'Let's get you home.'

Home? She stared at him for a second, utterly unable to pull herself together, and then he tucked her arm in his and forced her to begin walking along the wet, shiny pavement, the dull, opaque glow from the street lamp at the corner of the road making a soft circle of gold on the ground.

What would it be like if he *really* began to make love to her? She almost missed her footing, and his arm tightened as he drew her more securely against his protective bulk. If his kisses could reduce her to this, what would she feel then? Heaven. Heaven on earth—devastating, shattering, fantastic.

And when he left? a separate part of her brain asked coldly. Because he *would* leave; he had already told her so. An affair with Conrad would be a finite thing, subject to tight limitations even as it happened. He would terminate their liaison as he terminated certain business deals; swiftly and without regret.

She shivered, but it was nothing to do with the bitterly cold night air and all to do with the brief glimpse her heart had revealed of a bleak, hopeless, unthinkable future. He would eat her up and spit her out and she wouldn't even leave a taste in his mouth. He wouldn't set out to hurt her, she believed that, but the end result would be the same.

And it was that vision that enabled her to say, once they reached the door leading up to her flat, 'Thanks for tonight, Conrad,' in a tone that was intentionally dismissive as she extracted her arm from his. 'I've enjoyed it.'

'It should be me thanking you,' he said quietly, his eyes glinting down at her. 'You paid for the meal.'

'But you paid for the wine and it was as much as the food,' she returned smilingly, determined to keep it light and easy.

'I gather I'm not being asked up for coffee?' He didn't sound particularly concerned about it, and perversely it caught her on the raw. It was no trouble for him to take her or leave her.

She didn't trust her voice not to betray what she was feeling so she merely shook her head coolly.

And to her surprise he didn't try to persuade her. He didn't even attempt to kiss her goodnight, he merely nodded, his voice pleasant but somewhat remote as he said, 'Goodnight, Sephy.'

That was it? She stared at him as he turned away with an easy smile and began walking down the street. After all he'd said and that kiss outside Giorgio's that was it? He was leaving?

Too late she remembered he had said to James he would call a taxi to take him home; she should have offered the use of her phone at least. He would think her so boorish.

Without even thinking about it she called after him, 'The taxi! Do you want to come up for a minute and call a taxi?'

'Don't worry, I've got my mobile with me.' He patted the big pocket of his overcoat as he spoke, but his stride didn't falter or check in any way and neither did he turn round.

And then he had reached the corner of the road and disappeared from view, still without looking back, and she was suddenly alone. And she felt alone, desperately alone.

She stood in the shadow of Jerry's shop doorway for a full minute without moving as a dark, consuming heaviness fell over her like a blanket. She felt bitterly disappointed and tired and drained—exhausted with too many emotions she couldn't handle or even define. But all connected with Conrad Quentin.

She had fought her own battles and overcome her own problems for years, and she knew that was what she had to keep on doing, that her stand against Conrad was right, but just at this precise moment she would have given the world for it all to be different. For *him* to be different.

But he wasn't. She raised her head and stared up into

the sky just as a scudding cloud revealed a brief glimpse of the white ethereal beauty of the crescent moon.

And tonight had told her one thing. She had to leave Quentin Dynamics, and soon, because if she didn't, if she allowed him into her life and ultimately her body, he would destroy her.

CHAPTER SEVEN

SEPHY was awoken early the next morning—after a night of continuous tossing and turning and weird, disturbing dreams—by the sound of the buzzer to her flat being pressed repeatedly.

She stumbled into the little hall, fastening the belt of her robe as she went, and spoke into the intercom in a voice still thick with sleep. 'Yes, who is it?'

'Delivery for Miss Vincent.' The female voice was young and bright and impossibly cheery for this early on a Saturday morning.

She was too dazed and drowsy to wonder what the delivery could be as she opened the flat door and stumbled down the stairs to the outer door into the street, but when she opened it and the most enormous bouquet was placed in her hands by a smiling, chirpy delivery girl it acted in the same way as a bucket of cold water straight in her sleepy face and suddenly she was wide awake.

'Have a nice day.' The pretty young face was openly envious as the girl glanced once more at the dozens of red roses and fragile baby's breath the Cellophane held. 'And, whoever he is, he's sure no cheapskate,' she added perkily over her shoulder as she turned towards the florist's van parked at the edge of the kerb.

'It's serious, then?'

Sephy came out of her mesmerised state to find Jerry peering at her as the van drove off into the mounting morning traffic, and when he indicated the flowers she felt her face turn as red as the roses. Jerry had a way of always being around at the wrong time.

'It's not like that, really,' she said quickly.

'Oh, Sephy.' He shook his head at her, his nice face deeply troubled. 'I saw the way he looked at you.'

After the foul weather of the night before the January morning was crisp and bright but bitterly cold, and as its icy chill quickly penetrated her thick towelling robe she shivered before saying, her voice flat, 'He's the original love 'em and leave 'em type, Jerry, and I don't go in for emotional suicide, besides which I don't work for him any more—his old secretary's back, and I'm thinking of leaving the firm.'

He nodded slowly. 'Sounds sensible,' he said quietly, 'and Maisie will be glad to hear you might be around a bit more. We've missed you.' He smiled at her, his face open and friendly.

There was an inflexion in the 'we' that made her ask, 'You two are getting on well, then?'

'Very well.' It was warm and said far more than just the mere words indicated. 'We might even make it permanent.'

'I'm glad.' She smiled at him and his smile widened, but as she stepped inside and closed the door she suddenly felt painfully alone in a way she hadn't done for years. Which was stupid—really, *really* stupid, she told herself bracingly as she hurried up the stairs to the snug warmth of the flat, because nothing had changed. And she and Jerry would never have worked in a million years.

She laid the flowers on the breakfast bar and then, as a thought occurred to her, she reached for the little envelope attached to the Cellophane. She, along with Jerry, had assumed the flowers had come from Conrad, but they might not have. Although she couldn't think of another person on the whole earth who would send her flowers—and so extravagantly!

'They are soft and beautiful and sweetly perfumed, just

like you,' he had written. 'But the thorns warn one to handle with respect, just like… C.'

Handle with respect! How could he be so manipulative and machiavellian and…and *hypocritical*? she asked herself furiously, before bursting into tears.

She felt better after a good cry, and once the roses were in water—all five dozen of them—she soaked in a hot bath for over an hour without letting her mind consider the future once.

She had just dried her hair into soft thick waves about her face, and was considering getting dressed, when the buzzer sounded again. It was going to be one of those mornings!

Maisie. It had to be Maisie. No doubt Jerry had related the latest and she had popped round to get the 'i's dotted and the 't's crossed, as was Maisie's wont, Sephy thought patiently. She flicked the switch on the intercom and said flatly, 'Okay, Maisie, a coffee and a croissant, right?' Whenever Maisie did this she always arrived with half a dozen croissants and a sweetly entreating smile and never failed to gain admittance.

'I've never been called Maisie before—' the darkly amused voice was deep and husky and made her heart jump into her mouth '—and I'm right out of croissants.'

'Conrad?' He was here, *now*, and she must look such a *mess*.

'Sorry to disappoint you if you're hungry,' he said drily.

He was here, right now! She glanced in the hall mirror and inwardly groaned. Her face was shiny, her eyes still carried the penalty of the good cry and she was only clothed in her nightie beneath the robe. Don't panic, Sephy, she told herself desperately.

'What…what do you want?' she stammered at last, somewhat ungraciously, before adding, 'Thank you for the flowers.'

'My pleasure.' There was something so sexy about his husky voice it made her toes curl, which, no doubt, was *exactly* what he intended, she told herself caustically. Tried and tested formula.

She took a deep breath but her voice still carried a faint tremor as she repeated, 'What do you want, Conrad?'

'You.'

She swallowed hard. Okay, she should have expected that.

'But then you know that,' he drawled mockingly. 'Don't you?'

'I'm…I'm not dressed yet,' she said, before she considered her words.

'And they say there isn't a Santa Claus.'

'Conrad, *please*.' She glanced again in the mirror and groaned.

'I want to take you out to lunch, Sephy, or is that a terrible crime?' he asked softly, but this time there was a thread of naked steel running through the words that she recognised from her time as his secretary. It told her he wasn't going to take no for an answer.

'I might have other plans,' she managed after a few frantic moments. But she was only prolonging the inevitable.

'Have you?' He clearly wasn't buying that one.

Some deep feminine instinct for self-preservation urged her to say yes, but the thought of a few hours with him was too tempting. Lunch was safe, nothing could happen during lunch, and she had already made the decision to leave Quentin Dynamics at the earliest opportunity. She deserved this day. She did. It was all she was likely to ever have.

She had hesitated too long, and now his voice was very dry when he said, 'Get dressed, Sephy, and be downstairs in ten minutes or I'll upset your friend—Jerry, isn't it?— by breaking this door down.'

'Don't be ridiculous,' she said indignantly. 'You wouldn't dare.'

'I'm never ridiculous, and just try me.'

It was arrogant and cold and so very Conrad that it made her smile in spite of the circumstances, but she managed to keep all trace of amusement out of her voice as she said tersely, 'Fifteen minutes, and don't you dare so much as touch that door.'

She put the phone down on his warm throaty chuckle, but the ache of longing it caused was harder to control.

They lunched at a small old-fashioned inn in Stratford-upon-Avon, where the steak pie cooked in Guinness was wonderful and the raspberry pavlova was homemade and melted in the mouth.

The drive out had been leisurely, and Conrad appeared perfectly relaxed, but from the moment she had caught sight of him as she had stepped on to the pavement Sephy had felt her nerves pull as tight as piano wire.

She had never seen him dressed casually before, he had always worn any one of a number of beautifully cut designer suits for the office, but today his black denim jeans and waist-length bulky charcoal-grey leather jacket emphasised his dark, virile masculinity a hundredfold and it made her—quite literally—weak at the knees. He was intimidatingly sexy and flagrantly male from the top of his ebony head to the soles of his shoes, and she felt she had caught a tiger by the tail. Although she hadn't caught him, she reminded herself silently, she hadn't remotely caught him, and therein lay the root of all her problems. He was a law unto himself and answerable to no one.

'What would you like to do for the rest of the day?' he asked lazily as they finished their coffee, his vivid blue eyes moving over her silky dark hair which she had left loose to fall in soft waves about her shoulders. 'We don't need to be back in London until sevenish, but I've booked a table at the Calypso Club for eight-thirty and no doubt you'll want time to put on your glad rags.'

She stared at him uncertainly. Rarely a week or two went by when some glossy magazine or other didn't have pictures of a host of celebrities enjoying themselves at the Calypso. It was the place to be seen, the haunt of the jet-set and the beautiful people, and you had to be worth a mint just to step inside its exclusive doors. This was so far outside her league as to be laughable. She had to make him understand.

'Conrad, this isn't going to work,' she said as firmly as she could. 'You do see that, don't you? All I said…I still mean it.'

'You mean about prostituting yourself or my seeing you just as a challenge?' he queried with shocking impassivity. 'Or perhaps you're referring to your accusation that I don't care about you as a person?' he added, his eyes watching her closely.

Oh, hell! She suddenly realised her words had cut deep. 'I…I shouldn't have said some of that,' she admitted awkwardly.

'No, you're right, you shouldn't,' he said calmly.

'But some of it was true,' she declared tersely. 'Your view on life is so different to mine that we're poles apart—'

'Cut the baloney, Sephy. At least say it as it is.'

Her breath caught painfully in her throat. Beneath the smooth, amusing, controlled exterior this was one angry man.

'You don't trust me; that's it in a nutshell,' he said coolly. 'You've listened to rumour and innuendo.'

'No, that is *not* it,' she shot back quickly, a welcome flood of anger dispelling the momentary guilt and confusion. 'You told me what to expect if I got involved with you and I don't like it, okay? Not every woman wants a wham-bam-thank-you-ma'am kind of love affair, Conrad.'

'A *what*?' Dark colour flared across hard cheekbones and the sparks in his blue eyes warned her it wouldn't take much for the smouldering rage to flare into a blazing fire.

'I'm not capable of going into a relationship knowing it is destined to fail,' Sephy said wretchedly. 'That's what I mean.'

'Who's talking about failure?' he ground out. 'Just because a couple move on to other partners it doesn't mean they have to part acrimoniously or that what they shared is spoilt. My exes have always been quite happy and reasonable when the time has come for us to go our separate ways.'

'How would you know that?' she dared to challenge. 'How would you *know*? You lay down the ground rules; you control the whole thing from beginning to end; you never let anyone get close to you! How would you really *know* what the other person is feeling? You fool yourself, Conrad. All the time,' she said wretchedly.

'I don't believe this.' If the whole thing hadn't been so devastatingly horrible she might have found a glimmer of amusement in the astounded affront and scandalised resentment he was showing. 'I really don't believe what I'm hearing.'

'You told me you weren't capable of being close to anyone,' she continued softly, knowing she had to say it all. 'That love is a myth. That's what you said, Conrad. Well, I can't think like that. I could never give my body lightly. It would have to be a full commitment and I'd want the same promise of commitment back from the man I loved. It's the way I'm made.'

'And this man who let you down? Did he promise you full commitment and eternal devotion?' he challenged grimly.

Oh, he was good. He was; she had to give him that. She had noticed the raised eyebrow so she should have known something deadly was coming.

'No, he didn't,' she said bravely, her chin lifting proudly.

'And yet you still loved him.'

'It wasn't like that, not like you're assuming,' she said tightly, praying for courage. 'I never slept with David.'

'You didn't?' His eyes narrowed and she could almost see that razor-sharp mind whirring and collating all the facts so far. 'But since him you said—'

'That I've only dated occasionally, yes.' Perhaps it had to be this way for this ridiculous affair that wasn't an affair to finish, she thought painfully as humiliation turned her cheeks vivid scarlet. Conrad Quentin liked his women experienced and well-versed in the art of love, and although he had known she wasn't exactly a Mata Hari type he had thought—at twenty-six years of age—she had had some sexual experience.

The silence stretched and lengthened, but she was determined she wasn't going to break it, although the hand that reached out for her coffee cup was shaking. She had drained the last of the coffee before Conrad said, his voice expressionless, 'You should have told me, Sephy.'

'That I'm a virgin?' she stated baldly. The time for delicacy was over. 'Why? It's nothing to do with anyone else.'

'I'm not anyone,' he said sharply, before moderating his tone as he added, 'Hell, don't look like that.'

She couldn't help how she looked; he ought to be glad she hadn't dissolved into hysterical weeping the way she was feeling. Nevertheless, her chin went up a notch or two and she gripped her hands very tightly together under cover of the small pub table.

It had taken every drop of courage she possessed when she'd made the decision to leave her home town and move to London. The incident with David Bainbridge had shattered her self-confidence—which had always been pretty fragile anyway—and caused her to go into herself, but at the age of twenty she had known she had to climb out of the rut she'd made for herself and spread her wings.

The bedsit—which had been all she could afford—had been grotty to say the least, but she had persevered and worked hard and forced herself to go out on the occasional date so she didn't fall into the trap of becoming a recluse.

Her salary had risen nicely, she had found the flat of her dreams and a whole bunch of new friends, and then had come the chance of bolstering her career by standing in for Madge for a few weeks or—as it had turned out—months.

Every step along the way she had had to make herself reach out and be resolute in her determination that the episode with David would not spoil her life. From the start she had ignored the whispering and the nudges and sly looks as word had got about, and even though it had nearly killed her she had held her head high and refused to hide away, licking her wounds in private.

All that couldn't be for nothing, she told herself now. It was ironic that after all the years of keeping her feelings for the opposite sex in cold storage they had melted only for her to fall for the wrong man, but she would rise above this as she had risen above everything else. She loved him, she would always love him, but that was her problem, not his.

'So.' His eyes were still narrowed on her pale face. 'Where do we go from here?'

She took a deep breath, calling on the fortitude the silent pep-talk had given her, and said lightly, 'Back to London?'

'Don't be facetious, Sephy, it doesn't suit you,' he growled quietly.

'What do you expect me to do?' she snapped back swiftly, stung beyond measure. 'Dissolve into tears? String you along, knowing all the time it could never work?

Pretend? Coo and simper like your other women? That's not my style, Conrad.'

Her words fell into a taut silence, and then he completely took the wind out of her sails—and nearly sank her boat in the process—when he reached out and stroked his hand down the silky smooth skin of her cheek. 'You think I don't know that?' His voice was husky and smoky-soft. 'One thing I've come to know is that I always get the truth from you, even if it's like a punch in the stomach at times. And honesty deserves honesty. I can't give you what you deserve, Sephy, but I can't let go of you either. I *won't* let go of you.'

'That's so unfair,' she whispered weakly.

'Yes, it is,' he agreed quietly. 'So…how about if we get to know each other a while, without sex?'

'What?' The baldness of the last words had left her gasping.

'I respect you, Sephy, and I enjoy your company,' he said evenly, 'and I haven't said that to many women. But…I can't change the way I am. I don't believe in love and marriage and happy families and I won't insult you by saying there's a chance I might change. You say you couldn't accept anything less in a sexual relationship, so we cut the sex part.'

'But… I don't—' She was floundering; she had to pull herself together. 'Why?' she asked shakily. 'Why would you do that?' Knowing Conrad, there was a well-thought-out motive behind this.

'The only way I would want you in my bed is because you want to be there,' he said coolly. 'Regardless of what you think, I'm actually not an advocate of casual sex, neither have I ever enticed a woman with lies or my wealth or even the emotion of the moment. When eventually you come to me it will be knowing exactly what you are doing and because you have decided it is what you want too. And

I can promise you that as long as we are together I will be faithful. That's a darn sight more than most men commit to even when they are saying their marriage vows.' One dark raised eyebrow dared her to disagree.

'This…this is crazy.' And dangerous and scary and against every sensible and logical conclusion she had come to regarding Conrad Quentin. 'What if I say no?' she asked shakily.

'Then I'll make you change your mind,' he said softly, but with such cold purpose that her eyes opened wide.

'It will be for nothing; you say you can't change and neither can I,' she warned faintly. 'Not ever.'

'We'll see.' He smiled slowly and she felt her heart pound as the sky-blue eyes crinkled sexily. 'Not ever is a long, long time, and in the meantime we'll be having fun. There's nothing too terrible about that, is there?'

Sephy didn't know how to answer. She was aware, knowing Conrad as she now did, that he wasn't joking when he said he would determine to make her change her mind if she said no to this crazy scheme. It would make her a double challenge in his eyes, if nothing else.

And if she said yes? Her heart changed its rhythm into a mad gallop. It would mean a few weeks, maybe months, in his company with no strings attached. Memories. Memories that would have to last her a lifetime. And then when he at last accepted she wasn't going to sleep with him and they parted, he would at least remember her a little differently from all the rest. The one that got away? She bit on the soft underside of her bottom lip. And she would have to make sure she *did* get away.

But it was dangerous, too, too dangerous, loving him as she did. And she was the antithesis of his normal choice of female consort. How would she cope with his expectations of sparkling companionship? But then, she didn't have to.

She stared into the dark lean face wordlessly. The only way he would leave her alone would be when he lost interest. She didn't have to glitter and shine like all the society beauties he had been used to; she didn't have to worry that she didn't have an Armani or a Dior to her name and that she didn't know all the right people; she didn't have to try to be anything but herself. Sephy Vincent, with her old-fashioned views about love and marriage, her inexperience, her off-the-peg clothes and average good-looks.

The conclusion of this unlikely affair could only come one way; Conrad's tenacious, inflexible nature made it so. *He* had to end it because he didn't want her any more; she saw it clearly now. She just hoped she had the strength to endure it without giving him her body as well as her heart in the meantime.

'So, friends, then?' The smile she gave as she held out her hand was worthy of an Oscar if he did but know it.

'Not quite friends, Sephy, if you want that total honesty,' he said drily, his eyes hot as they roamed over her possessively. 'But I'll behave…for the time being. How about that?'

It was the best she was going to get, and far more than she could have hoped for that morning when the roses had arrived.

'It's a deal.'

And then, as he took her proffered hand and, instead of shaking it as she had expected, to seal the pact, raised it to his warm firm lips, the thought came that she had possibly just made the worst mistake of her life.

CHAPTER EIGHT

THE next few months were bittersweet. Sephy alternated between ecstasy and deep despair at regular intervals, sometimes on the same day, but in it all she sensèd she was growing up fast and had left something of the old Sephy behind for ever. And that wasn't all bad.

It was impossible, as Conrad's 'companion', to avoid the glittering galas and functions his wealth and influence demanded he be at, and the first few times she accompanied him to a première or sat next to a famous personage at some dinner or other she felt totally out of her depth.

But then she discovered that even the most wealthy and well-known people were quite ordinary under their Guccis and sparkling diamonds, and that a ten-thousand-pound frock and jewellery from Cartier didn't necessarily make a lady.

At first Conrad tried to insist that she take a dress allowance from him for such occasions, but she objected so vehemently he had the good sense to desist. However, Sephy was aware that a man in his position couldn't have someone at his side who looked badly dressed, and here Maisie turned up trumps.

Under Maisie's rainbow-coloured hair was a brilliant clothes designer as well as an astute businesswoman, and when Sephy confided her predicament Maisie and her assistant got to work with their patterns and sewing machines.

The first dress, made just a week after she and Conrad had come to their arrangement, made Sephy's mouth fall open in sheer delight. 'Maisie, it's *gorgeous*,' she said as she tried on the sky-blue silk evening dress and watched what it did to her creamy skin and hair in Maisie's mirror. 'But how much do I owe you?'

'Nothing,' Maisie said offhandedly. 'I shall sell it in the shop when you've worn it. A woman in your position can't be seen wearing the same dress twice.' She grinned at Sephy, who smiled weakly back. 'You're a perfect size twelve so there won't be a problem; just don't spill red wine down it or something. And don't be shy about saying where you got it if any of the precious darlings ask, okay? Jenny and I will do something different for every do you go to—exclusives. Don't forget to mention they're exclusives.'

'Right.' Sephy looked at the vibrant, confident face in front of her and said, a touch regretfully, 'You'd be much better at all this than me, Maisie.'

'Possibly.' Maisie eyed her laughingly through her exotic eye make-up. 'But I'm not the one he's got the hots for, kiddo.'

Sephy gave an embarrassed laugh. 'He'll soon come to his senses,' she said quietly.

She had told Maisie the full story at the first fitting. It had been the first time she had shared how she felt about Conrad with a living soul and the relief had been tremendous. And Maisie had been tremendous too. She had listened without interrupting until Sephy had finished and then she had given her a big hug and muttered, 'He's a rat. A rich, sexy, drop-dead gorgeous rat, I admit, but a rat nevertheless. And he doesn't deserve you, sweetie.'

'He hasn't got me,' Sephy had answered with a wry smile.

'Just make sure you keep it that way!'

Part of keeping it that way was to follow through on her decision to leave Quentin Dynamics, which Sephy did at the end of February, when she joined a very elite and prestigious agency.

Conrad hadn't liked it when she'd told him she'd decided to join a temping agency for the foreseeable future, but she hadn't expected him to. Whilst she was still working for Mr Harper there was always the chance she would run into Conrad—in the lift, in Reception or one of the offices—and she didn't like the thought of that, now word had got out they were an item, but it was more the issue of independence that prompted her action.

She didn't feel comfortable in being reliant on Conrad for her bread and butter, and that was what working at Quentin Dynamics boiled down to. It didn't sit right. Also—and she found herself skirting over this thought even as she berated herself for not facing the inevitable—working somewhere else would make things much easier when their tenuous relationship was over.

And so she worked for the agency in the day and entered a different world at night; Conrad's world. A breathlessly exciting, fast-moving, exhilarating place where anything could—and frequently did—happen.

She found herself drawn into all aspects of his life, but during the times when she began to hope that Conrad cared for her more than he was prepared to admit she had to remind herself that her presence was still carefully controlled by that cool, analytical mind. She was aware he allowed her to get only so close, and then a remoteness, a very distinct withdrawal, would take place.

This happened more often after they had spent time together and it was just the two of them; quiet evenings at Conrad's beautiful home, long walks when they talked and laughed together, the odd meal at a little pub somewhere far away from the glitzy glamour restaurants Conrad normally frequented. If she was honest Sephy enjoyed these simple pleasures more than anything else, and as she had never been very good at hiding her feelings she suspected Conrad knew that. But he didn't know the underlying cause, that it was because she loved him and treasured the time alone when she had him all to herself.

Through the months leading up to the summer Conrad kept to his word. He kissed her often—he'd made it very plain in the first week of their new arrangement that he considered that perfectly permissible under the terms of their agreement—and he kissed her passionately, petting and cuddling her, but only up to a point.

He would fit her body into his when they sat watching TV at his home, his arm round her shoulders and his square chin resting on the silk of her hair so the delicious scent and warmth of him was all around her; draw her closely against him on their walks, his hard thigh nudging hers and the powerful height and breadth of him seeming to enclose her; hold her so close on the dance floor that she could feel every hard male inch of him. But always that restraint was there.

He was controlled and in command of himself at all times, coolly curbing his desire when he caressed or kissed her and checking any moments which had the potential to get out of hand.

Cool, calm and collected—the epitome of the composed, successful, imperturbable potentate. *And it was driving her bananas.*

How many times she'd felt an almost irresistible urge to just leap on him Sephy didn't know, but by the beginning of June it ran into the hundreds and it was sending her mad. *He* was sending her mad. Her nerves were frayed and she barely knew herself any more.

He was playing with her; they both knew it. Beneath the innocent guise of friendship, or whatever else he cared to label their strange relationship in the icy confines of that freezer which passed as a mind, he was playing a strategic game of emotional chess. He was sensual and sexy in a million provoking little ways, drawing forth a response from her body, inflaming her senses, rousing her and stimulating her libido until she didn't know what to do with herself, Sephy told herself bitterly as she sat picking at a slice of toast one morning after a terrible night's sleep.

Conrad had taken her to the theatre the evening before for the opening night of a play which was predicted to take London by storm. They had been invited to the champagne supper afterwards where they had met the cast before dancing the night away. And Conrad had been at his most devastating.

It hadn't just been the black dinner jacket and tie, although the formal attire suited his wicked dark looks to perfection, or the fact that he had towered head and shoulders above most of the other men present which had had her heart racing most of the night, but the way he had been with her.

Protective, proud, tender, attentive... He'd had the technique down to a fine art, as normal, she thought aggressively, jabbing marmalade on to an unfortunate piece of toast with enough force to reduce it to a pile of crumbs. No one watching them would have doubted that he was anything but madly in love with her.

She'd floated through the night, revelling in every magical second she'd spent in his arms, and then—just as they'd been thinking about leaving—another couple had come to their table to talk to them for a few moments.

The woman had been bubbly and flirtatious, with cute blonde curls and the biggest baby-blue eyes Sephy had ever seen, and her husband had been a tall, lean Richard Gere type, who'd clearly worshipped the ground his taffeta-clad wife walked on. They had made a striking couple, and had apparently only got married the month before, but from the first moment the other woman had looked at her Sephy had known the blonde had been one of Conrad's affairs and, moreover, that she still cared about him.

The knowledge had shocked her out of the state of euphoria the evening in his arms had produced and back into the real world with a bump.

'Who is she?' All the time the couple had been with them Sephy had promised herself she wouldn't ask, but the minute they were alone again the words had just popped out of their own accord.

Conrad didn't try to prevaricate after he saw the awareness in her face, but there was a cool, cutting note to his voice when he said, 'It was a long time ago, Sephy.'

'She still wants you.'

'They only got married four weeks ago, for crying out loud; they're still in the first flush of married bliss,' he said with a cynical, mocking smile. 'And Brian's rich enough to satisfy her.'

'She still wants you,' she repeated flatly.

The sapphire eyes narrowed and hardened, and then he shrugged off-handedly, his face taking on the sardonic, derisive expression Sephy hated. 'So?'

'Don't you *care*?' she asked painfully. This woman and Conrad had shared total intimacy, explored each other's bodies, probably done all sorts of things that she only dared to think about in the quiet darkness of her bed at night, and he could be so stone-cold about her. She didn't understand him; she really didn't.

'I told you, it was over a long time ago.' It was dismissive and curt and told her the conversation was over, but she couldn't leave it alone. She knew she ought to, and that the only person she was going to hurt was herself, but nevertheless she had to ask—even if she didn't really want to hear the answers.

'And you finished it, right?' She stared at him bravely.

The downward quirk to his bottom lip told her she was venturing on to thin ice but she found she didn't care. 'Didn't you?' she pressed tightly. 'You finished with her?'

'Yes, I did.'

'And you finish all your affairs.' It was a statement, not a question. 'The second anyone might get close or try to break out of the mould you deem acceptable, you terminate the liaison.'

He shrugged again. 'Don't waste any time feeling sorry for Katie, if that's how it is,' he said scornfully. 'The main thing she wanted in life was a generous meal ticket and that's what she's got. She was determined to live well, whatever it took.'

Sephy stared at him, her mind whirling with a hundred things she wanted to say but which suddenly seemed pointless in the face of his cold indifference.

The taxi ride home had been difficult and the conversation stilted—on her part at least—and she had barely slept all night. Her head was thumping now, and she felt weary and drained, but for the first time for months she was listening to what her subconscious had been trying to tell her all along.

There had been a part of her, a tiny core in her innermost being, that had hoped... Hoped he would mellow, that he would start to open up a little, that he would fall in love with her despite the bad odds. *Fool!* She slumped back in the chair, her eyes staring blankly straight ahead without seeing anything. She had been lying to herself all through this fiasco. Conrad wouldn't just give up and get tired of the chase; he wasn't like that. He was a hunter; she'd seen him in operation in the cut-throat world of business too often not to know that. And he always had to win.

The only way he would finish their liaison would be after she had become his and the chase was over, and if that happened she would never recover from the pain of it. If she gave herself to him it would be completely and for ever; he would drain her of everything she needed for the future, everything she had to give, and leave her empty and crushed and useless. She couldn't, she *wouldn't*, let that happen. This was self-preservation in its rawest terms.

At first she was too lost in her misery for the sound of the buzzer to register, and then, as it penetrated the blackness of her thoughts, she dragged herself up from the chair and walked into the hall. Conrad often sent her flowers at the weekend; no doubt it was a delivery.

'Yes?' Her voice was flat as she spoke into the intercom.

Then, as a deep, husky voice said, 'Sephy?', her heart started pounding before she warned herself to take control.

'Conrad? What are you doing here?' He was due to pick her up later that afternoon for an evening barbecue with some friends of his who lived in Windsor, and she had been meaning to use the day to pretty herself up. Her hair needed washing, the flat was a mess—why was he here *now*? And then, as the panic subsided, she thought numbly perhaps this was for the best, after what the night before had shown her. Maybe it was better like this.

She could let this farce limp on for another few days or weeks or she could finish it now, and suddenly the second option was the only bearable one. He was never going to change; life with Conrad would be a savage cycle of highs and lows until the final low. And one day, when it was long over, he might catch a glimpse of her somewhere or other and his beautiful blue eyes would be as empty and cold as they'd been when he'd looked at Katie last night.

The last months had been nothing but moves on a chessboard to him, a means to an end, and it hadn't even seemed as though he had had much of a struggle to keep his hands off her.

She heard him say, a touch of amusement in his voice, 'I'm here to see you, of course,' and then she pressed the buzzer, indicating for him to come up, but she just couldn't speak.

'What's the matter?' The second he walked into the flat,

his arms full of flowers, his eyes focused on her ashen face. 'Are you unwell?' he asked quietly, his voice concerned.

She was dying. It was melodramatic, but exactly how she felt, and she wondered what his reaction would be if she said it out loud. As it happened she was beginning to feel a bit dizzy, and odder by the minute, but she merely said, 'I have to talk to you.'

His eyebrows rose enquiringly even as the blue gaze wandered down the length of her. She had the flimsiest of summer nighties on under her robe, but she blessed the fact the robe was thick towelling and covered her down to her knees as she pulled the belt tighter. Nevertheless her cheeks were burning.

'Tousled and barefoot. It suits you,' he said huskily as he dropped the flowers on to an occasional table and came towards her. 'You'd be nice to wake up next to in the morning, Sephy Vincent.'

If she was stupid, really stupid, she could believe that look in his eyes meant something, she told herself bleakly. But last night had solidified all her buried doubts and fears and this was truth time. 'For how long, Conrad?' she asked quietly.

'What?' She had caught him off guard and he stopped just in front of her, his arms freezing for a second as they reached for her waist and then continuing until he was holding her just a few inches from his hard chest. 'What do you mean?'

'I said for how long?' she repeated with a calm born of the numbness that had taken her over. 'How long would I be around?'

He was dressed in a suit and tie rather than casual clothes, which meant he was probably going into work for a few hours, and he confirmed this in the next moment when he said, his eyes slightly puzzled as they stared into hers, 'Look, I can't really stop now, there's some sort of crisis I need to sort out in the office for an hour or two, but I just wanted to give you the flowers and say I'll pick you up at three this afternoon, okay?'

'No, it's not okay. I'm sorry, Conrad, but I can't do this any more.' His hands were firm and warm through the towelling and he was as impeccably groomed as always, whereas she must look as though she had been dragged through a hedge backwards. It somehow seemed to sum up their relationship.

'You can't do what any more?' His voice was quiet, lazy even, but she had seen the import of her words register for a second in the intent blue gaze, and she knew he understood what she was saying. And he didn't like it; she knew that too.

'This, us, being together and not being together. Seeing that woman last night—' She stopped abruptly. She didn't know how to put it. 'I don't want to end up like her,' she said tightly.

'*What?*' He let go of her abruptly, stepping back a pace.

Her heart was thudding so loudly now it was echoing in her ears, but at least she could think better without him holding her, and the distance between them helped her to say fairly coherently, 'That's what you're trying to do, turn me into someone like her.'

'The hell I am!' He glared at her, his mouth pulling into a thin line as he said coldly, 'It might have slipped your memory, but this charade of being together and not being together was very much your idea, not mine, so don't try that little tack, Sephy. I don't know what meeting Katie has to do with anything—damn it, I haven't seen the woman in a couple of years—but if anyone should be griping it's me, not you. You've had this all your own way.'

'How can you say that?' Anger had flooded in, melting the numbness and bringing a rush of adrenalin that brought her ramrod-straight in front of him. 'How can you *dare* say that? I told you at the beginning I didn't want an affair with you—'

'And we both knew you were lying,' he said insolently, moving a pace nearer and staring down at her with glittering blue eyes. 'You want me, Sephy, and it's nothing to be ashamed about, for crying out loud! And you're not the only one who's had enough of this damn travesty. I've waited for you to come to your senses—longer than I've ever waited for any woman, I might add.'

'What do you expect me to say? Thank you?' she spat sarcastically, the pain in her heart enabling her to fight back.

'No, you can show your appreciation for my patience another way,' he said with hateful mockery.

'Not in a month of Sundays!' she shot back furiously, hiding the sudden dart of fear under her blazing rage.

'A month of Sundays?' He was towering over her now, and as he reached out and jerked her against him he said softly, 'I wouldn't have to wait two minutes, let alone a month of Sundays, and you know it. Tell me. Tell me you don't want me and I'll leave right now. Tell me to get out of your life, Sephy.'

'I—I don't want you,' she stammered. 'I want you to go.'

'Little liar.' He smiled, but it was a mere predatory twisting of his lips a second before they claimed her mouth.

'Let go of me!'

As she jerked her head away and struggled in his arms he made a low sound of irritation in his throat before renewing his assault on her senses, moulding her closer against his hard body.

If he had been rough or violent, if he had hurt her, she could have fought him and kept fighting, but his attack was warm and thrilling and frighteningly perceptive. She could feel his heart slamming against the hard wall of his chest and her own was an echo, her mouth opening under the continued assault and her head falling back against the sinewy strength of his arm.

The feel of him, the warmth and scent of his body, was wildly intoxicating, and as his hot hungry mouth trailed fire over her ears and throat before returning to take her mouth with gentle ferocity she knew the restraint· he had been employing over the last months was all used up. He was going for the kill.

He was whispering her name, touching her and caressing her until her body was trembling, and she was moaning softly in her throat without being aware of it as she strained closer to him.

It was only when she felt cooler air on her hot flesh that she realised the robe was on the floor and she was only clothed in the dubious covering of the wafer-thin nightie, which exposed more than it concealed. It should have mattered but it didn't.

His hands were on the soft swell of her breasts, their peaks hard and urgent against his knowing fingers, before they moved to her slender waist and womanly hips, and as he fitted her soft feminine curves against the hard thrust of his arousal she could feel the alien raw power of his manhood through their clothes.

'Say you want me, Sephy, say it,' he muttered hoarsely against her lips, and as she opened her dazed eyes she looked into his and they were hot and midnight-blue. The cool façade had been well and truly blown apart—this was a man intent on possession. 'Tell me I'm right.'

What was she doing? As she stared into his face the thought hammered in her head. This was about more than proving one of them right, didn't he understand at least that? But, no, he didn't. If he could fit her into a nice convenient slot in his mind that was all he needed. But she didn't fit like the others, she just *couldn't* think and feel like them—she wanted all of him, not a taste now and again until even that was taken away.

'I do want you.' She knew exactly what she was doing as she spoke the next words that would provide the ultimate wedge between them. 'But it's because I love you. And not because of the sexual chemistry between us or your wealth or your looks or anything else that could be taken away or lost with fate or time. I love *you*, all of you, the complete man—warts and pimples and all. If you lost all your money tomorrow or were hurt or injured nothing would change in my feeling for you.'

'No.' One small word but it had the power to make her feel as though she was nothing. The look on his face, the stark disbelief and rejection was all she had feared and more. 'You're mistaking something very natural, the sexual chemistry you spoke of, for something that doesn't exist. You'll come to realise that in time, believe me.'

His hands had moved to her upper arms now and he was holding her slightly apart from him as he stared into her drowning eyes. 'If you had known other men you'd under-stand—'

'I don't want to know other men, Conrad.' She suddenly felt so weary, so drained, that even standing was an act of will. They were at opposite ends of the world, of the uni-verse—there was no meeting point; there never had been. He wanted someone who was content with material things, someone he could buy, a woman who wouldn't make the mistake of caring. And right at this moment she felt that was what he deserved.

'You will,' he said tautly. 'In time you will.'

And then she understood. His childhood and youth, bad as they had been, weren't all of it. And unknowingly she repeated the essence of the words he had said to her months before. 'Who was she?' She should have known there was something—*someone*.

He let go of her, walking across to stand with his back to her as he stared out of the window into the sunny street below. As she struggled into her robe, shaking from head to foot, he said expressionlessly, 'She was just a female like any other, but I was young and idealistic and thought there was such a thing as love in those days. I was seventeen years old and she was the new French mistress at the school. Funny, eh? Like one of those bawdy jokes that make people laugh?'

He turned to face her then, and his countenance was dark and stony. 'Knowing what I know now, she must have been around some to get the experience she had, but she didn't look her age—she was twenty-six—and she lied so beautifully she could have made the devil himself believe black was white. She was tiny, petite, and she made every lad in the school feel like Tarzan, so the fact that she was sleeping with me... We were going to get married, as soon as I'd finished my A Levels and was out of that place. And then some weeks into the summer holidays, when I was waiting for my results and for her to join me after she'd settled things in France, I got a letter.'

A 'Dear John', Sephy thought painfully. She swallowed once, twice, before she managed to say, 'I'm sorry, I'm so sorry.'

'She'd married the local big-wig in her hometown,' Conrad said evenly. 'Apparently she'd been engaged to him for years but he was twenty-five years older than her and a gangster type with plenty of women on the side. She'd caught him out a few times and come to England in a fit of pique. Anyway, true love triumphed, or in her case a mansion of a house and her own Ferrari etcetera, etcetera, etcetera. A seedy little story involving seedy little people.'

'And that's when you went abroad,' she said softly, sinking down on to the sofa before her legs gave out. She felt sick for him, heartsick, but her misery was all the more acute for knowing that this was the death knell on any faint hope she'd had that he would ever understand how she loved him. He might want her, he might even care about her in his own way, but the ability for anything more had been burnt out of his soul long before he had met her. She had met him far, far too late.

Her head was swimming now, and she felt nauseous, but she forced herself to sit quietly. She sensed he had never spoken of all this before and he might never again, and she had to hear it all. She had to *know*.

'Yes, I went abroad,' he agreed expressionlessly. 'The original angry young man with money in his pocket and no one to answer to. I made a few mistakes—hell, I made a lot of mistakes—but it was beneficial in the main. I grew up, learnt what my strengths and weaknesses were and I found I was more like my parents than I cared to admit. I didn't need anyone to make good.'

'Everyone needs someone, Conrad,' she said sadly.

'That's where you're wrong, Sephy,' he said with disturbing conviction. 'Society perpetuates the myth that we're pack animals because it makes it easier for governments to control the hordes, that's all. Marriage, family units—they aren't necessary, believe me. I'm living proof of that.'

If she hadn't been so tired and her head hadn't been pounding so badly she might have thought more about what she said, but as it was the words were out before she had time to consider how they sounded. 'That's such rubbish,' she said flatly. 'Such utter and absolute rubbish. It's the most natural thing in the world for two people to fall in love and want to create a family. When it goes wrong it can be the most devastating thing in the world, like in your case, but that doesn't mean it's not necessary. If anything I would say you are living proof *for* a secure family unit rather than against. Proof of what a mess someone can become when they aren't loved and cherished by the very people they have a right to expect it from.'

He stared at her for a moment, the slash of colour along his chiselled cheekbones deepening as her words hovered in the taut silence. 'Thank you so much for that vote of confidence,' he said coldly, the tone of his voice cutting, 'but I don't think I've done too badly on the whole.'

'Materially you've got the world at your feet,' she agreed quietly, 'but that's nothing. Money and possessions are nothing.'

'There are a good number of women out there who would disagree with you.' It was bitterly cynical.

'Yes, there are.' This was it; this was the end. She had offended him beyond the point of no return. It was there in the blazing blue eyes and savagely tense jaw; he looked as though he would like to strangle her with his bare hands. 'And they are as emotionally crippled as you,' she said softly. 'No good to themselves and no good to anyone else. Life is more than performing well in bed, Conrad, more than making people fear and tremble when you walk into a room to conduct a business deal.'

'Here endeth the first lesson?' The sarcasm was raw and deadly. 'What makes you such an authority on human relationships anyway?' he said with biting control.

'I'm not an authority; I've never pretended to be,' she shot back tightly. 'But I know what I know and you're wrong, so wrong.'

'Oh, to hell with this,' he ground out furiously. 'I've a deal worth millions hanging in the balance. That's real life! And if I can have a few of them in fear and trembling this morning that'll suit me just fine; it'll have been a successful day.'

'Then I feel sorry for you,' she said bravely, lifting her chin as she stared up at him from the sofa. 'If that's all you've got.'

'Keep your pity for someone who needs it, Sephy,' he said with sudden chilling softness. 'Because I don't.'

'No, of course, I'd forgotten.' She was so *angry* with him; he would never find anyone else who would love him as she did and he was throwing away her chance of happiness along with his. This was so *unfair*. 'You don't need anyone, do you?'

'Dead right.'

She knew he was going to walk out on her and she steeled herself not to move or speak as he left, nodding at him with almost clinical detachment as he turned in the doorway to survey her one last time. The look on his face chilled her to the bone.

And then the door closed behind him, she heard his feet on the stairs outside—a brief pause—and then the sound of the door into the street being slammed with some force. He had gone. She turned her face into the upholstered plumpness of the sofa and let the pent-up tears come in an overwhelming flood. She had known it was going to happen—that it *must*. There had only been one way this could all finish from the start, so why—knowing that—did it still hurt so much?

It was a good half an hour later before Sephy roused herself from the sofa, and by then she had realised—her desolation taken as read—that she wasn't feeling physically well.

Her throat was burning, there were a hundred little men with hammers inside her head and she felt as exhausted as if she had just completed the London Marathon.

In spite of her consuming misery she fell asleep immediately she crawled back into bed, and it was some time later—how long she had no idea—that she became aware of Maisie's voice talking to her as a soft hand shook her awake. 'Sephy, Sephy, are you all right? For goodness' sake talk to me, kiddo. What's wrong?'

'Wh-what's the matter?' she asked groggily, the urgent, almost tearful note in Maisie's voice penetrating the consuming heaviness as she struggled to open her eyes.

'I've been pressing the buzzer for ages, and then I tried ringing; we were supposed to meet for coffee and croissants this morning, remember?' Maisie said earnestly. 'So I got the pass key from Jerry; he's waiting in the living room.'

'Is he?' She tried to sit up but every bone was aching and she felt indescribably ill. It was easier to fall back against the pillows.

'You've got a fever. I'm calling the doctor,' Maisie said firmly.

She heard Maisie speak, but it was too much effort to answer, and it was the same through the doctor's visit. She was aware of people in the room, but it was as though they were at the end of a long foggy corridor, and although she struggled to answer the questions put to her she wasn't at all sure she was making sense.

'Shouldn't be left alone...' The odd few words filtered through the pounding in her head. '...need me, don't hesitate to call.' She tried to sit up and protest that she would be perfectly all right if only everyone would *go*, but the room started to revolve into a spinning kaleidoscope of colour and sound that took the last of her strength with it.

The next twenty-four hours passed in a blur of images and weird disjointed dreams. She thought she heard Conrad's voice at one point, and then Maisie, if not exactly shouting, then coming pretty near to it. She was conscious of trying to claw her way out of a deep abyss, but every time she thought she was going to make it it all got too much, and the world became narrowed down to a thick heavy blanket that drew her down and down...

When she did finally awake properly she lay for some moments without opening her eyes, aware that the terrifying headache was gone, along with the swirling voices and distorted images which had populated her head. She felt tired, she didn't think she had ever felt so tired in all her life, but her mind was her own again.

She forced her aching eyelids open, and then blinked and shut them again as golden sunlight turned everything white for a moment.

'Sephy? Sephy, it's Maisie. Open your eyes again, love.'

Maisie? As her gaze focused on her friend's face Sephy saw to her consternation that Maisie looked as tired as she felt. 'What…what are you doing here?' she asked through dry lips.

'Looking after you,' was the rueful reply. 'You've been on planet Zargos for the last twenty-four hours, kiddo. Don't you remember?'

'A bit.' And then, as her thirst became overwhelming, 'Can I have a drink, Maisie?' But by the time the glass was placed to her dry lips she was fast asleep again.

By Sunday evening Sephy had skimmed in and out of sleep several times, but was sufficiently recovered to sit up in bed and drink the bowl of steaming vegetable soup Maisie gave her at six o'clock. She didn't feel at all hungry but she tried to please Maisie.

'You had us going for a time there, kiddo,' Maisie said breezily as she plumped herself down on the duvet. 'The doctor thought it was this rotten summer flu, but I was beginning to doubt he knew what he was talking about. He said you're absolutely knackered as well, which didn't help. Asked me if you'd been burning the candle at both ends,' she added pointedly.

'And you said?'

'Too right.' Maisie grinned cheerfully. 'I told him you'd got this rat of a boyfriend who'd been giving you the run-around.'

'You didn't!' Sephy was horrified. 'You didn't, Maisie?'

'I did.' Maisie's kohl-blackened eyes narrowed. 'And I

told the boyfriend the same thing, as it happens. He didn't take too kindly to being told he was a git,' she said with some satisfaction.

'*Maisie!*' The soup nearly went all over the bed.

'Now don't excite yourself,' Maisie said imperturbably. 'It won't do him any harm in the long run.'

'He…Conrad came round here?' Sephy asked weakly. She had purposely been blanking that part of her consciousness until she felt strong enough to deal with the memory of their last meeting.

Maisie nodded. 'I think he wished he hadn't by the time he left,' she said with some relish, the stud in her nose shining as she wrinkled her nose gleefully at the memory.

'Oh, Maisie.' She felt too weak to deal with this development.

'Don't ''Oh, Maisie'' me,' the other girl said firmly. 'From what you mumbled when you were delirious, I got the impression he'd chucked you. Right?'

Sephy nodded silently. Words were beyond her just at this point, with the picture of an angry, bristling Maisie facing the tall, remote figure of Conrad Quentin and giving him what for. She was one in a million; she was really.

'Yes, that's what I thought,' Maisie said comfortably. 'So I told him he ought to be down on his knees thanking God or Buddha or whoever else he prays to that they threw you across his path. You're special, Sephy.' Now all trace of belligerence was gone as Maisie leant forward and gripped her hand hard. 'Very special, and he's a fool. I told him that as well.'

'Oh, Maisie.' She didn't seem able to say much else, but the other girl's fierce championship was making her want to cry. She had never been one to make close friends in the past, her inferiority complex as a child and adolescent had worked against her in that respect, but now she realised there was a whole realm of warmth and friendship open to her she had never guessed at.

'Anyway, that's enough of that.' Maisie jumped to her feet, her psychedelic hair, bright green waist-length cardigan and tight rainbow-coloured skirt all—miraculously—blending into one very attractive whole as she said, 'You've wasted enough tears on that rat; you're not going to shed another one. You've finished the soup and now you're going to eat a chicken sandwich prepared by my own fair hand. Okay, kiddo?'

'Okay.' Sephy nodded obediently.

She only managed to eat about a third of the chicken sandwich before she found herself snuggling down in bed again and falling asleep, but an hour later when the buzzer went she was wide awake in an instant, as though she had been programmed.

She could hear Maisie speaking in a low voice into the intercom, although she couldn't distinguish what was being said, but when the other girl popped her head round the bedroom door a few moments later Sephy was sitting up in bed with her eyes fixed on the door. 'I heard the buzzer. Who is it?' she asked nervously.

'He wants to come up for a few minutes.' Maisie's voice was flat and low and Sephy didn't have to ask who 'he' was.

To her eternal shame Sephy was less concerned with the ethics of it all than the fact that she hadn't bathed in forty-eight hours and her hair was tangled and she must look a sight. 'No.' She stared at Maisie and the bizarrely painted face stared back. 'Not now. Say…say I'm still too ill or something.'

'Sure.' She certainly wasn't going to get any argument from Maisie. 'Let the creep squirm for a while.'

She didn't want him to squirm. Ridiculous in the circumstances, but she really didn't want him to squirm, Sephy thought miserably, as she slid down under the duvet again.

It was a few minutes before Maisie walked back into the bedroom, and this time she was carrying a huge bunch of flowers and a box of chocolates that outdid the colossal absurdity Conrad had taken in to Madge. 'Okay, so he's a generous creep,' Maisie said offhandedly before grinning at her and adding, 'I told him to come back tomorrow, but that's about as far as I can push my luck, I think. As it is he's phoned the doctor himself and got the lowdown on what's happening. Dead cheek if you ask me.'

'He didn't?' And then she refused the ray of hope before it had a chance to develop into something more hurtful. He was probably only feeling a bit guilty, she told herself silently. As well he might! But it didn't make any difference to the overall situation and she'd forget that at her peril. 'How did he know my doctor?' she thought out loud. 'I've never told him.'

'Probably from his personnel department,' the ever practical Maisie said in reply. 'You did work for him for six years, remember.'

As if she could ever forget!

Sephy insisted on sending Maisie back to her own flat to get a good night's sleep, but after the other girl had gone the hot bath and long soak she'd promised herself degenerated into a hasty lick and a promise followed by brushing her teeth. She couldn't believe how exhausted she felt once she'd tottered into the bathroom, and by the time she slid back under the rumpled covers her legs were shaking and her eyelids just wouldn't stay open.

The next morning she awoke very early and lay looking at the vases of flowers—the bouquet wouldn't fit into less than two—sitting on her dressing table. The freesias and stock had scented the room with summer, and red and gold chrysanthemums and coneflowers were a blaze of colour against the graceful belladonna lilies standing at the back of the profusion of flowers.

Maisie had already told her that the blooms Conrad had previously bought on the Saturday morning were filling the sitting room's large windowsill, and for a moment—just a moment—Sephy found herself resenting the inoffensive flowers.

It was too easy to send bouquets and buy chocolates and other expensive presents, she told herself wearily. They only cost him money, and for someone as rich as Conrad money wasn't a consideration. A fistful of garden daisies or buttercups given with love would have sent her to the moon, but he wouldn't understand that, or even perhaps believe it. And that wrenched her heart.

She had often looked at film stars or top models in the past who had all but destroyed themselves in some way—drink, drugs, depression leading to attempted suicide—and wondered how they could fall apart when they had the world at their feet and everything they wanted, but even the best things counted as nothing if you didn't have your soulmate to share them with.

But Conrad wasn't her soulmate, however much she wished it different. She couldn't turn him into something he wasn't any more than he could make her give up the loving, giving part of herself that made her what she was, the part which would become an irritation to him—at best—if she put both feet into his world.

He wanted a cool, worldly Caroline de Menthe clone and she needed roses round the door and happy ever after, something he just wasn't capable of providing.

Maisie breezed in just before eight and insisted on cooking her fried eggs and bacon with two rounds of toast before she disappeared to the boutique, with promises she would return at lunchtime with sandwiches. 'Don't you dare try and do a thing today,' she warned firmly as she placed the loaded tray across Sephy's knees. 'The doctor said a week in bed at least.'

'Maisie, I hate staying in bed!'

'Well, you can get up and lie in the sitting room,' the other girl conceded, 'but that's all. Have a bath, drift around looking pale and interesting and prepare to twist the knife when he - who - deserves - his - comeuppance calls. Okay, sweetie?'

'Maisie, you're the most unlikely mother hen in the whole of creation.' Sephy grinned with genuine warmth.

'I know it.' There was a vivid shade of purple coating Maisie's eyelids today which exactly matched her mini-dress, and as the other girl winked at her Sephy laughed out loud. As desolate as she was feeling about Conrad, there was something irrepressible about Maisie that lifted one's spirits in spite of oneself.

Once she was alone Sephy forced down a few mouthfuls of food and then slept most of the morning, before rising just after eleven and running herself the promised bath. She had been feeling so warm and sticky that the silky water felt heavenly, and after soaking for some minutes she washed her hair, luxuriating in digging her fingers into her scalp and washing out the staleness of the weekend.

Once out of the bath she wrapped a big fluffy bath sheet round herself sarong-style, and peered into the mirror. A brief glance was enough to inform her that the pale and interesting look Maisie had mentioned was definitely in evidence, although she wasn't sure the interesting part applied.

Her face was lint-white, the sprinkling of freckles across her nose standing out like a scattering of nutmeg on thick cream, and she actually looked thinner. 'Every cloud has a silver lining,' she muttered wryly to herself as she walked through into the bedroom to dry her hair.

When the buzzer sounded she grimaced to herself and

then glanced at her little bedside alarm clock. Twelve o'clock—Maisie was nothing if not punctual.

She padded quickly through to the hall, surprised to find how much the bath had tired her, and flicked the switch on the intercom as she said, 'Come on up, mother hen. Your chick's just drying her hair,' before opening the flat's front door and walking through to the sunlit sitting room.

And it wasn't until she heard footsteps that definitely were not Maisie's that she realised Maisie would have used Jerry's key.

CHAPTER NINE

THERE was no time to think, let alone move, and as the tall, lean figure of Conrad walked into the flat Sephy faced him from the middle of the sitting room, her hair falling in thick, damp, rich brown waves about her pale face and bare shoulders, and her honey-gold eyes open wide with shock.

He stopped still in the doorway as he saw her, and in spite of herself she let her eyes feast on him for a moment; she really couldn't help it. His hard, handsome face was full of very sharply defined planes and angles as a shaft of sunlight hit him, and his coal-black hair and impossibly blue eyes, the tailor-made suit and silk shirt and tie, completed the picture of a man who knew exactly where he was going and woe betide anyone who got in his way on the journey. A man at the top of his profession.

Cold, hard and ruthless; he could definitely be called that on occasion, and yet she had seen the other side of the coin, and it was that which made her heart ache and her senses tighten to breaking point. And it was that weakness she had to fight now.

She had never felt so vulnerable and defenceless, and something of what she was feeling must have shown in her face because he said, his voice soft and steady, 'It's all right, Sephy. I'm not here to fight.'

'I...I thought you were Maisie,' she murmured breathlessly.

'Ah, the coffee and croissants, right?'

It was the smile that did it.

He could smile. He could actually *smile* like that, as though nothing was wrong, when he had all but ripped her

165

heart out by its roots in this very room not three days ago, Sephy thought bitterly. But at least his casual demeanour had the effect of putting adrenalin in her veins and steel in her backbone.

He probably expected her to beg and plead or cry buckets, but she'd rather be hung, drawn and quartered! Pride and dignity were poor bedfellows but they were all that was left to her, and by golly she intended to hang on to them.

In the past she had always tried to make things easy between them by filling in any awkward silences with chatter, but now she lifted her head slightly and continued to stare at him without speaking. She was blowed if she was going to speak next.

'How are you feeling?' he asked after a few endless seconds.

'I'm fine,' she said tightly.

'Rubbish. How are you feeling?'

Typical Conrad! Well, if he wanted the truth he could have it. 'Tired, my throat's sore, the headache I thought had gone is returning—' since you walked through the door '—and I ache all over. Okay?' she snapped testily. 'Satisfied?'

'You really are in a bad mood, aren't you?' he drawled lazily, and then, as she opened her mouth to fire back, he added, 'I'm sorry I didn't realise you were ill on Saturday, Sephy.'

She shrugged, and then as the towel slipped a little decided she wouldn't do that again. 'It wouldn't have made any difference. We had things to say and we said them,' she said shortly.

Why did he have to look so good in a suit and tie? Why did he have to look so good in *anything*? she asked herself silently.

'The doctor told me you are extremely run down and

could do with a break,' Conrad said quietly. 'All those months of working all hours for me started a downward spiral, no doubt.'

She had to get something on other than this towel! 'Look, I won't be a moment,' she said curtly, before walking quickly into the bedroom and shutting the door. She stood for a second, her heart thumping so hard it made her feel dizzy, and then pulled on a baggy T-shirt and a pair of panties before slipping into her robe and jerking the belt tight. Psychologically fortified, she opened the door and walked into the sitting room, saying, 'Conrad, why did you come back on Saturday? Maisie told me.'

'Ah, yes, Maisie.' He frowned, and then said with grudging generosity, 'She's a good friend.'

'Yes, she is.' And Maisie knew as well as she did that her present exhaustion was due to the fact she'd lived on her nerves from the first day she had worked for Conrad Quentin. And it had got worse, a million times worse, since she'd agreed to his preposterous demand that they see each other. And she also knew, as she stared at his dear face, that she could never go back to that, even if the pain of losing him continued to the day she died. She felt light-headed, and sank down quickly on the sofa as she said, 'Please go.'

His guilt she could do without, and it was clear pity was the only thing he felt for her. Not once since he had walked through the door had he made any attempt to touch her, and she found she couldn't bear it. She just couldn't bear it.

'Not yet.'

To her horror he walked across and knelt back on his heels in front of her, the pose stretching material tight over hard male thighs and bringing the scent and warmth of him too close for comfort. He was looking straight into her eyes now, his dark head on a level with hers and the blue of his eyes piercing.

His voice dropped an octave as he said, 'Do you trust me, Sephy?' The tone was cool and almost expressionless.

'What?' Of all the things she had expected him to say it wasn't this. 'What are you talking about?'

'I need to know about this man, this David.' His eyes watched his words sink in, and as hot colour stained her white face he leant a little closer, not touching her with any part of himself yet enveloping her with his magnetic pull. 'I've no right to ask—after Saturday I haven't even got the right to be here, as Maisie's pointed out more than once— but nevertheless…'

'I…I can't.' She took a deep breath and managed to say, 'We're not seeing each other any more so what's the point?'

'I need to know, Sephy,' he said softly, his eyes never leaving her face for a moment. 'Believe me, I really need to know.'

She expelled a shuddering breath as her stomach churned violently. She could see this meant a great deal, but she didn't understand why, and the humiliation and pain of having to tell was too much. And it wasn't fair to ask, not now.

'Please?' It was said very, very softly.

He had never said that word before, and he had never looked at her as he was doing now. She couldn't read what was in his eyes but it was clear he was in the grip of something that was tearing him apart. And in spite of everything she couldn't bear that.

Her profile was white and fragile as she turned slightly, her voice low and strained as she began. 'There were a whole bunch of us who grew up together and David was one of them. He…he was the handsome one, the charmed one; everyone was crazy about him and wanted to be with him. And then…'

It didn't take long to tell, but when she had finished she sagged against the sofa as though she had been talking for hours. She hadn't looked at him once as she had spoken, and he hadn't said a word, so when his voice came, dark and deadly, saying, 'I would like to kill him, Sephy,' she was actually shocked.

'It was a long time ago; it's in the past,' she said quickly, feeling it had been a terrible mistake to tell him.

'I'm going to hold you, just hold you.' He had taken her in his arms before she could demur, lifting her as he rose and then sitting on the sofa so that she was cradled in his arms with her head resting against his throat.

She held herself rigid—it was either that or turning in to him and saying she would take any terms, any conditions, as long as he didn't go. But it would be a mockery of a relationship. He didn't love her; *he didn't love her*.

'Listen to me for a minute without saying anything,' he said huskily, after what felt like a lifetime. 'You're ill now, tired and low and at the end of yourself, and I should have realised it weeks ago. The doctor said you are completely exhausted.'

'But—'

'No, just listen, Sephy. I want you to do one last thing for me. I want you to let me send you away somewhere hot and lazy, somewhere where you can recover in peace and quiet and get strong again. Will you let me do that, please? And soon?'

She swallowed once, twice, but she still couldn't speak. He was sending her away, that much had registered, along with the knowledge that for a moment—just a split second of a moment—she had hoped he was going to say something else. That he had grown to love her, that their quarrel on Saturday had opened his eyes and he understood he felt more for her than he'd felt for the others. Had there ever been such a fool as her in the whole of time? Would she never learn?

He was breathing hard, she could feel his muscled chest rising and falling, and then he cleared his throat and said, 'Will you let me do that? The doctor says you need to convalesce.'

Nothing more than a weak whisper could force its way past the painful constriction in her throat as she fought the tears. 'There's no need, really. I am strong, or I will be in a day or two. It's only a touch of flu.'

'You haven't had a holiday in over a year and you're physically and mentally exhausted. I want to do this, Sephy. I've a place in Italy that I bought years ago, when Daniella's father first made contact with me again. It was a means of being around my niece now and again but still having home comforts and being able to work when I needed to. There are people there who will cook and clean and take care of things while you relax and get well again.'

'You mean live in your home?' she asked dazedly.

'This is not a means of getting you into my bed whilst you're ill and weak,' he said evenly, his voice slightly clipped now. 'I don't operate like that.'

'I know.' She hadn't thought that for a moment. 'I know that.'

'I shan't be there, of course, but I'll know you're recovering in beautiful surroundings and that there are people to assist if you need anything. You have my word I won't visit or harass you.'

His duty—as he saw it—taken care of and this whole unlikely affair finished on a clean note. She knew what he was about, but with the warm fragrance of him all about her and his body touching hers she couldn't think clearly.

'I can't…let you do that,' she said after a while.

She heard him sigh impatiently and then her heart stopped beating as she felt his hand smooth back a tendril of hair from her cheek, and he said, 'Yes, you can. Madge has sung your praises more than once for the way you handled things when she was away, and she's let me know it was totally unreasonable of me to expect you to work the hours she does. You're young; your whole life isn't taken up with Quentin Dynamics like she's chosen for hers to be.'

No, her whole life was taken up with him, and that was a hundred times worse than the position Madge was in.

So... Madge had obviously been on at him, and Maisie had put in her twopenny-worth, and now he felt he had to do something for her. She didn't like that, it was humiliating, but, knowing Conrad as she did when he had the bit between his teeth, he wouldn't take no for an answer, and besides... She bit her lip hard as she faced the truth of it. She would love to see this other home of his, live somewhere that had the imprint of him all around, even if it was just for a week or so. It was crazy and smacked of masochism but it meant she didn't have to let go for just a bit longer, that she was still on the perimeter of his life in some way. She closed her eyes and drank in the closeness of him for a moment. And she couldn't feel worse than she was feeling now. At least this way she would start to face the rest of her life without him bronzed and well instead of pale and pathetic.

'Look on this as a bonus for the job you did for me,' the deep, husky voice above her head said softly, 'if that makes you feel better.'

It didn't. It only confirmed what she'd known all along— that he was making this offer because he felt uncomfortable about the way things had finished and wanted to end their relationship on a better note. However, once he had touched her, once he had shown that other side of himself which was so dangerously tender, her earlier resolution regarding pride and dignity seemed to have flown out of the window.

She sighed inwardly at her inconsistency, and at the fact that she would be quite content to sit here like this for the rest of her life, and took a deep, steadying breath before she said, 'You don't have to do this, but if you really want to then…thank you. A holiday would be nice.'

If he was surprised at her easy capitulation he didn't show it, but, never one to miss pressing an advantage, he said quickly, 'A month away should have you back on your feet.'

'A month!' She straightened then, twisting to face him, and wished she hadn't as his face came disturbingly close. For such an uncompromisingly masculine man he had ridiculously long eyelashes, and his mouth was fascinatingly uneven. And sexy. Definitely sexy. It made you want to kiss it, to draw his firm bottom lip between yours and explore its taste…

'Okay, you've twisted my arm. Six weeks.'

'I can't possibly stay away a month,' Sephy said flatly, pulling the belt of the robe tighter before she twisted and rose carefully to her feet. She noticed—with a dart of pain that was confirmation she'd been stark staring mad to agree to anything but a swift clean break with this man—that he made no effort to restrain her or pull her back into his arms. 'Ten days at most.'

'A month minimum,' he said coolly, 'and of course it goes without saying I pay your rent here while you're away.'

'No way.' This was the Conrad she could fight, the imperious, overbearing, lordly tycoon who thought he only had to speak and the world listened. '*I* pay the rent.'

'Okay, I'm willing to compromise. *You* pay the month's rent,' he agreed smoothly.

She stared at him uncertainly. Somehow she had agreed to a month's holiday and she wasn't quite sure how. 'Conrad—'

As they both heard the downstairs door open, followed by a 'Yoohoo! It's only me!' Conrad's eyebrows rose mockingly.

'Mother hen?' he murmured silkily as he rose to his feet.

How could you love someone and hate them at the same time? 'Conrad, we have to discuss this,' she said a trifle desperately.

'No time.' And then he had pulled her into him roughly, kissing her hard and hungrily for a heart-stopping moment before he let her go, a second before Maisie breezed into the room.

'Hallo, Maisie,' he said easily, the mocking expression intensifying as he took in the look of absolute amazement on Maisie's face. 'How nice to see you again.'

'You… How did you—'

'Sephy will explain,' he said smoothly. 'By the way, she's going away for a few weeks the day after tomorrow. Help her pack, there's a good girl, and a taxi will be here at eight on Wednesday morning.'

'Conrad, I need to know about everything,' Sephy said flusteredly, her face flushed and the feel of his mouth still burning her lips. 'I have to get plane tickets and—'

'All taken care of.' And as she started to protest his eyes narrowed and he said warningly, 'I told you, Sephy, I want to do this and I don't do things by half. You should know that by now. Madge will phone you tonight and give you all the details; all you have to do is to get well enough to travel on Wednesday. Your passport is up to date?' he asked suddenly, as the thought struck him.

'Yes, but—'

'Good.' He turned briefly to Maisie, who for once was speechless, her startlingly mauve eyes blinking helplessly and the plate of sandwiches she had brought in wobbling precariously in her limp hand. 'I'll see myself out,' he said with silky politeness. 'You take care of your…chick.'

And then he was gone, leaving the two girls staring at each other as the sound of his footsteps on the stairs outside faded into the street.

CHAPTER TEN

PARADISE. This was one place which was paradise on earth and she wished with all her heart she didn't have to leave it tomorrow.

Sephy stretched on the sun lounger and reached for her sunglasses before sitting up and looking out over the glittering blue water of Conrad's Olympic-size swimming pool.

She drew her knees up to her chest, wrapping her arms round them and feeling a dart of pleasure at the smooth, golden-brown intensity of her tan.

From the first day she had arrived in Northern Italy the weather had been wonderful, day after gloriously sunny day turning her golden brown and highlighting her hair with shades of chestnut and dark auburn, and now she was as brown as Daniella.

She had been surprised to find Conrad's niece waiting for her at the airport when she had emerged from a luxurious first-class plane ride; Madge had merely said she would be met by a member of Conrad's Italian family but that was all. However, it had emerged that Enrico's time at the London hotel was finished and Conrad was setting the couple up with their own restaurant in their hometown, much to the delight of Daniella, who had apparently been homesick for Italy.

And Sephy had soon been able to understand why. She hadn't realised that the country held such vast contrasts; golden, powdery beaches and azure seas, rolling hillsides and magnificent mountain ranges, enchanting valleys and rich meadows where swathed figures still herded animals with tiny bell necklaces, small picturesque villages which hadn't changed in hundreds of years and great modern bustling towns where it seemed as though every other car was a Ferrari—Daniella had shown her it all.

Conrad's villa, set high in wooded hills above the town where his relatives lived, was an old mansion he had had completely refurbished when he had decided to buy the dignified, crumbling, graceful old residence. And Sephy had fallen in love with it the moment she had seen it.

Mellow, honey-coloured old stone, arched leaded windows, exquisite wrought-iron balconies cascading with bougainvillaea of vibrant red and mauve, all topped by a rich terracotta-tiled roof—the house had it all. It was surrounded by beautifully landscaped gardens, sheltered by massive oak trees and cypress, and with the huge swimming pool and orchards at the back of the house the grounds were extensive.

An old Italian couple—distant relatives of Daniella's father—kept house for Conrad and resided in a large, spacious flat above the row of garages converted from the original stables, and a gardener and a cleaning lady who lived in the town visited on a daily basis.

Sephy had been amazed Conrad had never mentioned the villa in all the months she had known him, but when she had said as much to Daniella the Italian girl had shrugged extravagantly in true Latin style before saying, 'Conrad, he like to keep it separate, *si*? He very private man, very independent. This different.'

At Sephy's puzzled look, Daniella had continued, 'He never bring no one here from outside, from his other life. Not ever, *si*? This is where he is himself, I think.'

'He's brought me.'

'*Si.*' Daniella had looked at her oddly then, her nutbrown eyes slanting above finely moulded cheekbones. '*Si*, he bring you, Sephy.'

Sephy had wondered, at first, if Conrad would visit whilst she was staying, but as day had followed day and then week had followed week she'd realised he intended to keep to his word and remain in England. However, he'd made a point of phoning her every night at the same time without fail.

At first their phone conversations had been stilted and awkward, and had lasted no more than five minutes or so, but gradually they had lengthened into interesting, often laughter-filled discussions, and after two weeks it hadn't been unusual for the phone to be occupied for over an hour. And, perhaps predictably, Sephy had found she was measuring time from call to call and only really coming alive when she heard the deep, dark voice on the other end of the line.

Conrad had talked about all sorts of things he had never discussed before; his plans for the future regarding the Quentin empire, difficulties or triumphs he encountered day by day, even Angus's emergency trip to the vet, when the big cat had taken on a bunch of the local feline mafia and exited from the scrap minus part of his left ear.

'Of course he managed to bleed all over the car,' Conrad had said drily, 'and Madge was so upset I bought a bottle of brandy on the way home, not realising she'd never had spirits before. She was so out of it after two totties I had to sleep the night on her settee in case she fell down the stairs or something.'

The girls in the office at Quentin Dynamics would never have recognised the cold, unemotional, heartless tycoon and his dragon of a secretary, Sephy had thought with an inward chuckle. Which, for no reason at all that she could name, had suddenly turned into an overwhelming urge to have a good cry.

She had restrained herself until she was off the phone but then had bawled half the night. At three in the morning she had given herself a stiff talking-to, followed Madge's example of getting legless, and then slept like a top until two the next afternoon.

After that she had kept a firm hold on her emotions, both before, during and after the telephone calls, but it still hadn't stopped her *aching* to hear his voice.

'Which doesn't help anyone in the long run, old girl,' she told herself now, levering herself off the lounger and walking idly to the edge of the swimming pool. Tomorrow had to be cut-off point. Once she was back in England she had determined she'd move right away from London, probably up north, maybe even as far as Scotland. She could possibly think about moving abroad later too.

She had to make a new life for herself; she saw it now. Not back in her hometown—much as she loved her mother, that wouldn't work—but somewhere fresh and challenging. And far away from London.

She stood gazing down into the flickering water, immersed in sober thought. It was a baking hot, airless afternoon, and the sun was beating down fiercely on her skin now she had moved out of the shade the large parasol fixed over the sun lounger had provided, but still she didn't move.

Maisie had called him a rat, but she couldn't think of him like that. In his own way he had always been very honest with her. She wished she didn't love him. Her eyelids smarted and she told herself, Don't. Don't do this; it's pointless. Look forward. She wished she didn't keep dreaming about him, longing for the feel of his arms about her. She wished she knew for sure if she'd done the right thing in not taking what he could give for as long as he could give it so she'd got memories of waking up beside him, feeling him inside her, knowing the ecstasy of full intimacy.

'Sephy?'

She froze for a second before giving herself a little shake. She was imagining things now—all she needed. Nevertheless, something told her to turn round, and there he was. Not more than a few feet away.

She would have loved to be able to behave as he expected. Like a Caroline de Menthe would have behaved. But she couldn't. A glib, cool response was beyond her.

She stared at him, at the big, dark, *magnificent* sight of him, and she began to tremble. He looked calm and composed, impeccably dressed as always, in charcoal-grey trousers and a short-sleeved silk shirt in a lighter hue, and here she was in a minuscule denim bikini she had worn non-stop practically since arriving in Italy and which, she had noticed yesterday, was showing signs of wear in several strategic places.

'You look wonderful,' he said softly, taking another step towards her and then stopping as she instinctively jerked backwards, almost disappearing into the pool in the process.

'Conrad.' It was a faint murmur but all she could manage through the wild beating of her heart which was sending the blood tumbling through every nerve and sinew.

Pull yourself together. Funnily enough it was Maisie's voice she heard through the feverish rush of adrenalin and it worked to some extent, enabling her to take a long deep breath and say fairly coherently, 'I didn't know you were coming. No one said.'

'I told them not to.'

'Oh.' That look on his face was a lie; it wasn't real. She was imprinting what she wanted to be there, she told herself desperately. She hadn't learnt anything over the last weeks.

'Don't you want to know why?' he asked softly.

'I...I'm sure you must have had your reasons.'

'Oh, yes, I did.' He was watching her as though he couldn't take his eyes off her, and now, when he moved towards her, Sephy held still. 'I wanted to see if you still looked at me the way you did for an instant that afternoon in England when you told me you loved me,' he said quietly. 'You were open then, without your guard up. Nothing to lose, I suppose. It was the cards laid bare and I failed you. I failed you completely.'

Her heart was pounding against her ribcage so hard it was actually hurting, but she still managed to say, 'That's…that's gone, in the past. I…I'll be all right.'

'I love you, Sephy.'

She knew she couldn't have heard right.

'I love you so much it's a physical ache, all the time, no matter what I do. I've loved you from the first day you worked for me, or the first evening, to be precise, and I've fought it just as long. You were so brave that day, telling me how you felt and to hell with the consequences, and I smacked it all back in your face. Like I did when you said you loved me.'

The raw pain in his voice was real, the look in his face was real, but she couldn't believe what he was saying.

'You…you said—' She couldn't go on, and now he reached out and tenderly cupped her face in his strong hands.

'I know what I said. The big fellow—doesn't need anyone and doesn't care about anything. But I do need you and I care about you. You have to believe me.'

'No.' She couldn't. She *couldn't* dare to trust he meant it. 'You haven't been here, not in four weeks,' she said brokenly.

'And it's torn me apart to keep away.' He stroked his hand over the silky smooth skin of her cheek and she had to force herself not to turn her face into the caress. 'Why do you think I called you every night? I was desperate to hear your voice, to have something of you, but you were so ill in England, so fragile, and I owed you the chance to think clearly. If I'd asked you to marry me then you'd have always wondered if I meant it or if you were manoeuvred.'

What was he talking about, manoeuvred? she asked herself silently. If she thought he really meant this she would have swum back to England to see him.

'I had to give you the chance to get well and then decide, when your mind was clear and you were physically strong,' he said quietly. 'I owed you that if nothing else.'

Had he said *marry* him a few words back, or was she taking a trip on Maisie's planet Zargos again?

She strove for calm and said, tremblingly, 'You told me you don't believe in love and marriage and happy families. You said you couldn't change.'

'I also said that when you came to me it would be knowing exactly what you were doing and because you'd decided it was what you wanted,' he said softly, 'and I think the phrase is "hoisted with my own petard". I want you, Sephy, I want you so much physically it's driven me half mad. But then you know that.'

Did she? She hadn't known she had!

'I want the whole caboodle, Sephy—children and dogs and cats and whatever. I came here today to tell you that I love you, that I've loved and wanted you always. The thought of this other guy, this David, and not knowing where he'd fitted in your life was making me want to do murder. That's why I had to ask you that day, to find out what had happened and if you still loved him.'

'Love him? I didn't even know him,' she said shakily. She could feel the tears trickling down her face, and she hated that she was crying but she couldn't do a thing about it.

'Can you forgive me?' He bent and kissed the tears on her cheeks and she shuddered violently. 'Have I ruined everything? I know you love me, I saw it in your eyes when you turned round and saw me, but can you forgive me for what I've done to you?'

She was trembling so much he drew her close against the hard wall of his chest, and as she felt the accelerated beat of his heart she murmured helplessly, 'I'm frightened.'

'So am I.' He understood instantly and his voice was soft on the sun-warmed silk of her hair. 'There are parts of this love thing that aren't all they're cracked up to be; putting the whole of your life in someone else's hands, giving them the power to make or destroy you, thinking what it would be like if you had to live in a world without them—'

'Don't.' She moved back enough to gaze up into his face. 'Don't say that.'

It was an answer in itself, but still he said, 'Will you marry me, Sephy? Will you be my wife and let me love you and adore you and worship you all my life? Will you bear my children and be with me when their children are born? Will you sleep with me every night and wake with me every morning? Will you be my breath, my reason for living, the beat of my heart?'

'Oh, my love.' It was what she had always wanted to say but never had the right to express, and now she fell against him as he rained kisses on her face and throat in an agony of love and need. They clung together as though their bodies were already merging.

'I love you. You've got no idea how much I love you,' he murmured at long last, when she was flushed and bright-eyed, her lips swollen and her body straining into his. And then he reached in his pocket and brought out a little red velvet box, opening it to reveal an exquisite diamond engagement ring. 'For ever, Sephy.'

They were married in Sephy's hometown, in the little parish church in the village, and it seemed as though the world and his wife had turned out to see the local girl who had snared one of the biggest catches in the country.

The day was bright, and unseasonably warm for early October, and Sephy looked radiantly lovely in a long ivory gown trimmed with tiny gold daisies, her headdress and bouquet made up of fragile white baby's breath and a profusion of tiny gold daisies and fragile little gold and ivory orchids.

Maisie, as Sephy's bridesmaid, looked amazingly solemn and sedate for once, in her long gold dress and carrying a smaller version of Sephy's bouquet. She had even dyed her hair all one colour: a rather alarming shade of red, which should have clashed horribly with the dress but—Maisie being Maisie—actually looked rather good. But then with Sephy's mother giving the bride away and little Madge Watkins as Conrad's best man the wedding was never going to be a traditional one anyway. Just one filled with lots of love.

The winding path from the church door was thronged with well-wishers who hadn't been able to fit into the small thirteenth-century church as Sephy and Conrad emerged to the peal of church bells.

They stood for a moment, Conrad gazing down at his bride as Sephy looked adoringly up at her handsome groom, and no one seeing them could have doubted that this marriage was anything but a love match. 'Have I told you in the last minute that I love you, Mrs Quentin?' Conrad whispered in her ear as they began to walk down the confetti-strewn path.

'Yes, but don't let that stop you,' Sephy whispered back as the ribbon of smiling faces on either side of the path called out congratulations and good wishes. They had just reached the gnarled wooden gate at the end of the path when a red-faced, somewhat bloated man stepped straight out in front of them for a moment.

'Remember me, Sephy?'

It was said with confidence, but as Sephy glanced up for a moment it was clear she had no idea who he was, and then Conrad had whisked her away to the gleaming white Rolls-Royce he had hired to take them to the most exclusive hotel in the district where he had arranged a reception for family and friends and half the village.

David Bainbridge's eyes followed the car as it left the village green and his eyes, already bloodshot with the alcohol he'd consumed in large quantities daily since his father had lost all the family wealth on the Stock Exchange, were puzzled. That wasn't the girl he remembered; this one was a beauty. And she'd ignored him! Damn it, she hadn't even recognised him. And everyone had seen it.

But Sephy wasn't thinking about David Bainbridge, or anyone else but Conrad, as the rest of the day unfolded hour by entrancing hour. After a wonderful meal they danced the evening away, and Conrad was mean enough not to share her with anyone. Which suited the new Mrs Quentin just fine.

And then the evening drew to a close, all the guests were gone, and it was just the two of them alone in the magnificent bridal suite the hotel boasted.

They undressed each other slowly, and Sephy was surprised to find she felt no shyness as she stood naked before him. Perhaps the wonder and love in his eyes had something to do with it.

His passion was restrained at first, sensuous and coaxing as he held her close to him and stroked and petted her, his lips covering her face in tiny burning kisses before moving to her throat and then her breasts, teasing their peaks into taut hardness with his mouth and tongue.

When he finally lifted her into his arms and carried her over to the huge four-poster bed she was trembling and moist, her hands roaming over the hard-muscled wall of his chest as he leant above her for a moment, his blue eyes open and loving as he allowed her to look into his soul. 'I love you, my sweet wife,' he whispered softly. 'More than you could ever know.'

'Oh, Conrad...' She gripped his shoulders, pulling him down on her as she took his mouth with touchingly inexpert hunger.

'Shush, my darling, slowly, slowly,' he murmured with a faint touch of laughter in his voice. 'This has to be right for you.'

And then he took her into a time of pure enchantment, his lips warm as they kissed every inch of her body and his tongue entering all the secret places until she was crying out with abandoned pleasure, her body surging against his hands and mouth as she arched and pleaded for the release only he could give.

But still his control held, even though his body was betraying the fact that his desire was white-hot, as he continued to bring her to the very brink of fulfilment time and time again, only to draw back at the crucial moment and then begin the passionate ritual again.

When he finally possessed her he had brought her to fever-pitch, and the feel of him inside her, the knowledge that she was joined body and body to the man she loved with all her heart, made the exquisite physical pleasure unbearable.

As she felt his body convulsing with hers in perfect unity Sephy found herself transported to the outer spaces of time, a place where there was no tomorrow and no past, just a consuming present that utterly possessed her.

It was much later when she stirred in his arms, turning her head to open heavy-lidded eyes as she looked at him. And the devastating blue eyes were waiting for her, his voice slightly uneven as he said, 'Thank you, my darling. Thank you for giving yourself to me so completely.'

'I never guessed it was so...' She could find no words to describe the ecstasy. 'Is it always like that?' she asked dazedly.

'Never before. Not for me,' he whispered against the silky skin of her cheek before taking her mouth in a kiss that was tender beyond description. 'But I promise you, my darling, it will be like that for both of us from this night on.'

And Conrad Quentin had never been a man to break a promise.

Alison Roberts was born in New Zealand, and says, 'I lived in London and Washington D.C. as a child and began my working career as a primary-school teacher. A lifelong interest in medicine was fostered by my doctor and nurse parents, flatting with doctors and physiotherapists on leaving home and marriage to a house surgeon who is now a consultant cardiologist. I have also worked as a cardiology technician and research assistant. My husband's medical career took us to Glasgow for two years, which was an ideal place and time to start my writing career. I now live in Christchurch, New Zealand with my husband, daughter and various pets.'

A CHANGE OF HEART

by

Alison Roberts

CHAPTER ONE

HEARTSTOPPING!

David James knew his heart had stopped because he was a doctor and knew about such things. He also felt the distinct thump a second later which indicated that the organ in question had decided to make up for its momentary lapse. The surprising force of the thump still failed to break the mesmerising effect of the moment.

David James was a firm believer in lust at first sight but this was definitely one for the books! She had to be the most stunning woman he'd ever seen and so far he was only getting a profile. Tall, slim, shoulder-length wavy, dark blonde hair, expertly streaked with threads of silvery gold. He couldn't see her eyes but they would have to be blue… David finally became aware that the voice beside him had continued unabated. With an effort he managed to change the static-like buzz back into words.

'So we had a bit of a reshuffle. This office seemed the perfect choice, being at the surgical end of the cardiology suite.'

'I hope I haven't put anyone out.' The husky drawl was a bit of a giveaway but had certainly not been intentional. Was it wishful thinking or did his voice have the effect of causing a momentary freezing of her decisive movements? The box was almost overflowing in any case.

'Oh, no. Lisa didn't mind a bit.'

Lisa. Perfect! It went with that elegantly tailored

5

clothing. That fitting black skirt with the provocative
little slit that went from the above-knee hem to halfway
up her thigh. David rearranged his face into what he
hoped was his most charming expression as the head of
Christchurch Hospital's cardiothoracic surgical team
launched into a formal introduction.

'Lisa, this is our new consultant surgeon, David
James.' Alan Bennett's smile reminded David of a
proud parent. 'David, I'd like you to meet Lisa
Kennedy, senior cardiology registrar. You two will
probably be seeing quite a lot of each other.'

Play nicely, children, his tone suggested. Not a problem, David's expression assured his senior colleague as
the vision turned her head towards them for the first
time. Her eyes weren't blue, they were brown. Dark
brown. Even better!

'I'll look forward to it,' David said aloud. He felt his
smile widen further than he'd intended. It felt disturbingly close to a leer. Hastily he cleared his throat. 'I
seem to have been a disruptive influence, even before
walking in the door. I do apologise, Lisa. I had no idea
I'd be kicking anyone out of their office.'

'As Alan said, it was the obvious choice. Like everything else in the public health system, floor space is at
a premium. And, as Alan also said, I don't mind a bit.'

The tone was sweet. It just didn't match the flash of
annoyance in those velvety brown eyes or the defensive
tilt of her chin. Lisa Kennedy minded all right. Fair
enough, too. It was a very nice office. The window had
a view out to the Avon River with the glorious backdrop
of the botanical gardens. Where was she going now?
Probably some windowless cubbyhole down behind the
exercise testing laboratory. Never mind, he'd make it

up to her. His smile was understanding. Sympathetic—
but helpful.

'Let me give you a hand with that.'

'No, thanks, I can manage.' Lisa hurriedly added a
couple of items to the top of the carton and folded her
arms around its edges. David's glance took in the elegantly tapered fingers of her left hand. Not a ring in
sight! He was straightening, ready to prove his helpful
intentions by insisting on carrying the box, when his
companion's beeper sounded.

'I'll have to go and scrub,' Alan Bennett informed
them. 'I'll leave you to get settled in, David, and we'll
continue our tour later. You'll find quite a few of the
old crowd still around so you should feel at home pretty
quickly.'

'I do already.' David smiled. 'It's good to be back.'

Alan nodded and returned the smile as he turned
away. 'You were a very popular choice for the consultancy. I wonder if so many people would welcome me
back if I disappeared for a few years.'

David laughed easily but he had been surprised himself by the warmth of the welcome he'd received up
until now. Up until he'd stepped into this office, in fact.
Decisively, he moved forward.

'Do let me take that, Lisa. It looks heavy.'

'I *said* I can manage.' Lisa took a sideways step to
evade his touch on the box. The slippery journal covers
on the top layer refused to support the final item added
and it slid with remarkable speed to land on the floor
with a thud. A large, plastic, anatomical model of a
heart, it now lay in several pieces.

David swore softly but then felt the corners of his
mouth lift and couldn't suppress the smile.

'I seem to have broken your heart, Lisa.'

She *could* smile. Even the fleeting glimpse of the accomplishment was enough to make something inside David tighten with a very pleasurable sensation.

'Par for the course for you, from what I've heard, Mr James. Still, I imagine it takes first prize for speed.'

What did she mean? The tone did not suggest an attack but there was an edge to it that made David's hackles rise defensively.

'I'm sure anything you've heard is grossly exaggerated, Lisa. Pure fiction. Such rumours generally are.' He stooped to pick up the pieces of the model. 'Let me see if I can repair the damage. I'm a doctor, I know about things like this.' His smile was back in place as he straightened. He would give her the benefit of the doubt and try again.

'I wouldn't worry about it.' Her tone was offhand. 'I can assure you my heart's quite indestructible.'

This time the message was clear. David's smile finally wilted under what could only be described as a chilly stare.

'I have a ward round I should have started ten minutes ago,' she informed him crisply. 'Just put anything else in that empty box and I'll come back for it later.'

David found himself staring at the chunks of moulded plastic in his hands after Lisa swept past with her carton. She was right, of course. The solid model clipped together with a series of small brass hooks and eyes. Even its stand was unscathed. Had she intended the innuendo that the genuine article was equally impervious to damage? Quite possibly, David conceded. Lisa Kennedy obviously liked to project an image that advertised strength and competence. If the packaging hadn't been quite so attractive she might even come across as intimidating. Certainly not the type of woman David James gravitated towards.

He had to admit that her indifference to their introduction rankled. Rejection was not an experience David was accustomed to, especially from women. Taking over her office might not have been the best start but was an obstacle that could easily be overcome. Even rumours concerning any past relationships—and he had to admit there *had* been a few—could be laid to rest. Unfortunately, it was more likely that Lisa Kennedy was firmly attached elsewhere even if she wasn't married and would therefore be immune to any amount of charm he could turn on. That was a far more likely explanation. Who could look like that and not have been snapped up long ago?

With a resigned sigh, David deposited his briefcase onto the desk top and flipped open the catches. Never mind, it was still great to be back. As his indrawn breath caught the lingering trace of perfume in the office David found himself smiling. She might come across as being tough but there had to be a sensual side to a woman who wore Chanel to work. The decisive head shake as he unpacked and connected his laptop computer should have been enough to clear the distracting images of the woman from his mind, but David James was vaguely delighted to find that it failed so noticeably.

He was actually grinning as he sent himself an e-mail to test his new connection. Unexpectedly, it reminded him of his fourth-form science class when that new student teacher had taken over. Miss Drummond. Blonde hair down to her waist and legs up to her armpits. Memories of words in the science textbook blurring into total irrelevance and an entire classroom of adolescent boys squirming uncomfortably at their desks widened

David's grin even further. Even he had been in danger of dropping his position at the top of the class until he'd realised that the most effective way to get Miss Drummond's attention was to excel.

It had been a valuable lesson that had served David well over the years but until now had been simply a distant memory. Had Lisa Kennedy had that much effect on his circulating levels of testosterone? Yes. He had to admit that it seemed the only explanation for the uncharacteristic sprint down memory lane.

With a determined effort David turned his thoughts back to his surroundings and left the office. He had worked too hard to get here to have his concentration undermined the instant he walked through the door. He poked his head through an adjacent doorway.

'Hello again, Sue.'

His secretary looked up from her typing. Her smile was welcoming. Very welcoming. 'Is there something I can do for you, Mr James?'

'You can call me David, for a start.' He watched the faint flush of colour stain the girl's neck as she nodded. 'I'm just off to chase up a white coat and collect my pager. Perhaps you could give me a beep in half an hour so I can test it.'

'I'll get them for you if you like,' Sue offered eagerly.

'No. Thanks anyway, Sue, but I'm rather looking forward to exploring my old stamping ground. I'll expect a beep from you, though.'

The call came precisely thirty minutes later and David smiled as he put down the phone. A reliable and helpful secretary was a definite bonus. Like a lot of the nursing staff, Sue had probably still been at high school the last time David had worked here.

The familiar faces were all amongst the senior staff and David was thoroughly enjoying their surprised and delighted reactions as he came across them. Like Jane Maddon, who had had changed her surname but looked just the same and who was now the nurse manager of the twin cardiology wards that flanked the intensive coronary care unit.

'I knew you'd come back eventually,' she informed David, having given him a hug. 'You were so determined.'

'I love Christchurch.' David nodded. 'And a few years out of the country makes you appreciate what we've got even more.'

'I kept up with the occasional bit of news. Last I heard you were in Washington, D.C.'

'That was over two years ago. I had eighteen months in Europe after that and then had some time with a transplant unit in London. I think that experience might have been what swung the decision for this consultancy in my favour.'

'There were a lot of applicants,' Jane confirmed. 'Some were a lot older than you, too. Well done, David.'

'Thanks.' David smiled modestly.

'The parties were never as good after you left,' Jane added with a wistful grin. Then she frowned. 'You haven't gone and got married or anything, have you?'

'No chance. I was hoping you'd wait for me.'

'Oh, sure!' Jane's expression was knowing. 'I'm delighted to say you're too late.' Then she laughed. 'I'd forgotten just how cute you were, mind you. All those curls and those wonderful dark blue eyes. They're going to be queuing up around here. You haven't changed a bit, have you, David?'

'I'm older and wiser.' David's smile was relaxed but he felt disturbed. Just how much of a reputation *had* he left behind? OK, so he'd played hard. But not that often and only as a counterbalance to the effort he put into his work. At thirty-three, David knew he was exceptionally young to have gained this surgical consultancy. He also knew that he deserved it, and he was looking forward to proving his abilities and commitment, as well as undoing this idea that he was a good-time Charlie, which might be an obstacle to professional acceptance.

'I'm just on my way to check out the surgical ward,' he told Jane. 'I don't start officially until tomorrow.'

'You should be impressed. It's a great set-up.' Jane Maddon switched from old friend to professional colleague without blinking. 'Post-Cardiac Surgery Intensive Care is attached to the main ICU and the ward is right beside that. Come and have a look at CCU on your way. We've just upgraded the whole monitoring system. State-of-the-art technology.'

Jane was right. The technology was impressive and David was particularly interested by the screens which gave closed-circuit-television coverage of the most acutely ill patients. The group of staff standing by the bedside of number eight was headed by an unmistakable figure. He couldn't hear what Lisa Kennedy was saying but the examination seemed to be complete. The staff were moving away, Lisa pausing to have a final word with the patient, who was still smiling as he watched his doctor leave. David's glance flicked down to the other monitors attached to bed eight.

'You've certainly got all the bases covered.' He indicated a small button. 'I suppose this gives a printout of the ECG?'

Jane nodded. 'It does it automatically when it recognises an arrhythmia.'

'His blood pressure's low.' David was staring at the screen. His eyes narrowed slightly. 'In fact, it's still dropping.'

'Is it?'

David's eyes were back on the television screen. The curtains had been pulled open again around bed eight and he could see Lisa's back as she stood near bed seven. He heard Jane's muttered curse as she moved quickly away from the control desk and he caught the change in the ECG pattern out of the corner of his eye, but it was Lisa Kennedy he was watching. How had she known to turn back to her previous patient at precisely that point? A lightning glance at the monitor confirmed that the rhythm had slipped into the uncontrolled squiggles of ventricular fibrillation that heralded a cardiac arrest and the printout of the thin rhythm strip had begun, but it was several seconds before the alarm began to sound.

By that time Lisa had pushed the cardiac-arrest button on the wall to summon the crash team, had knocked the bed end into a horizontal position and removed the patient's pillows, pushing his bedside table out of the way as another doctor replaced it with the unit's crash trolley. Jane Maddon hurriedly pulled the curtains to screen the emergency from the horrified gaze of other patients but David had a bird's-eye view thanks to the television screen.

The staff worked as a close team. David, frustrated at his own inaction, watched as conduction pads were slapped on, positioned over the apex and bottom of the patient's heart, his bedding and clothing hastily thrown aside. It was Lisa who held the defibrillator paddles and he could almost hear her command to stand clear as other staff stepped back. He cringed inwardly as the patient jerked convulsively and then his gaze moved away from the screen as the crash team arrived at a run.

Despite the seniority of the extra staff, Lisa continued to direct the resuscitation and David's eyes were riveted to the screen as he watched the CPR, intubation and further defibrillation of the patient. He found he had been holding his breath, which he released in a sigh as the spikes of a normal sinus rhythm began to drift across the screen in front of him.

'Too slow,' he muttered, surprised by the murmur of agreement behind his shoulder. He had been totally unaware that other staff members had joined him to observe the crisis. Nobody had switched off the automatic recording of the abnormal rhythms and the strip of ECG paper was now pooling around his ankles. They all watched as Lisa injected the drugs she had ordered, presumably including atropine, and there was a collective sigh of relief within the next minutes as the observers saw the evidence of the patient regaining consciousness.

'Score one for our side, I think,' a nurse pronounced as she moved away.

Score another one for Lisa Kennedy, David amended silently. He was still watching as the crash team left and Lisa and the other unit staff tidied up. He could hear the laughter and joking and recognised the sense of euphoria he knew existed between staff in the aftermath of a desperate situation. He would very much have liked to have been included but could only smile his congratulations as Lisa and her companion passed the desk on their way out.

'Well done, Lisa,' he said warmly. 'I'm most impressed.'

'Thanks.' The smile didn't quite reach those brown eyes. 'But you must be easily impressed. It's just part of the job around here.'

'I'm sure Mr Steel wouldn't agree.' David enjoyed the surprised flicker in her expression at his knowledge of the patient's name. Then he saw her glance towards the monitors and the television screen. Her expression changed as she realised how closely David had been able to observe the incident. Fascinated by her changing expression, David wondered if Lisa Kennedy had any awareness of how her face revealed her thoughts. Her body language was expressive too. Like the infinitesimal shrug that said it was of no importance that he'd been watching her. He could almost see the effort with which she made her gaze carefully neutral when she transferred it back in his direction.

'I don't think you've met our junior registrar, Mr James. This is Sean Findlay.'

'Call me David.' He held out his hand to the registrar. 'I'm not big on formality.' His gaze included Lisa but it only Sean who nodded and returned the smile. He sighed inwardly. Was establishing a friendly relationship with Lisa Kennedy always such an uphill battle or was it something about him?

Perhaps he shouldn't have accepted Jane's offer of a tour around the cardiology wards but it hadn't occurred to David that it might coincide with Dr Kennedy's round. Neither had he had any intention of staring at the woman every time she came into view. It had to be coincidence that she managed to catch his eye every time she glanced in his direction. Or could it be that she felt the same attraction and found, like him, that she seemed to have lost automatic control over her visual targets? If so, she was very good at covering it up. Her expression became increasingly exasperated and David felt it was not before time that he headed off to explore the surgical set-up.

The unfortunate timing of his exit from the ward was more than coincidence. It was sheer bad luck. The last thing he wanted was to irritate her further by disrupting her day yet again. But what could he have done? The woman coming down the corridor was the size of an elephant. The bars on her walking frame looked seriously strained and David instinctively stepped aside to remove himself from the path of what appeared to be a human steamroller. The momentum was deceptive, however, and David found himself blocking the purposeful approach of Lisa Kennedy.

'Excuse me.'

There was nowhere to go. Jane was behind him. Lisa in front. The mountain of flesh on his left had rolled to a standstill and was breathing with alarming difficulty.

'Use your puffer, Mrs Judd,' Lisa ordered calmly. 'Have you got it with you?'

The incongruously small head nodded slowly. Sausage-like fingers inched along the bar towards a fold in a baby pink candlewick dressing-gown that looked like a bedspread. David's lips twitched. Hell, it probably needed to be a bedspread. He wanted to catch Lisa's eye to see if she was sharing any amusement in the situation but Lisa was looking over his shoulder at Jane.

'Do you have any idea where Mr Benson is?'

'Having an echo, I think.'

Mrs Judd was having difficulty locating her pocket. She tilted towards David who stepped forward involuntarily. Lisa was forced to step backwards. She looked annoyed.

'And Mrs Chisholm?'

'She was on the list for a nuclear scan but she might still be in the shower.'

Mrs Judd had found her inhaler. It seemed to be an effort for her to raise it to her lips. David heard her gasp and had a horrifying vision of trying to resuscitate Mrs Judd here in the corridor. He drew in a deep breath and was again aware of the evocative scent of Chanel. But Lisa Kennedy was looking anything but sensuous.

'It would be nice—just occasionally—if I could find my patients in their beds when I wanted to do a ward round.'

Jane laughed. 'I'll see what I can do, Lisa.'

Mrs Judd was moving again and David found himself deserted. He watched as Lisa disappeared into the ward office with Jane, before moving off himself with a small shrug. Why did he have the feeling that he was a major contributor in what was shaping up to be a bad day for Lisa Kennedy? And why did his thoughts keep returning to the senior registrar even hours later when he had finished his tour of the respiratory wards and lunched with their senior staff.

It had to be the novelty of an attractive woman apparently disliking him on sight that had sparked this preoccupation. It wouldn't take long to readjust to a professional standpoint and then they'd probably get on just fine. She was obviously good at what she did and she would soon recognise that he was also more than competent. He would gain her respect at least. And after that? a small voice whispered. David ignored the question. After that, who knew what might happen? Things had a habit of sorting themselves out. It was really only a matter of time.

And time could often pass more quickly with a little

push. David's attention was caught by the display outside the hospital's gift shop but he hadn't expected to find Lisa in residence when he managed to track down her new office. He had intended to simply leave the single red rose along with the other items in the small box he carried. With dismay he now realised that the gesture might not have been such an inspiration after all.

'I felt bad about the office,' he explained. The rose now seemed totally inappropriate but he handed it over anyway. Her expression was unreadable but maybe there was just a trace of amusement there.

'Thanks.' She tilted the rose towards the box he carried. 'I see you've fixed my heart as well.'

'My pleasure. It's what I was trained for after all.'

The reward of a smile was encouraging but David was uncomfortably aware of the reverberation of a treadmill gaining speed next door. When Sean Findlay entered the office it also felt distinctly crowded. The young registrar dumped a pile of case notes onto the second desk and vanished with a cheerful grin. The sound of the treadmill increased. David glanced out of the small window and found he could see directly into a side room of one of the cardiology wards. Mrs Judd was standing at the window. Divested of her candlewick bedspread, she was now wearing an unfortunately diaphanous nightgown. Lisa had followed her gaze.

'Just as well you weren't given this office,' she commented lightly. 'It wouldn't do to provide a surgeon with such blatant distractions.'

Something about her inflection made David's gaze transfer swiftly. 'You've got something against surgeons?'

'Nothing personal.' Lisa's smile looked mechanical.

'I'm sure you get a lot of job satisfaction.' She toyed with the rose she was still holding.

David leaned his back against the windowframe. So this was what the attitude was all about. He smiled encouragingly. 'What's so wrong with being a surgeon?'

'Oh, there's nothing *wrong*. Quite the opposite.' Lisa's eyebrows moved up expressively. 'A surgeon is the best thing to be. Ask any patient. Wait for that awed gaze when they know they're going to be referred. They're going to see the real thing.' Her chuckle was genuine enough. 'God holding a knife. A chance of a *real* cure.'

David held onto his smile with increasing difficulty. 'OK, so it's a bit more glamourous. That's not my fault.'

'More glamourous, more important, more skilled and more highly paid. A hell of a lot more highly paid.'

'Ah! Now we get down to it.' David's smile was forgotten. 'You're jealous!' David felt a flash of annoyance at her belligerent attitude and his control slipped significantly. 'So what stopped you becoming a surgeon, then? Course too tough?'

'Typical!' It was a wonder the rose didn't wilt under the heat suddenly generated around it. 'You're not good enough to be a cardiac surgeon so you take the easy route and become a cardiologist. Exactly the attitude from most surgeons and more than most of the general public. What you—and they—fail to appreciate is that you couldn't function without us.'

'Really?' David's anger had been overridden by a very different emotion. He had never been tempted to try the line that a woman looked beautiful when she was angry but, then, he wasn't in the habit of making women angry. Passionately angry, judging by the play of expression before him now. The rose was tossed aside.

'*Really.*' It was a snap like a steel trap. 'Who diagnoses these patients? Keeps them alive and makes the decision about whether surgery is even necessary?'

David couldn't take his eyes off her. Her guard had really slipped now. He had never seen a face quite so alive. 'I think we might have a little input into that one,' he suggested evenly. Lisa ignored him.

'Who continues the care after the surgery? They're *our* patients from go to whoa. Sure, we might need the technical assistance with a bit of replumbing in the interim but that's as far as it goes. We create your workload and we pick up the pieces afterwards. And *we* carry the can for any less than successful interventions. Envious! Listen, I know who the *real* doctors are.'

The end of the tirade coincided with the abrupt termination of the neighbouring exercise test. The silence was startling. David was still staring at Lisa. He had been watching her mouth with fascination, the soft, mobile lips now set into an uncompromising line. He met her eyes, disappointed to find that the fire had been extinguished. David raised an eyebrow eloquently but said nothing. The blush he saw appearing was unexpected.

'Sorry.' She looked away and her voice dropped to a mutter. 'I shouldn't take it out on you.'

'Take what out?' David's curiosity was aroused. Perhaps there was more going on than an irrational professional intolerance.

'It doesn't matter.'

'It seems to matter quite a lot.' David tilted his head thoughtfully. 'If I'm stepping into some political minefield, I'd prefer to get some idea of whose toes I should avoid treading on. Apart from those I've irreparably damaged already.'

'Oh ? Like whose?'

'Yours. You weren't exactly happy at being evicted from your office—at least not by a *surgeon*.'

'I don't give a damn about the office. I knew it was only a temporary luxury. It wasn't that I was...' She shook her head and then pushed a stray curl back from her face. 'Never mind. Don't concern yourself about *my* toes, David. They're indestructible.' The smile was apologetic, embarrassed even, and David was happy to return it despite the attack to which his specialty had been subjected.

'Like your heart, yes?'

'You got it.' Lisa nodded, reaching for the phone as her beeper sounded. The silence was brief. 'What's the blood pressure now? OK, stop the TPA infusion. I'm on my way.'

She was gone. David moved slowly as he followed her example. Without her physical presence he found himself thinking more about exactly what she'd said. So, he was a glorified plumber, was he? Nothing personal, though. Strangely enough, the attack hadn't felt personal at the time, but David found a new wariness nibble at the edge of his confidence. If that was the general attitude of the whole cardiology department then the obstacle to gaining respect might be a much bigger hurdle than simply exorcising any rumours about his past.

Thank goodness for a friendly face. It was late that afternoon that David encountered a welcome he'd been waiting for. It came at the end of what now seemed like a very long day.

'Mike! Where the hell have you been hiding?'

'Cath lab all morning. Then we had an emergency angioplasty this afternoon. Some of us have to earn a living, mate.'

David shook his head, confident that Lisa Kennedy's opinion of surgeons was not being reinforced from this quarter. 'It's good to see you, mate. You've been the world's worst correspondent.'

Michael Foster grasped the outstretched hand and then slapped David on the shoulder. 'Look who's talking! We must have about five years to catch up on. God, it's good to see you, Dave.'

'Likewise. Got time for a coffee?'

'I'll make time. What's the point in being a consultant if you can't manage that?'

'I thought you'd be head of the cardiology department by now.'

'Give me time. I've had a rough couple of years.'

'Oh?' David's face was concerned as he followed his friend into the small staffroom. 'What's happened, Mike?'

'Anne and I split up six months ago. Things were pretty difficult for a long time before that.' Mike spooned coffee into the mugs but glanced up to catch David's expression. He laughed ruefully. 'You were right all along, mate. Marriage is the quickest way to ruin a good relationship.' He handed David a steaming mug. 'I should have listened to that lecture you gave me. I just wish you hadn't waited until my stag night.'

David smiled but was disturbed by the shadows in Mike's eyes. He tried to lighten the atmosphere. 'You should have listened,' he said sternly. 'Like I always said, "Why buy a book when you've got a whole library to choose from?"'

The incredulous snort from behind David made his head turn sharply. In his concern for Mike he had managed to walk right past the figure curled into the armchair beside the door. Mike followed his glance.

'Have you met my registrar, Dave? This is Lisa Kennedy.'

'We've met.' David winked at Lisa. 'In fact, I've already broken her heart.'

Mike laughed. 'That was quick even for you, mate. But I don't believe a word of it. Lisa's the one that leaves the trail of broken hearts around here. The job description for that vacancy is a bit hard to measure up to, isn't it, Lisa?'

'Oh, *please*!' Lisa uncurled her long legs from the depths of the armchair and reached for her shoes. 'I'm sure David James isn't remotely interested in my love life, Mike.'

'Oh, I wouldn't say that,' David murmured. He watched appreciatively as Lisa eased on her narrow, heeled black shoes. Very elegant footwear, he concluded. And a perfect match for the rest of her outfit.

'Well, I'm not remotely interested in sharing it.' Lisa stood up gracefully. With her heeled shoes she was only an inch or two shorter than David's height of six feet.

Mike laughed. 'That's the problem, isn't it? You'd better watch out, though. You'll probably be well up on David's required reading list.'

Lisa deposited her mug into the sink, turned and met David's eyes with a direct stare.

'My collection doesn't include paperbacks, sorry. Or over-popular fiction. I prefer something with a bit more quality…and durability.'

Mike's exaggerated indrawn breath feigned fear at Lisa's attack beautifully. Much to David's relief, it was enough to break the hold that Lisa's eye contact was having. Her short chuckle was dismissive. 'See you later, Mike. Some of us have work to do.'

David wasn't included in the farewell. Something flicked off at the dismissal and David was acutely aware of an emotional U-turn. OK, he'd been attracted but now he'd come to his senses. He'd been wrong in his assumption that the woman was attached and now he could see why. With blinding clarity. She was rude, snooty and totally unapproachable. And as for her attitude towards surgeons! Well, David James knew where he wasn't welcome and he certainly wasn't going to waste any more time trying. Lisa Kennedy wasn't going to be on any list as far as he was concerned.

Mike hadn't failed to notice the line of David's intense stare.

'Gorgeous, isn't she?'

'Mmm.' David's tone was carefully noncommittal. 'Shame about the personality.'

CHAPTER TWO

PERHAPS it wasn't so great to be back after all.

Feeling out of sorts was such an infrequent experience that David was seriously disturbed. Lack of sleep hadn't helped. Had it been a medical emergency that had kept him awake most of the night he wouldn't have thought twice about it. In fact, the adrenaline would still be running and he'd be in top form for at least another twelve hours. It was his accommodation that was problematic. The temporary arrangement for the room in the staff quarters had seemed perfect, but the walls were thin and the young medic next door had clearly scored in a big way with a woman who seemed to find the whole business excruciatingly funny. A pneumatic drill would have been much less disruptive than her giggles. Even when he'd finally managed to fall asleep the experience had been less than restful.

'It was a nightmare,' he related solemnly to Mike Foster. 'Crushing chest pain, electrodes plastered all over me and Lisa Kennedy standing at the end of the bed... Smiling.' He punctuated his tale with a woeful groan.

Mike grinned. 'Lisa's OK. Don't judge her on the basis of one bad day.' He pointed to a fire-stop door coming up on their right. 'Let's take a short cut.' Mike led the way up the stairs. 'If anybody's kept me sane over the last year it's been Lisa.' He shot his companion a quizzical glance. 'In fact, she's a lot like you.'

'What a ghastly thought!'

'She works bloody hard, plays just as hard, great sense of humour...' Mike was sounding breathless. 'And a body to die for.'

'I plan to keep living,' David muttered.

'You'd be perfect for each other.'

'I doubt it. She thinks I'm a glorified plumber. A knife-wielding technician with a God complex. Surgeons suck.'

'Ah! Well, there's a bit of a history there.'

'Oh, yeah?' Despite himself David felt curious. By tacit agreement the two men paused at the top of the stairs, screened from the corridor by another set of fire-stop doors. 'Perhaps you'd better fill me in.'

'Have you met Lewis Tanner yet?'

David shook his head. The hospital's third cardiothoracic surgeon had not put in an appearance during his tour of introduction yesterday.

'Lewis arrived about eighteen months ago—about the same time Lisa started here. ''Sex on wheels'', as one nurse was heard to report. Wealthy, confident, charming and...single.'

'And Dr Kennedy fell for him.' David nodded, feeling somehow disappointed.

'Not exactly. He fell for Lisa—in a big way. She did go out with him a few times.'

'And?'

Mike glanced around them and lowered his voice. 'Lewis presented her with an engagement ring. A rock that could have given her carpal tunnel syndrome if she'd worn it for any length of time.'

'A generous man.'

'Mmm.' Mike bit back a smile. 'Unfortunately he was overheard by a secretary telling your predecessor that he had no intention of marrying Lisa. The engagement seemed to be the price he'd have to pay to get her into the sack, so he was happy to fork out and with a bit of luck he might even get the ring back later.' Mike cleared his throat expressively. 'Word got around, you know?'

'I know.' David smiled wryly. He looked at Mike curiously. 'So Lisa knew what was going on, then? I take it she didn't accept?'

'Oh, she accepted it. She returned it a day or two later. Lewis was not impressed.'

David said nothing. He had a feeling there was more to the story. Sure enough, Mike laughed quietly but gleefully as he gave another quick glance over his shoulder.

'Lisa had the ring valued. She put it in a clear plastic envelope with the formal valuation. She also put in an address of a local house of pleasure with a suggested list of services—all couched in the most tasteful euphemisms—that added up to the exact worth of the ring. Then she posted it in the internal mail system.'

David whistled silently. Half the hospital had probably seen it before it arrived at its destination. And the other half would have heard about it.

'Photocopies of the list still surface occasionally,' Mike added wonderingly. 'It was a major form of entertainment for months, trying to guess what some of those services might actually be. Even Lewis came to see the funny side—or pretended he did. I suspect it bumped up his estimation of Lisa Kennedy no end but he had no show after that.'

'I'll bet.' David shook his head. 'No wonder she's not too keen on surgeons.'

'Don't take it personally.'

'Funny, that's what she said.'

'She goes out with Alan Bennett now.'

'What?' David was appalled. 'He's old enough to be her father.'

'It's a convenient arrangement. They accompany each other to medical functions. Lisa's great company.'

'So it would seem.' David's tone was ironic. 'Is there anyone she doesn't go out with?'

Mike laughed again. 'Yeah—Lewis Tanner.'

'Can't wait to meet the guy.'

'You don't have to wait,' Mike promised. He pushed the door open. 'Let's go and see if he's putting in an appearance at this meeting for once.'

Lewis Tanner would be in his early forties, David guessed. He was charming, sure enough. His welcome for David and apologies for missing his visit the day before were quite sincere. David eyed dispassionately the tall, impeccably dressed figure, the smooth, glossy black hair, the blue eyes and the automatic smile. David had more than a passing interest in keeping up his own appearance but Lewis Tanner made him feel distinctly scruffy. Perhaps it was the silk handkerchief or the miniature carnation in his buttonhole. Or maybe it was the unnaturally high sheen on his black shoes. Instinctively, he disliked the man and he spent the first ten minutes of the meeting trying to fathom out why.

The meeting was a regular weekly occurrence. Cardiology staff presented their referrals for surgery and decisions were made on priorities and theatre lists. The cardiothoracic team had a similar meeting later in the week with the respiratory department. David was only half listening to Lisa as she went through the scoring system on the sixty-two-year old woman being referred.

'Severe triple vessel coronary artery disease,' Lisa stated. 'Left main stem was normal but there is a seventy to eighty per cent stenosis on the left anterior descending. Dominant right coronary artery with an eighty per cent lesion in its mid-conduit portion and further fifty per cent lesion prior to the origin of the posterior descending artery.'

David watched Lewis Tanner who was watching Lisa. There was no hint of any personal animosity or long-held grudges. It was interesting to note that Lisa could hold a professional relationship with someone who had failed so stunningly to make it on a personal basis. There was hope for David yet. Lewis was nodding occasionally in agreement and his expression suggested that he was impressed at Lisa's presentation. From the angle David was sitting at he could follow the line of Lewis's gaze quite accurately, however.

Lisa had crossed her legs and David had to admit that the glimpse of thigh offered by the split skirt was arresting. When Lisa paused momentarily in her summary he glanced up and was startled to find her eyes fixed on him in a baleful glare. She looked away as soon as David caught her eye and continued her presentation, but he could have sworn her lip curled fractionally. It was only then that he realised what had caused her disgust. His tie felt suddenly over-tight. He adjusted the knot with a casual movement but his lips were pressed firmly together. Damn the woman! Now she assumed he had been sitting there thinking of nothing but her legs!

'Class one angina with ongoing pain at rest,' Lisa finished up. 'The echo shows a well-preserved left ventricular function with an ejection fraction of eighty per cent. We recommend urgent revascularisation.'

'Of course,' Lewis murmured. 'Let's get her on the list for this week.'

That was it. David forgot about Lisa—her legs, her attitude problem and even her scary ability to publicly humiliate surgeons. He found himself nodding but his agreement had nothing to do with the patient. He realised why he didn't like Lewis Tanner. The man was assuming a controlling influence in the group even though the heads of both departments were sitting nearby. He oozed confidence in his own opinion and reeked of assumed power.

David's glance shifted to Alan Bennett. The older surgeon's face was impassive as he nodded agreement but David could sense the undercurrent. He swore silently. What kind of interpersonal warfare had he stepped into? He resolved to keep silent until he got a better feel for what was going on.

He didn't have long to wait. Mike Foster launched into a polite but clearly personal criticism of Lewis Tanner.

'We don't seem to have resolved the communication difficulties between departments, Lewis. The Monday morning elective angioplasty slot is required to have surgical back-up for any emergency. You were covering this slot yesterday.'

Lewis raised his hands, palms upward, the diamond on his signet ring catching the light. 'I know, I must apologise again. It was—'

Mike interrupted him. 'It was a potential disaster. We had our patient on the table, sedated and finally psyched up for what she viewed as a major procedure. We were unable to contact you to confirm your availability.'

'That's because I wasn't available.'

'Precisely. Owing to the lack of communication, the only indication we received was the message that your cellphone was switched off.'

'I had an emergency at Greenpark. As you know.' Lewis Tanner's tone suggested that the explanation should not have needed repeating. David's brow creased thoughtfully. Greenpark was a private hospital. He had declined his own offer of operating privileges there.

'Our patient was highly stressed by the delay and eventual cancellation of her procedure. She went on to have an acute myocardial infarction and required emergency angioplasty yesterday afternoon. For which, fortunately, surgical back-up is not mandatory.'

Lewis's shrug was barely noticeable. 'She got her procedure done, then, didn't she?' He shot back a cuff to expose a discreet gleam of gold. 'I'm running out of time here. Is that it for today? Looks like we've got a full case load for the week.'

'No, that's not it for today,' Lisa snapped.

David rather enjoyed the look of irritation on Lewis Tanner's face but it was gone as quickly as it had come.

'I would like further discussion regarding the case of Desmond Knight. He was readmitted yesterday with intractable angina. In the last four weeks he has spent eighteen days in the coronary care unit. His need for surgery has become progressively more urgent.'

This time the shrug was pronounced. 'I reviewed the man last week. He's not a good risk. He's hypertensive, hyperlipidaemic and overweight. Above all, he's still smoking. As I told him, he has to be prepared to take some responsibility for the outcome of his surgery. I'm not prepared to operate until I have concrete evidence that he's given up smoking and is making an attempt to lose weight.'

'His level of angina precludes any form of exercise.' Lisa was clearly angry. 'He had cut down to one cigarette a day. The stress of receiving your letter suggesting

that surgery would not be available was enough to push
him back into it. He's forty-three years old with four
children to support. He hasn't been able to work for six
months. I'm quite confident that a chance to live a normal life will be more than enough incentive for him to
make the appropriate lifestyle changes post-surgery.'

'It hasn't been enough of an incentive so far.'

David's resolve to stay silent evaporated. 'Is this a
departmental policy?' he enquired.

'No, it's not.' Alan Bennett broke the tense silence.
'Lewis's principles are well known but not necessarily
shared to the same degree. Desmond Knight was referred initially to Lewis but I think a change of consultant at this point might be advisable.'

'I've got a theatre slot tomorrow morning,' David
announced. 'Has that been filled?'

'No.' Alan Bennett smiled. 'We planned to ease you
in gradually.'

'I'm more than happy to start operating immediately,'
David offered. He smiled at Lewis Tanner. 'As long as
you don't object to me poaching one of your patients?'

'Not at all, old chap.' Lewis smiled back. 'Are you
sure you want to? Operating on no-hopers like Mr
Knight will play merry hell with your statistics.'

'I'll take the risk.' David felt as if his smile was glued
on. The eye contact with his colleague was challenging.
He definitely did not like this man. No wonder Lisa
Kennedy was prepared to loathe cardiac surgeons on
sight—particularly when they made it obvious they
found her attractive. The thought made him shift his
glance. The expression on both Lisa's and Mike's faces
was enough reward for any risk he might be taking,
politically or otherwise. If there was a line drawn in the
sand here it seemed that David had unintentionally cho-

sen which side to stand on. He was surprised at how good it felt.

'Did you hear the one about the cardiac surgeon who told his patient that he had some good news and some bad news?'

'Probably.' David grinned. 'I reckon I've heard them all by now.' Desmond Knight was a bit of a character and they had established a quick rapport during the introductory interview David had just concluded. 'Is the good news that you have twenty-four hours to live and the bad news that I should have told you yesterday?'

'No.' Desmond Knight chuckled. 'The bad news is that he's only got a week to live.'

'And the good news?'

'Well, the surgeon points to a nurse who's really...'

'Stunningly gorgeous?'

Desmond nodded enthusiastically. 'And he said, "You see that great-looking nurse over there?" The patient looks and then he nods eagerly and looks back at the surgeon kind of hopefully and the surgeon says, "Well, the good news it that I'm taking her out on Saturday night."'

David laughed with genuine amusement. He even looked in the direction Desmond had been pointing, but there was no nurse, stunningly gorgeous or otherwise. There was, however, an impressive expanse of pink candlewick—a back view of Mrs Judd, her walking frame parked in the doorway as she stopped to catch her breath. David caught Desmond Knight's eye.

'Rather you than me,' Desmond murmured.

The pink tidal wave receded, replaced almost instantly by the slim figure of Lisa. The contrast was astonishing and Desmond's face brightened considerably.

'Hi, Doc.'

'Hi, Des. I see you've met our new surgeon.'

'He tells me I'll never play the violin again.'

'You couldn't play it before.' Lisa's smile was only for her patient but David could sense its warmth and felt oddly excluded.

'I've just been explaining the surgery to Desmond here. We're scheduled for 8 a.m. tomorrow.'

Lisa nodded. 'I wondered if you had the time now to review everything. I've got all the notes and I've set up the cardiac catheter film in the viewing room if you want to see it.'

'Of course. I was about to call you.' David turned back to Desmond. 'Try and have a good rest and I'll see you in the morning.' He leaned forward conspiratorially. 'I'd better check out the home movie you had done in the cath lab. I wouldn't want to miss a bit of plumbing that needs attention.'

'Make sure you do the bolts up nice and tight. That's what bothers me.'

David could see the fear beneath the levity. He reached out and gripped Desmond's hand briefly. 'No worries, mate. I'll get you running on full bore *and* leakproof.'

The faint pink flush he could see on the back of Lisa's neck indicated that she had not appreciated the interchange as much as Desmond Knight, but David hadn't been able to resist rubbing her nose in it just a little. He would never admit to the extent that her attack had nettled him yesterday, but between that and the paroxysms of mirth from the neighbouring bedroom last night David had been sorely tempted to pack his bags and return to a more congenial hemisphere.

'What time did Desmond come in yesterday?'

Lisa was flicking a series of switches, dimming the lights in the angiography viewing room. 'About two o'clock.' She moved swiftly towards the projector. 'Why?'

'Just curious.' David took a seat, leaning back and resting his chin on one hand. The admission must have been just before he'd turned up in her office with her remaining belongings and that stupid rose. So that was what she'd been taking out on him—her frustration at being unable to provide the treatment her patient needed so desperately. Understandable. Commendable, even. But it didn't excuse her earlier rudeness or that cutting remark about library books. Lewis Tanner may well have soured her opinion of newcomers but it was still inexcusable to act on it so blatantly.

'You've got his hypertension under good control,' he commented, picking up the case notes. 'And coronary perfusion's not looking too bad.'

'Surprisingly,' Lisa agreed. She started the projector. 'We got these shots this morning.'

They both watched the screen—the shadowy background of the heart pumping, the outline of the main arteries and their filigree of branches darkening clearly as each dose of dye was injected.

David grunted. 'Not pretty.'

'No,' Lisa agreed quietly. 'It's not.'

They went through the film twice. David held the catheterisation report in his hand the second time, checking the diagram that documented which arteries were damaged and to what extent. 'We're looking at a

quadruple graft here,' he murmured. 'Should keep me
out of mischief for the morning.'

'Would you mind if I stood in for a while? If I get
the chance, that is.'

'Not at all.' David deliberately gave his tone a professional detachment. Scrutiny was only to be expected
as a newcomer, and David had never suffered from
nerves due to an audience. This time yesterday his pulse
rate would have jumped at the thought of being observed by Lisa but he was delighted to find himself
unmoved today. Sure, the woman was physically attractive but his initial reaction had been ridiculous. She
was a colleague. One who had advertised her ability to
be antagonistic and would therefore need to be treated
cautiously. The idea that she might be anything other
than a colleague had fortunately vanished completely.
He was no longer remotely interested despite Mike
Foster's advocacy of her virtues and suitability. That
teenage-like surge of testosterone had been nothing
more than part of the excitement of starting a new job
and the pleasure of renewing old friendships. The novelty had worn off amazingly fast.

The theatre team was fantastic. David was delighted to
find that the anaesthetist was Gerry Greene, a contem-
porary and one of the old party crowd. Now married
with three children, he was still keen to arrange a get-
together. The nursing staff were welcoming and the selection of CDs for some relaxing background music was
surprisingly good. David's choice of Dan Fogelberg
was met with general approval. By the time Alan
Bennett slipped in to observe, David had opened the
chest, separated the sternum, retracted the ribcage and
was carefully opening the membranous sac of the per-

icardium which enclosed Desmond Knight's heart. His registrar was doing a very competent job of harvesting the leg veins required for the grafts.

'I'm about to cannulate for bypass with aortic arterial and venous RAIVC lines,' David informed Alan.

The transfer to bypass on the heart-lung machine was smooth, and by the time David applied the cross-clamp and stopped the heart by injecting the cardioplegic solution he was thoroughly enjoying himself. David loved surgery. Politics were non-existent. The goal was defined, everybody was working on the same side and he had the skills to lead them and deal with any complications. It was a dramatic occupation. David had often thought 'theatre' was a very appropriate name for the room. It was also often highly stressful, especially when unforseen difficulties presented themselves, but David thrived on the pressure.

'7.0 Prolene, thanks.' David handled the floppy section of empty vein gently as he sutured one end of it carefully into place. 'OK. Let's check the run-off.' The adjustment of the clamp allowed blood volume to move through the graft and David nodded with satisfaction, before turning his attention to attaching the other end of the graft to the wall of the aorta.

He stood back and stretched some time later but the break in the long procedure was brief. 'Let's move on to the anterior descending, folks. We're doing well.'

Lisa did not appear in Theatre until the last graft was being attached to the aorta. It would have been easy to miss her arrival, due to the number and activity of the theatre staff, but something made David glance up. The brown eyes were magnified by being the only exposed part of her face. Even by themselves they were remarkably expressive. David dismissed the faint jolt the recognition gave him but acknowledged Lisa's presence with a slight nod.

'Let's get this cross-clamp off and check out the plumbing,' he suggested, his smile hidden by his mask. David knew quite well that he'd done an excellent job. Even Lisa should be impressed. Alan and the theatre staff certainly were. Desmond Knight was weaned from bypass uneventfully and his heart restarted spontaneously.

The atmosphere in Theatre relaxed progressively as David wired the sternum back together and closed the chest. Gerry Greene's plans for a dinner party had been finalised and other staff members were talking excitedly about an upcoming cardiovascular conference in the South Island tourist mecca of Queenstown.

'Will you be going, David?'

'I doubt I'll be eligible for conference leave for a while.'

Alan laughed. 'I forgot to tell you—we've got you down as one of the speakers. I don't think leave will be a problem and it's only for a weekend.'

David grinned. Speaking at a national conference on short notice shouldn't be any problem and could only speed up his acceptance. It sounded great. Unconsciously, he found his gaze searching for the cardiology registrar, wondering whether she would be attending the conference. But Lisa had vanished and David merely shrugged mentally. It was of no great importance after all.

'*No!* You musn't do that, Donald.'

Both David and Jane Maddon turned at the sound of the alarmed protest. The familiar pink candlewick, wedged between the bars of the walking frame, was quivering ominously.

David's eyes widened. 'Don't tell me that's *Mr* Judd.' He eyed the pencil-thin, late-middle-aged man with some awe.

'Sure is,' Jane whispered. 'He absolutely adores her. He comes in every day to look after her and do her washing.'

'So I see.' David was just as awed by the size of the pair of knickers Mrs Judd was pulling from her husband's hands. Her voice had quietened due to the exertion of her protest but was still quite audible.

'If you put them in the drier they'll shrink, and then what'll I do, Donald?'

David grimaced at Jane. The alternatives didn't bear thinking about.

Jane smiled. 'We have a laundry where patients and relatives can take care of their nightwear and smalls. Donald Judd uses it more than anyone.'

'Smalls?'

Jane glanced at the item of clothing Mrs Judd had now draped over the bar of her walking frame. She elbowed David as she cleared her throat. 'What can we do for you, Mr James? Are you on the hunt for new patients? I hear Mr Knight is doing very well.'

'He is, indeed. I like the set-up in the post-surgery intensive care unit. Very impressive.'

Jane was watching Donald Judd hovering anxiously near his wife as she rolled slowly back to her room. 'Mrs Judd is in need of some attention to her coronary arteries, I believe.' She eyed David with amusement. 'We just need to get her diabetes under better control and see if we can get on top of the asthma. Lisa has her scheduled for a cardiac catheter next week.'

David was backing off. 'I really only came to find Mike. Is he around at the moment?'

Jane grinned. 'I guess Mrs Judd will have to wait, then. Mike was helping Lisa with an admission a while back. Try the staffroom.'

Half expecting to find Lisa with her consultant, David was relieved to find Mike sitting alone. The feeling changed to one of concern as he saw how morosely Mike was hunched over half a cup of coffee.

'What's up?'

'Upsetting admission.' Mike shook his head sadly. 'Fourteen-year-old boy with cardiomyopathy, Stephen Taylor. He's been on the waiting list for a cardiac transplant for over six months. Went up to Auckland a couple of months ago but it all fell through. He's not looking good right now.' Mike sighed heavily. 'Stephen's a great favourite around here. He's got a brilliant attitude to life. He's particularly attached to Lisa Kennedy. She'll probably be here all night, watching him like a hawk.'

'Are you planning to hang around as well?'

'No.' Mike stood up and emptied his cold coffee down the sink. 'Lisa's more than capable of handling things and knows when to call me if she isn't.'

'Are you otherwise free?'

'Of course. Permanent state of affairs these days.'

'Good.' David was determined to cheer his friend up. 'Gerry Greene's invited us both for dinner. Probably wants to rehash unsavoury memories. Could be just what you need.'

'Could be.' Mike was looking more cheerful already. 'Sounds great. Gerry's over the other side of town. Do you want me to give you a lift?'

'No, thanks anyway. I've bought a car and this will give me the opportunity to give it a test run. I'll meet you there at seven.'

*   *   *

The car was a heap but it had been all David could afford without putting himself into serious hock. Maybe it hadn't been such a great idea, buying his parents that town house as a present to celebrate his father's retirement. Property in central Auckland didn't come cheap. Hell, it didn't even come reasonable. Then he grinned as the engine on the aging Toyota finally caught and held. Of course it had been worth it. His parents had struggled financially all their lives and it had been their sacrifice that got him through medical school. The look on their faces when he'd presented them with the keys!

He had flown home for the occasion, having had his younger sister, Melanie, and a real-estate agent make all the arrangements. The project had had the useful spin-off of keeping Melanie out of trouble for longer than usual. His parents had been pleased enough about that—they couldn't believe it when the reason for their daughter's preoccupation had been revealed. The Jameses had only ever lived in rented houses and retirement had simply been yet another financial challenge. Now they could look forward to having the time of their lives. They were both fit and healthy.

Maybe when he got back on his feet again he'd shout them a trip through Europe. His own two-month jaunt, before returning to New Zealand, had been a wonderful experience but had also been responsible for clearing the last of his savings.

David joined the still heavy stream of traffic circling Hagley Park. At the first set of traffic lights the engine on his car died suddenly. David swore softly but got it started again just as the car behind gave him a blast on its horn. He began to feel concerned about his purchase but it seemed to be running fine until he had to slow for the roundabout at the next corner. The engine cut out without so much as a cough.

David tried to restart repeatedly as the traffic banked up around him. Cars tried to edge into the other lane to pass the obstacle he had created but other motorists were having none of it. Angry shouts and blaring horns contributed to the build-up of road rage. David opened his door, having released his handbrake. He ignored the insults thrown from a car of youths beside him and began to push, one hand on the steering-wheel, the other on the roof above the door opening. Nobody offered to help.

Once rolling, the car gathered speed and David fought to control the steering while he aimed for the side of the road. A front wheel mounted the kerb and David dived for the handbrake as he saw the cyclist on the footpath. Now he was stationary but only the front half of the car was off the road. He was still causing a traffic hazard. With an apologetic grin at the alarmed cyclist David released the catch and opened the bonnet. Surely someone would be able to offer a hand with his distress so clearly advertised.

Sure enough, a car pulled up, neatly mounting the kerb to park on the footpath, well out of the way of the traffic. A shiny, low-slung, convertible MGB. Bright red. A car buff! Just what the doctor ordered.

The driver climbed out. High-heeled shoes, long, slim legs, a neatly fitting skirt with a slit up the side.

'No...' David groaned. 'It couldn't be!'

It was. Lisa Kennedy had swapped her white coat for a tailored jacket in the same fabric as her skirt. She looked as though she would have a briefcase and several cellphones on her passenger seat.

'Having problems?'

'You haven't got a cellphone on you, have you?'

'Of course.'

'Could you ring someone for me? A breakdown service?'

'Let's have a quick look first. What happened?'

David was feeling very tense. His popularity with the general public of Christchurch was rapidly plummeting. He'd heard some pretty colourful abuse in the last ten minutes and the traffic wasn't showing any signs of abating.

'The car stopped,' he said sarcastically. 'I'd think it was fairly obvious.' He glared at the elegant figure in front of him. 'I also think it would be a good idea to clear the obstruction I'm causing.' He shut his eyes briefly. 'Now.'

'Sure.' Lisa was looking amused. 'But it would probably take half an hour for a tow truck to get here. Do you really want to wait and listen to that?'

'Get a horse!' someone yelled. Lisa's mouth twitched but she controlled her expression admirably.

David gritted his teeth. 'I don't know anything about cars.'

'Hop in,' Lisa ordered. 'Turn the key and push gently on the accelerator.'

David didn't move. 'I do know how to *start* a car,' he said coldly. 'If that had worked, I wouldn't be standing here now. And, yes, it *does* have some petrol in it.'

Lisa silently stepped around him and got into his car. The engine started first try and David swore profusely under his breath. He already felt embarrassed enough by his situation. Now he was going to look a complete idiot. The engine ran for thirty seconds and then died. Lisa turned it over but it failed to start. David was perversely relieved.

Lisa moved swiftly. Opening the tiny boot of her car, she pulled out a toolbox. Removing a torch, she marched back towards him. 'Get in, turn it on and press suddenly on the accelerator,' she commanded. Her attention was on his engine as she shone the torch into its depths.

With a frustrated grunt David did as he was told. At least he was partially hidden, sitting in his car. The insults had become appreciative whistles and hoots as Lisa leaned over the bonnet. David slumped a little further down in his seat.

'Looks like it could be a problem with your fuel line.' Lisa's voice floated through the window. 'Stay there.' She collected some items from her toolbox, including a glass jar.

'Turn the key—briefly,' she called a minute later. David complied. 'And again. OK, stop!'

David stuck his head out of the window. He watched as Lisa reconnected some tubing and then emptied the jar of petrol into the gutter.

'Blocked fuel line, I think. Try her again.'

The engine caught, held, but then died. 'For God's sake,' David muttered. 'I did ask you to call a tow truck.'

'This will only take a minute,' Lisa snapped. 'I'm going to check the spark plugs.'

David sat, drumming his fingers on the steering-wheel. The minute passed. And another. He jumped out. 'I thought you were staying in the hospital overnight.' He refused to be impressed by the confident manner with which she selected the socket and wrenches.

'I am. I'm just going home to grab a change of clothes. Stevie's asleep.' Lisa shook her head. 'Look at that. Black! It hasn't even been firing. And this one's oily, see?' She held the spark plug under his nose. 'Probably a shot PCV valve. When did you have this car in for a service last?'

'I only bought it yesterday.'

Lisa's look suggested that there was one born every day. She replaced the spark plugs and David watched as she continued working rapidly. 'You need new spark plugs, your wiring's just about had it and the battery's corroded to hell. Did you even look under this bonnet when you bought this car?'

David grinned. The funny side of the situation finally struck him. A feminist plot to destroy a manhood. A role reversal to die for. 'How come you know so much about engines?' he countered.

'I like old cars.' Lisa nodded at the gleaming machine parked nearby, wiping her hands on a rag. 'I could never have afforded to keep one on the road if I hadn't learned to look after it myself. I've had this since I was a student.' She looked back at David's car. 'How much did you pay for this?'

'Two thousand dollars.'

'Take it back,' she suggested. 'It's worth about five hundred.' She glanced at her watch. 'I've got to go. Have another try.'

The engine started instantly and chugged happily. Lisa listened for a minute. 'Your timing's way off.' She shrugged. 'Sounds like it might get you home, though.' She slammed the bonnet shut. 'I'll follow you for a block or two, just in case.'

He didn't really have any choice. Somehow it was far more unnerving to have the glimpse of the whole of Lisa Kennedy's face in his rear-view mirror than it had been to have those brown eyes critically assessing his surgical technique in Theatre that morning. Then he had been the star performer. In control. David kept his eyes on the road ahead. The tables had turned again and it annoyed the hell out of him. Another glance in the mirror a minute or two later revealed the fact that he had been abandoned. He felt even more annoyed. Then he realised that he hadn't even thanked her! David groaned aloud.

He was not only a member of a specialty that couldn't be trusted and a man with a reputation for wild parties and wilder women. He was an imbecile who couldn't purchase a decent vehicle and didn't even have a real man's ability to fix it. He had accused her of rudeness and now hadn't shown any appreciation at being rescued from an embarrassing situation. What a nightmare!

Not that he was interested in Dr Kennedy any more. Not a chance. But it wasn't very nice to feel that one's ego had been reduced in size to something that wouldn't distort a matchbox. If he kept this up, how on earth was Lisa ever going to have any idea of what she was missing out on?

CHAPTER THREE

'You fancy her, that's the problem, mate.'

'No way!'

'It's a gender problem, then. You don't like being shown up by a female.'

'I don't like being put *down* by a female. Or a male. Or a bloody transexual, for that matter. It's a question of whether somebody's a nice person or not.'

'Lisa's a *very* nice person,' Mike stated firmly.

Gerry nodded an enthusiastic agreement. 'She rides in like a knight in shining armour and rescues you. And you sit here, complaining that she's giving you a hard time.'

Mike and Gerry both laughed. Mike leaned over and gave David a friendly shove. 'She's just casting aspersions on your manhood, that's what it is.'

Gerry nodded again. 'And if you didn't fancy her you wouldn't be so upset about it.'

'Hey, I'm not hung up on gender roles,' David protested. 'I'm sensitive—new age. I'm not the one to have to wear the pants in a relationship.'

Mike hooted. 'That'd be right. Get them off as fast as possible, eh?'

David rolled his eyes. 'Forget the manhood issue. She's cast aspersions on my career as well.'

'She was very impressed with your surgery on Desmond Knight. Told me so herself.'

'Did she?' David was momentarily distracted. Then

he shook his head. 'Not only that. She's cast aspersions on my character.'

'Difficult to do that,' Gerry said seriously.

'Yeah.' Mike grinned. 'You'd have to work hard at it—for at least ten seconds.'

'OK, OK.' David gave up. 'But you guys haven't had your personality likened to a pulp-fiction paperback. Lacking quality and durability. She's out to get me, I tell you.'

'Lucky man,' murmured Gerry.

Mike was still grinning. 'Just because you think she's after you doesn't mean you're paranoid, mate. Don't worry.'

Gerry looked thoughtful. 'Perhaps *she* fancies *you*!'

The three men all laughed, though David's mirth was less genuine. Why was the prospect of Lisa Kennedy finding him attractive so amusing anyway? He'd never really had to entertain the possibility that he might, in fact, be *unattractive*. He watched Gerry and Mike both squash their empty beer cans.

David did not like the idea of being unattractive. He especially did not like the idea of being unattractive to Lisa. A desire for revenge was a completely alien emotion for David but he toyed with the thought as he raised his own can of lager to his lips. Wouldn't it be nice if she really did fancy him and he could cut her down to size with a subtle but spectacularly effective campaign? The thought of seeing the heat of desire in those large brown eyes did something peculiar to his gut. He dismissed the whole concept with some relief as the conversation turned.

The three friends had a great evening. Even the rug-rats Gerry had accumulated weren't a problem, having been discreetly tucked up into their beds before David had arrived. It had been the explanation for his lateness which had led to a confession of the embarrassing encounter, and they returned to the topic late in the evening after Gerry's wife had excused herself and retired, and yet another six-pack of beer had appeared from the fridge.

Mike popped the tab from a fresh can some time later. 'Yeah,' he agreed, seemingly to himself. 'They're too much of a hassle all round.'

'What, cars?' David queried.

'Women.'

David grinned at Mike's morose expression. 'What's the difference, mate? Take them for a test drive. If they feel good keep them until they conk out or get too expensive. Then—'

'Trade them in?' Gerry interrupted, shaking his head. 'Just as well everyone doesn't think like you, mate. Some of us are very happy to keep the same model and develop a more meaningful relationship.'

David groaned. 'Nappies, mortgages, more nappies. School fees, chicken pox…a partner who's too tired to talk let alone anything else by the time you finally get to bed.'

'You can't build a relationship by just having a good time.' Gerry reached for another can of beer. 'They just confirm what's already there. It's the bad times that really count.'

Mike leaned towards David. 'Lisa could give you a great bad time, Dave. She could make your life hell.'

'She already is, thanks.' David grinned. 'Why don't you ask her out yourself, Mike? You're free.'

'Damned right I am.' Mike was going to regret his alcohol intake in the morning. 'We'll go out together, mate. Forget marriage and meaningful relationships. I'll settle for loads of sex.'

David shook his head. 'It's not that easy.' He sighed heavily.

'Who are you kidding? They trip over themselves to fall at your feet.' Mike echoed David's sigh. 'Must be because you're a surgeon.'

'God, don't you start. No, the problem is age. Being thirty-something isn't great. Most of the attractive women our age are either attached or soured by a bad relationship and don't want anything to do with you. Or they've got rugrats in tow. The rest are so young they seem like kids themselves. They want commitment and deeply meaningful romance. Or loads of sex and forget the rest.'

'I'm not complaining.' Mike yawned. 'Lead me to them.'

'You'll get bored,' David warned. 'You'll end up like me, happier to go to bed with a good book.'

Mike wagged his head wisely. 'A whole library of paperbacks. I'm ready for anything.'

'You're ready for bed,' David told his friend. 'I think we'll share a taxi. My car probably wouldn't start anyway.'

The three men stood looking at the car while they awaited the arrival of the taxi.

'I had a better car than this when I was in high school,' Gerry commented.

Mike laughed. 'Hell, this probably *was* your car when you were in high school.'

'It's a heap,' David agreed calmly. 'But the guy started telling me what hard times the business was having and that's why he was prepared to sell so cheaply.

Then he started talking about all the orthodontist work his daughter needed.'

Mike put his arm around David's shoulders. 'You always were a soft touch, mate. It'll get you into trouble one day.'

'It has already,' David said ruefully. 'In fact, I may never live it down.'

'If you hadn't told them where to put those operating privileges at Greenpark, it wouldn't be problem.' Gerry shook his head sadly. 'You'd be driving a Porsche in no time.'

Mike straightened his shoulders and looked suddenly sober. 'That's right, mate. You'd earn ten times what us poor public consultants get. Big drawcard for the women, too.'

David's mouth twisted in distaste. 'I expect Lewis Tanner drives a Porsche.'

'Sure does.' Mike grinned. 'Customised number plate as well. "HEART".'

David snorted. He kicked the rear tyre of his car which had deflated considerably since that morning. 'I've got better things to do. Like research. You can't do that in private.' He glanced at Mike. 'We must have a chat about the project I want to get under way. I'm keen on looking at modified surgical techniques and their effect on the risk of cerebral damage during by-pass.'

The taxi rolled up and drew to a halt. Mike reached for the door. 'It's Lisa you should talk to. She's got a project of her own on that very subject.' He grinned over his shoulder. 'I told you you had a lot in common. Maybe she can collaborate with you.'

'Maybe she can stay out of my way.' David climbed

into the car. 'I have every intention of staying well out of hers.'

It should have been relatively easy to keep a good distance away from the aggravation that Lisa seemed so good at engendering. The respiratory and cardiology wards were well separated, there were three different cardiology teams that could call David in for referrals, and communication post-surgery or outpatient follow-up was usually done by letter. So why did Dr Kennedy have such an uncanny knack of appearing in unexpected places?

He had found her visiting Desmond Knight in the post-surgical ward yet again only this morning. The patient was doing fine. The chest and leg wounds were healing well, pain was now minimal, medical observations excellent. He was using the shower and toilet independently and had managed a full circuit of the ward without assistance at seven days post-surgery. He would be discharged and sent back to Dr Kennedy for follow-up soon enough. But the woman seemed to have a mission to personally supervise the care of every patient admitted under her team no matter what department they might be sent on to. Very admirable but a bit over the top, David thought.

And why did people around her always seem to be laughing? Or at least smiling. It had the effect of making David feel left out of something. It also had the effect of making him overly conscious of Lisa's presence, even at a distance. He could recognise her laugh anywhere—a contagious, throaty gurgle. But she had never laughed in his company and David had always been aware of his own ability to lighten almost any atmosphere with a joke or two and make people laugh.

With Lisa his comments fell like lead balloons. She refused to be amused when he was around, unless it was at his expense.

Like yesterday, when he'd been sitting in CCU, reading a patient's notes, and Jane had gone past and ruffled his hair. He had felt obliged to chide her on her disrespect but Jane had merely laughed.

'Couldn't resist,' she had excused herself. 'It's so…' She'd been searching for an appropriate adjective as Lisa had walked by with a length of ECG trace in her hands. Lisa had taken a long look at David's hair.

'Hmm,' she had murmured thoughtfully. 'Did you sue the hairdresser, David—after the perm?'

Jane had laughed again. 'It's always been like that. Gorgeous, isn't it? Like a mobile pot-scourer. It's even got that metallic gleam.'

David had scowled. His corkscrew brown curls with their natural highlights were distinctive, and he knew quite well they made him appear younger and less professional than he might have done, but his one attempt at shaving them off had been disastrous. With his thin face and wide smile he had looked as though he'd suffered through a particularly gruesome course of chemotherapy. So he was stuck with the curls, but David didn't like being labeled as 'cute'. He would have preferred a suave and sophisticated image—like that which Lewis Tanner seemed to project so effortlessly. On second thoughts, maybe he didn't. Curls were cool. David smiled.

'People have been known to pay big money to get a hairstyle like this,' he informed Jane. 'I happen to be fortunate enough to have it as a natural attribute.'

'It's natural all right,' Jane grinned. 'I love it.'

'Me, too.' The echocardiograph technician, Jenny,

had joined them at the control desk. 'Are you still OK for tonight, David?'

'Can't wait.' David gave Jenny his most brilliant smile, grateful for the change of subject. 'Eight o'clock, right?'

'Here we go again.' Jane gazed heavenwards. 'Another one bites the dust.'

Lisa had found the set of notes to file the ECG strip into. She snapped them shut and moved away with Jane. 'Perhaps Jenny has some pots that need scouring,' she said clearly. Both women were laughing as they left the unit.

Perhaps he was simply overreacting to her barbs. Perhaps it was because she treated him so differently to other colleagues. She had a close friendship with Mike. Was he jealous of their easy rapport? No. Mike was a great guy. Renewing their old friendship, that had, so far, been the best aspect of his return. He was glad that his mate had good friends who had been around to help him through a difficult patch. Lisa had a similar rapport with many other staff members and the patients thought she was wonderful. Desmond Knight was smitten.

'She's the best,' he had told David on more than one occasion. 'She really cares, you know?'

Most registrars kept a personal distance from consultants or at least some degree of deference. But Lisa seemed to be welcomed as an equal. Especially by Alan Bennett. He saw his boss with Lisa now, beside the photocopying machine, as he headed back to his office after lunch. Kissing her, no less! On the cheek, admittedly, but it had prompted David to slow down so that Lisa was alone by the time he reached her.

'You seem to get on well with Alan.'

Lisa glanced up. The raised eyebrows and cool expression informed David that it was none of his business. David lowered his voice. 'How does Alan get on with Lewis Tanner?'

Lisa looked startled. 'Why do you ask?'

'I have to work with them both. I've already got the strong impression that Lewis has a rather consuming personal agenda. Not one that I find particularly attractive.'

Lisa kept her eyes averted. She carefully positioned a journal page on the glass top of the photocopier. 'Lewis Tanner is committed to his private interests. Public hospital work provides a useful extension.'

'Useful?' David was puzzled.

Lisa's glance was searching. It was long enough for David to register just what a rich shade of brown they were. Velvety. Dark. Like the chocolate on expensive after-dinner mints. A man could drown in eyes like those. David brought his attention to heel sharply. Not this man! She seemed on the point of making a decision about whether or not she could trust him. On the point of speaking, in fact, until the machine light flashed and Lisa lifted the journal to turn the page. 'Ask Mike,' she suggested. 'My opinion is a little too biased to share.'

'Why does Alan put up with him?'

'Alan's a peacemaker,' Lisa said carefully. 'And he has a foot in both camps.' She collected the sheaf of photocopied pages, before looking up at David. 'He is also an exceptionally diplomatic person. He's very good at what he does and he avoids causing offense if at all possible. Unfortunately, he will probably head back to Australia. He came here after his wife died but he misses his children and has a grandson now. I suspect he'll go as soon as a suitable position becomes available.'

'That's a shame.' David was now feeling uncomfortable. How could she make the description of someone else feel like a personal criticism of himself? Or was it simply another overreaction?

'Lewis will probably go as well,' Lisa continued evenly as she turned to leave. 'He'd much prefer to work full time in private.' She flicked David another glance, this time a little calculated. 'You might find yourself head of department before you know it.'

David stood back to let her pass. 'You're not too impressed by cardiothoracic surgeons, are you, Lisa?'

Her gaze was now a challenge. 'Should I be?'

David should have stepped a little further back to let her pass. That way she wouldn't have brushed his chest with her shoulder as she moved. That way he wouldn't have been aware of the sensation the touch generated, a sensation that seemed to make it difficult to draw breath. He forced a grin onto his face. 'That's your decision, Dr Kennedy. Maybe one day you'll change your mind.'

'Maybe.' Lisa's smile also looked as if it had taken an effort to produce. 'One day.'

Aggravating, opinionated and arrogantly superior. He should loathe the woman. So why did he have this sneaking admiration for her unshakable standpoint and the feeling that he was missing out on something important due to the force field she had erected? Especially, why did he feel the need to impress her? He only wanted a professional rapport. The same as she allowed everybody else, with the understandable exception of Lewis Tanner. He didn't want a personal involvement. God forbid! Even if she was panting for him he wouldn't touch her with a barge pole. Not even for a sweet taste of revenge.

So why should he feel any inclination to impress her, let alone a preoccupation that was threatening to become disruptive? David was on his way to answer a request for a consult on the respiratory ward. A patient didn't seem to be responding to the treatment for a pneumothorax and his consultant wondered if surgical intervention might be necessary.

David stalked through the corridors, his mind not yet on the patient he had been called to see. It came down to personal esteem, he decided. His ego had taken a distinct battering, thanks to Lisa Kennedy. Word of his embarrassing mechanical problems had leaked out. He suspected that Gerry Greene had been keeping theatre staff entertained by embellishing the story. He had the horrible suspicion that because it had been Lisa involved the comparison between himself and Lewis Tanner would be established on a personal basis. That was only a step away from being likened to his colleague professionally and that was definitely unacceptable.

Lisa was the key. If he could impress her then the link would be broken and David could restore his own pride.

A registrar introduced him to the patient, thirty-four-year-old Wayne Drummond, and David made a quick examination of his chest and the drainage system in place.

'You're right,' he told the registrar, folding his stethoscope. 'The lung's not fully inflated yet but I think it's just a matter of keeping the suction going for a bit longer. I don't think surgery's indicated.'

'Hallelujah!' his patient muttered. 'This place gives me the creeps as it is. Reminds me of my father's fate.'

'What was that?'

'Keeled over and dropped dead when he was forty,' Wayne said. 'I was just a kid.'

David glanced at the registrar who raised her eyebrows and looked worried, probably because it wasn't detailed in the patient's notes and could be an important issue. He turned back to Wayne.

'Have any other members of your family had a sudden death at an early age?'

'My uncle died when he was in his thirties. I never knew any of my grandparents. Not a great track record, is it?'

'No, it's not,' David agreed cheerfully. 'Maybe I'll check you out a bit more carefully.'

'No. Sooner I get out of here the better. I just wish I'd been a bit more careful on the stairs.'

'Can you remember exactly what happened?'

'Not really. I think I just tripped and landed on the bannister post and broke my ribs. All I remember is waking up on the floor with a bloody sore chest.'

'Waking up?' David had his hand on Wayne's carotid pulse. 'Did you hit your head?'

'No, don't think so. It's not sore.'

'Is it possible you blacked out and that was what caused the fall?'

Wayne shrugged. 'I can't remember.'

'Have you ever had any dizzy spells or blackouts?' David was unwinding his stethoscope again.

'Get a bit light-headed occasionally,' Wayne said thoughtfully. 'Jeez, Doc. I'm not going to conk out like my dad did, am I?'

'Not if I can help it.' David was silent as he listened,

the stethoscope positioned above the chest drain over Wayne's heart. 'OK, Wayne.' David straightened. 'I'm going to get you out of bed for a minute.' He unhooked the drainage bottle from the bed-frame and held it in one hand, the disc of his stethoscope still held in his other hand.

'Hang onto the bed with the arm on your good side,' David instructed the young man. 'I want to listen to your heart while you squat and then stand up.'

He nodded as Wayne complied with the manoeuvre. As he had expected, the abnormal murmur he'd detected diminished when his patient was in a squatting position and increased markedly on standing. He and the registrar helped Wayne back onto the bed as the registrar's beeper sounded.

'Sorry, I'll have to go,' she apologised.

'No worries.' David's smile was casual. 'I might keep Wayne company for a bit longer. You don't have a twelve-lead ECG machine around here, do you?'

'Sure, in the treatment room.'

It had been a long time since David had done a twelve-lead ECG himself. He was rather enjoying a return to some basic cardiology. Lisa was renowned for her care of patients not necessarily strictly within her own specialty. Perhaps two could play at that game. When he had successfully placed the electrodes on Wayne's ankles and wrists and positioned the rest in a pattern around his heart, he stood back, his finger poised over the start button. Wayne was looking apprehensive, as though he expected to be electrocuted, but he smiled when he saw David's satisfied expression. David ripped off the page of trace results.

'I'm just going to make a quick phone call,' he told Wayne. 'Be back in a minute.'

Jenny, the echocardiograph technician, seemed delighted to hear from him. 'You're in luck,' she told him. 'I've got a gap right now. Wheel him over. You can do the echo yourself if you like.'

'Great. After your tutorial last night I might just manage it. Thanks again, Jenny.'

'My pleasure. You owe me a bottle of wine, don't forget.'

'I won't,' David promised. 'We'll be there in five minutes.'

An hour later David made another phone call, this time to the operator. 'Who's the cardiology team on take today?' he queried.

'Michael Foster.'

'Great. Could you page him for me, please?'

An unfamiliar voice answered the page. 'Do you have a message for Mike?' it enquired.

David gave the details of the referral. Then he went back to check on Wayne. He was looking forward to Mike's arrival. He knew his mate would be impressed. But it was Lisa who came through the door of the respiratory ward ten minutes later. Walking to meet her, David was momentarily disappointed but rallied quickly. This was even better. At last he had the chance to impress the woman.

'Mike's caught up with a temporary pacemaker insertion. He said he'd catch up with you later and not to forget about the double date you've got tonight.' Lisa spoke as though she were communicating information on a patient's test result. 'He said he's lined up the two best-looking cath lab nurses you've ever seen.'

David groaned inwardly. 'Mike wants to hit the bachelor scene again and thinks I'm some sort of expert. I think he'll be disappointed.'

'So do I.' Lisa fiddled with the stethoscope that protruded from the pocket of her white coat. 'Not by any lack of expertise on your part, of course.' Her gaze locked with his. 'He still loves Anne, even if he denies it. Did you know they have a baby?'

'No.' David was shocked. And then he felt angry. Mike was a special friend. How come Lisa knew more about his private life than he'd been allowed to share?

'It was all part of the problem. Anne had a very difficult pregnancy and then mild postnatal depression. Mike was struggling with political hassles, thanks to our friend Lewis. It all got too much.' She sighed. 'Anyway, I hope you all enjoy your night out. What's the problem here?'

David wanted to talk more about Mike but Lisa had made it suddenly inappropriate. 'Come and meet him. Wayne Drummond, thirty-four. Came in yesterday with broken ribs and a pneumothorax. It's been slow to respond to drainage and when I was checking him I noticed a bit of a murmur.'

Lisa was nodding. They had reached the patient's bed. 'Hi, Wayne. I'm Lisa Kennedy. I'm a cardiologist and I'd like to have a listen to your heart, if that's OK?'

Wayne nodded, David stood back, listening and watching. She certainly did better than the respiratory registrar, eliciting the information about his family history within the first couple of minutes. She took a blood-pressure reading and then he watched her hand on Wayne's neck as she felt his carotid pulse. A plain gold bangle fell back against a slim wrist. He could imagine how gentle her touch was.

For a second he wondered how it would feel to have those delicate fingers touching his own skin and had to look away as he quelled an entirely unprofessional twinge of desire. Perhaps the night out with the nurses wasn't such a bad idea after all. His sex life had obviously been neglected for too long. By the time he looked back, Lisa was listening to Wayne's chest, front and back.

'I'd like to get you out of bed, Wayne, so I can check your pulse standing and squatting.'

'Not again!' Wayne groaned. 'It kind of hurts to move and Mr James has already done that one.'

Lisa looked taken aback. David suppressed his smile. He enjoyed every second as Lisa excused herself and they both moved away from the patient.

'There's a definite systolic ejection murmur,' Lisa said quickly. 'I'd pick mitral regurgitation or aortic stenosis. We'd better transfer him to Cardiology and do some more investigations.'

'Like a twelve-lead ECG?' David produced the page from his pocket. Lisa gave him a strange look, before turning her attention to the trace.

'Left bundle branch block,' she muttered. 'Still points to aortic stenosis. Q waves are pretty deep. Could be—'

'Hypertrophic obstructive cardiomyopathy?' David delivered the suggestion thoughtfully, relishing every syllable.

'Possibly. We'll need to do an echo.'

David produced the page of echo results from his other pocket. Lisa stared at the paper and then at David.

'You've already made the diagnosis and done the appropriate investigations.' Her tone became sarcastic. 'I suppose you've started treatment as well?'

'Yep.' David's grin sneaked out. 'Beta blockers. Propanolol 160 mg, four times daily.'

Lisa looked resigned. 'I suppose I deserve this.

You're trying to show me that cardiologists are redundant. Surgeons can do anything.'

'Not at all.' David could afford to be generous. He smiled placatingly. 'I just thought you might be impressed by the fact that we can be real doctors, too, sometimes.'

'OK, I'm impressed.' She didn't look impressed. She looked annoyed. 'I've just wasted half an hour, that's all.'

'I needed your authorisation to transfer him to Cardiology,' David reminded her. 'And I thought you'd prefer to make your own initial assessment. Will you follow up with a Holter monitor or catheterisation?'

'Possibly.' Lisa nodded. 'If he has a significant left ventricular outflow tract gradient we'll send him back to you for some surgery.'

'"Pass the Patient",' David grinned. 'Kind of like "Pass the Parcel" only there's less to unwrap.'

Lisa returned the grin. He had succeeded in amusing her! Not enough to make her actually laugh but it felt like a major triumph. David felt a glow of satisfaction.

'How did you get Jenny to do an echo at such short notice?'

'I have this incredible power over women.' David leaned closer. He could smell the Chanel and it suddenly seemed the most evocative perfume ever invented. 'I can get them to do anything I desire.'

Lisa edged away. Her look was exasperated but David realised that his physical proximity had affected her more than his words. She looked distinctly unsettled. He watched the faint pink flush enter her cheeks. The glow he had felt in his success at amusing her faded, replaced by a knot of tension that David failed to recognise. His lips seemed to move without any conscious direction.

'Come out to dinner with me, Lisa.'

'You have no power over me, Mr James.' Lisa took another step back. 'I'm a cardiologist, not a woman.'

It was an open invitation to allow his gaze to travel down the length of the elegant figure before him. Lisa had a dark yellow dress on today, slim-fitting and very smart. As far as David was concerned, she was *all* woman. Yet her comment seemed quite serious.

'Does being a *real* doctor mean that you can't be a *real* person as well, then?'

Lisa eyed him silently. For a second, David was sure he'd actually been allowed to step inside the force field. 'In my case, it could be true,' she said quietly.

David had to suppress the urge to reach out and touch her. To extend the moment of connection. The power of the urge was enough to rattle him badly so, instead, he just grinned. 'Thank God I'm only a surgeon, in that case.'

She didn't bother to answer that. She just walked off, shaking her head. Thank goodness. David breathed a sigh of relief. What would he have done if she'd accepted that impetuous invitation? An intimate dinner with this woman was the last thing he'd want.

Wasn't it?

CHAPTER FOUR

THIRD time lucky, David decided, stripping off his blue theatre gear.

It was the first time his Wednesday morning cardiac surgery had finished in time for him to attend the lunch-time meeting. He had particularly wanted to make this one, having seen the memo detailing today's speaker. It was a meeting open to all interested medical staff members. A rotation allowed all departments to put forward interesting cases for presentation. The purpose was to maintain a hospital-wide link, to provide information of perhaps the appearance of a new viral disease, improved diagnostic techniques or therapies. In some cases it gave an open forum for the input of suggestions to deal with a particularly troublesome case.

Lisa's presentation did not fit any of these criteria. As David eased himself through the door, to stand with others who had been too late to secure a seat in the packed lecture theatre, the lights were dimmed and an image appeared on the large screen—a young man, grinning in typical adolescent embarrassment at the attention of the camera, his hand held up to one side of his face with a triumphant thumbs-up gesture. It advertised an unusual approach. Patients were normally presented anonymously, identities protected by the use of initials and certainly no photographs.

Lisa waited for complete silence. Her voice, amplified by the microphone clipped to the lapel of her white coat, was soft but confident.

'We are all faced with a huge number of people need-ing our medical assistance. Some we instinctively like, some we can't stand, but we try our best to offer com-passionate and hopefully effective therapy...without be-coming too emotionally involved.' Lisa cleared her throat delicately. 'Occasionally we are faced with a case that makes it impossible to avoid that involvement. This is such a case. The case of Stephen Taylor.'

David, like everyone else in attendance, felt his at-tention focus sharply.

'Twelve months ago, Stephen Taylor was your av-erage thirteen-year-old boy, physically speaking. In other respects he was very far from average. Stephen's IQ had been estimated to be in excess of one hundred and fifty. His ambition to become a doctor seemed an easy goal. He was already doing university-level sci-ence subjects and taking an extracurricular course in anatomy. Not that he was a complete academic nerd...' Lisa waited for the ripple of laughter to subside.

'Stephen has a passion for old rock and roll, partic-ularly the Rolling Stones, an equal passion for classic cars and a girlfriend he has been keen on since primary school. He has three older sisters who adore him and parents who provide a stable and very loving family environment.

'Twelve months ago the world was Stephen Taylor's oyster and he was loving every minute of it. Last winter he caught the flu.' Lisa cleared her throat again. 'A few days off school. A bit inconvenient but not a major hassle. Something we—and our children—have to han-dle with monotonous regularity. He was back to school the next week but he couldn't quite shake off the virus. He seemed to be tired all the time, got short of breath with minimal exertion, had the odd palpitation and even a few spells of dizziness...' Lisa paused briefly. 'And his shoes felt uncomfortably tight.'

A few heads were nodding amongst the audience. Lisa was looking around as she continued speaking. 'One day, during a history class, Stephen collapsed. It could very easily have been a sudden death—the type of case we hear about more frequently than we'd like to. But Stephen Taylor was still alive when the paramedic team arrived. And he was still alive when he was admitted to our care in the CCU a short time later.'

The teenager's face disappeared from the screen and the lights came up as Lisa moved to an overhead projector and flicked the switch. The silence was still absolute. The case presentation so far had been very far from typical. Nobody presented a case in such a personal manner. What was she doing? David wondered as he watched the overhead transparencies detail the results of exhaustive tests. Had the lad died? Was Lisa going to discuss the implications of becoming too emotionally involved with patients?

He registered the data—the physical examination and findings, the ECG, chest X-ray, echocardiograph and the cardiac catheterisation. The diagnosis was clear-cut. Congestive cardiomyopathy—a complication of a viral infection which had led to a dilated, poorly contracting left ventricle and progressive heart failure. There was no need to discuss the results—or the treatment. Mike and Lisa had brought the heart failure under control with an impressive drug regime and had kept the boy under close observation.

Somebody's beeper sounded and they moved past David to get through the door. He found himself taking the empty seat automatically. His attention was not diverted. It was like reading a thriller. He had to know the ending of the story and the motivation for the main character. From his perspective right now, the main character was Lisa Kennedy. Did everyone else find their eyes riveted so totally on that slim figure on the podium? Did every inflection in her voice and subtle change in her body language elicit such an acute response of their own awareness, as David was experiencing?

'Stephen Taylor went on the waiting list for a cardiac transplant six months ago,' Lisa was saying. 'He carried a pager, waiting for the call that would mean a dash four hundred and fifty miles north to Auckland. He took it to school for the classes he still managed to attend. He kept it beside his bed at night. The call came two months ago at 4 a.m. A woman involved in an MVA in Wellington was available as a donor. The size match was perfect. Even the blood group was an exact match. By 5.30 a.m. Stephen, his mother and myself were in the Medivac plane *en route* to Auckland.'

The atmosphere in the lecture theatre was tense—almost a collective holding of breath.

'Stephen was prepped for Theatre on arrival. He was scared but excited. This was it! The miracle we'd all been hoping for. The donor heart arrived by helicopter at almost the same time. The patient was ready, the surgeons were ready. The anaesthetist was on the point of starting induction when we were told there was a problem.'

The sigh was also collective. Lisa's tone hardened. 'The heart was unsuitable. Hypertrophic. The donor had been an undiagnosed hypertensive, probably for a long time. There was also evidence of coronary artery disease. Nothing could be done. Stephen and his mother were offered accommodation in Hearty Towers, the facility for transplant patients and their families from out of town, in the hope that another donor might become available. Stephen refused. He didn't want to be away from his family or friends. And he didn't want to get behind in his schoolwork.

'The heart failure is end-stage and becoming very hard to control. Stephen has had three admissions since the abortive rush to Auckland. Each one has potentially been his last. This one probably will be.' Lisa looked down in silence for a second and then raised her face, her chin up. 'You're probably all wondering what the point of my presentation is. Even if a donor became available tomorrow, Stephen is too ill to travel to Auckland. We all have tragic cases that touch us very deeply. What's so special about this one?'

Lisa looked around at her audience. David had to admire her poise. She had them all in the palm of her hand. 'The point is that we have reached a turning point in the treatment of such cases in Christchurch. Thanks to a recent appointment, we have the skills available to perform a cardiac transplant right here. I'd like to introduce Mr David James to those of you who don't already know him by past acquaintance or reputation.'

The collective chuckle was friendly but David felt himself reddening. Lisa's eyes found David with an unnerving rapidity. Had she been aware of his presence all along? 'Could you stand up, please, Mr James? I'm sure everyone would like to see who you are and welcome you to Christchurch.'

Reluctantly, David got to his feet briefly, to a wave of applause. He felt embarrassed and vaguely threatened. What did Lisa expect of him? That he could somehow wave a magic wand and provide a miracle for a case that was now going to be a focus for the entire hospital community?

Lisa was collecting her overhead transparencies. 'I know it's not always easy approaching a family regarding the question of organ donation.' She looked up again and David's head turned, with many others, to the knot of people he recognised as representing the ICU. 'I just wanted to remind people of the other side of the coin. The story of a potential recipient. The story of Stephen.' Lisa dimmed the lights, reaching an unexpected and dramatic conclusion by again projecting the boy's photograph.

There was a moment's complete silence and then a general buzz of conversation broke out. David checked his watch and was astonished to find that lunchtime was now over. Lisa's presentation had filled the entire forty five minutes. Nobody else had said a word. They had been caught spellbound by the account and left with the lasting image of a courageous youth giving a thumbs-up signal.

Working his way through the throng of people dispersing towards their various destinations, David found himself unexpectedly eye to eye with Lisa. He bowed his head slightly.

'Bravo, Lisa. You missed your vocation, I think.'

'Sorry?'

'You had your audience captivated. You could do well on stage or screen.'

'Ah!' Lisa raised her eyebrows quizzically. 'Next act perhaps—enter cardiac surgeon, stage right. The hero of the hour.'

David frowned at her sardonic inflection. She was going to get squashed by the weight of the chip on her shoulder if she wasn't careful. He'd had enough of it. 'Look here, Dr Kennedy—'

Lisa ignored his growl, her gaze elsewhere. 'Enter, stage left, John Watson. Intensive Care consultant. Hi, John! Have you met David James?'

'I have, indeed. You might like to fill me in on his past reputation, though.' John's grin at David was friendly but his expression amused. 'What gossip have I missed out on yet again?'

'Ask a nurse.' Lisa laughed. 'Any nurse!'

David fixed Lisa with a steely glare as he gave an exasperated sigh, but John's grin widened. 'You'll have to let me in on the secret. Unfortunately, it's a bit late in my case.' His grin faded rapidly. 'Seriously, now, I'm glad I've caught you. Both of you.' John Watson looked from David to Lisa. 'We've got a young woman in the unit. Serious brain injury from an accident last week. The EEG hasn't picked up and we've got a family conference this afternoon.' The consultant spread his hands. 'I don't want to raise any hopes yet—it's only a possibility and I have my doubts about her husband's reaction.'

David was watching the glow ignite in Lisa's eyes. Fat chance of not raising hopes, he thought. The woman looked like she'd just been told she'd won first prize in a lottery. He found a smile gently curving the corners of his own mouth as his anger faded. Despite the superiority complex and all the angst, someone who cared that much about a patient couldn't be all bad.

'Act two, scene three,' he suggested quietly. 'Theatre.'

Lisa let out her breath in a long sigh. 'Let's hope so.' The glance she gave David was almost beseeching and David was shocked at the jolt it gave him. Whatever she was asking of him he was prepared to give—and more. Unsettled by his reaction, David turned away.

'Let's,' he agreed calmly. He glanced back quickly. 'It may be the only chance I have to salvage my reputation, thanks to you.'

'Your reputation is entirely your own,' Lisa retorted. 'If it needs salvaging it has nothing to do with me.'

He could swear he heard her added mutter of, 'And thank God for that.' But he couldn't be sure and he was now staring at a rapidly retreating back. Lisa certainly had the knack of needling him but his own response was too quick and too exaggerated. A personality clash, he concluded unhappily. He would just have to set a mature example and show Dr Kennedy how it could be dealt with without compromising a professional relationship.

That resolve lasted all of three hours. Until he was actually face to face with Lisa again. The brown eyes were flashing fire and David knew that something had hit the fan. Judging by the way she'd burst into his office and stood glaring at him, it was something that could somehow be directly attributed to himself. A wave of weariness washed over David as he pushed himself to his feet. An advantage of at least an inch or two in height seemed a good first line of defence.

'What have I done now, Dr Kennedy?' It was easy to make his tone exasperated. He really was fed up with being a target for this bolshy woman whose passions seemed rather misplaced—and wasted.

'You operated on Mr Waugh this morning, didn't you? Douglas Waugh?'

'Yes.' David straightened his spine a little more. 'A mitral valve replacement. Quite successful, I think.'

'Mike tells me you used a femoral arterial cannulation for bypass rather than a standard ascending aortic cannulation.'

'It's an acceptable alternative. Especially when patients are undergoing repeat surgery.'

'Mr Waugh was not undergoing repeat surgery. This was his first, and possibly only, procedure under bypass.'

'Well, let's hope so.' David frowned. 'Look, what is this all about, Lisa? Have you come here just to criticise a decision I made regarding my surgical technique? If so, I'd—'

'Did you have a reason for modifying the cannulation site?' Lisa interrupted him. 'Other than adding a little variety to the procedure?'

'Yes, I did,' David snapped. '*If* it's any of your business. I'm looking at the effects, if any, of modified cannulation and clamping sites on post-bypass cerebral damage. Mr Waugh is the first patient of a series I intend to extend considerably. It's a research project I've looked into before but I've never been based anywhere long enough to make it a feasible proposition.'

'Did you get a signed consent form from the patient regarding his participation in this trial?'

'It's not a trial. At this point it's an observational study. And I don't normally obtain signed consent forms regarding a perfectly acceptable modification of a surgical technique. Mr Waugh is not even one of your patients. I fail to understand what your problem is.'

Lisa took a deep breath as she stared at David. She seemed to be making an effort to control herself. When she spoke, her tone had calmed considerably.

'I have been working for some months to get a controlled, double-blind, randomised drug trial under way. I have received drug company, departmental and ethical committee approval. Have you heard of the drug Neuroshield?'

The name rang a bell but it was quite difficult to dredge up any details. A conversational topic or a media report at some stage in his travels. Wonder drugs were always being discussed—often years before they had any chance or making an appearance in clinical practice.

'It has some action on cellular metabolism, doesn't it? Specific to cerebral cells?'

'It has the ability to slow the metabolism radically. As far as the animal studies can predict, it gives close to perfect preservation of cerebral cellular function under some remarkable challenges. Its use as a prophylactic agent to prevent cerebral damage during bypass surgery has a lot of people interested.'

David was now interested himself. He was watching Lisa intently.

'Mr Waugh was the first patient I had enrolled. I obtained an informed, signed consent form from him and completed baseline anatomical and functional assessment two days ago, including a CT scan. I administered the dose of either Neuroshield or placebo myself. This morning.'

'What time this morning?'

'Six-thirty a.m. I came in specially. The protocol is to administer the dose two hours prior to surgery.

Six-thirty a.m. Thirty minutes before David had arrived to review his patient and prepare for surgery. 'I didn't see any warning marker on Mr Waugh's chart that he was enrolled in any trial or had been administered any drugs not charted by myself.' David's tone was icy. This was serious and could have unfortunate repercussions.

Lisa flushed. 'I had the stickers in my pocket,' she admitted reluctantly. 'I put one in his notes but not on his chart. One of the nurses had taken it to record his pre-op observations.' She met David's glance. 'Don't worry. Even if it wasn't the placebo, Neuroshield has no known interactions with any other drugs. I was excited about actually beginning the trial. I went to review the CT scan and book in the follow-up in three days.' Lisa sighed angrily. 'Not that there's much point now. Modifying your surgical technique adds conflicting data that I haven't allowed for in my protocol. I'll have to start again.'

'Randomly dosing my patients with a trial medication will confuse my own data. Perhaps we'd better agree to keep our studies completely separate.'

Lisa dropped her eyes. 'In that case I'll have to abandon the trial. I wouldn't be able to get the case numbers I need.'

'Why not? I only represent thirty per cent of the surgical team.'

'Lewis doesn't wish any of his patients to be involved. In fact, he was delighted to provide the only real obstacle I have had to contend with. That only leaves Alan's patients, and it would take me years to accumulate enough for even a pilot study. Someone else will have done it well before then.'

Damn it. Her disappointment and frustration were palpable. It should feel good. Lisa was not on top of this situation. Here was an opportunity to take revenge, presented on a plate. David could provide an obstacle just as big—even bigger—than Lewis had. He could block her research interests completely. But he didn't want to. Quite the reverse.

'There is another possibility,' he found himself suggesting.

'You'll give up your observational study?' The light of hope dawned in the brown depths of her eyes.

'No.' The light went out but David held her gaze and spoke slowly. 'We could collaborate.'

Her eyes widened. The stare was intense. David wondered if anyone had ever listened to him as closely as Lisa's face advertised she was about to.

'What about a multi-factorial study design? Four factors. Medication, modified surgical technique, nothing or both.'

'It wouldn't be double-blind.'

'The medication side would be. We could randomise the surgical technique as much as possible. It would give a lot more data. And be a unique study. I doubt if anyone else trialling Neuroshield would be making life more difficult for themselves by extending the factors.'

'We'd have to start again. Talk to the drug company, draw up a new protocol, get ethical committee approval—'

'We'd have to work together,' David added in an ominous tone. 'Closely. Could you do that? With a *surgeon*?'

She seemed not to have heard the warning. Her eyes were shining again. 'It would be a fascinating project.' Her bottom lip was caught between small, even teeth. 'I'd like to try.'

'Good.' David dragged his eyes away from her mouth. 'So would I. We're agreed, then.' He held out his hand. 'Put it there, partner.'

It started as a handshake, an agreement between colleagues both excited by a shared new scientific horizon. But the movement of their hands died and it suddenly became something else. Their hands seemed as glued together as their gazes. Who looked away first? Who made the first move to withdraw from the physical touch?

Perhaps it had been simultaneous. As simultaneous as the knowledge that this voluntary physical contact had underscored something far more significant than a professional agreement.

The pile of background material was impressive. Lisa must have spent considerable time collecting the journal articles, textbook references and drug company data. It filled a large carton which David carried home with him the next evening. Deciding it was too late to begin his review, David then changed his mind a short time later.

The occupant of the next room had scored again. This one didn't giggle, but in a way her appreciative groans were worse. It made him think about what was going on far more graphically than he felt comfortable with. Gritting his teeth, David rummaged through one of his own boxes for his portable CD player and a disc of classical music. With the headphones on, the sounds of the activity next door were obliterated, but the music was not enough of a distraction to prevent him reading a few journal articles.

David reached for the top layer of journals, while making a mental note to try and catch sight of the stud who lived next door. With his determination to outdo Lisa in at least the hours worked in the hospital, he had spend the last weeks leaving too early and returning too late to meet his neighbour. It really was indecent that some junior doctor had both the time and energy for such a vigorous social life. It hadn't been like that in his day. David smiled wryly, settling back against the pillow on his single bed, a notebook, pen and journal to hand. Perhaps it had been—but those days were long gone.

It was only a recent discovery that they were a part of the distant past. Memories to file along with that of the delectable Miss Drummond. Mike had been responsible for the unsettling discovery with that double date he had organised with those cath lab nurses. They certainly had been great looking. Not to mention young, keen and ready for fun.

Why was it that neither he nor Mike had been remotely interested in taking them up on their unspoken offers? It had been almost funny, that embarrassing leave-taking at the nightclub, when the nurses had gone in one direction, with somewhat amazed glances at each other, and he and Mike had gone in another. David had tried to catch Mike's eye, ready to make some crack about it not being the best start to a bachelor career, but Mike had been strangely withdrawn and obviously not willing to discuss his lack of interest.

David had caught the mood, feeling somehow let down—with Mike and, more, with himself. The ingredients had all been there. Ten years ago he would have asked for nothing more. Now he realised that he needed something more but was unsure exactly what it was he was looking for. Maybe he should talk to Mike about it.

The journal forgotten, David checked his watch. Tenthirty. He pulled his headphones off and reached for the bedside phone. It wasn't too late to call his old mate. It was time they had an evening out and few drinks. Just the two of them. They wouldn't include Gerry because he was too caught up in his own married bliss to understand. He and Mike needed a real talk so they could sort each other out and find out what it was they both really wanted out of life. It was Friday tomorrow, a perfect time for a well-lubricated philosophical discussion—something you couldn't have in feminine company. Forget marriages, babies and separations. Forget women in general and irritating cardiology registrars in particular. They were just strings, catches in an otherwise ideal existence. Maybe what he and Mike needed was just some good, plain, old-fashioned fun!

CHAPTER FIVE

'WHAT do you mean—you can't make it?'

David held the phone to his ear with his shoulder as he pulled up his jeans and fastened the stud. 'I've got it all arranged, mate. Pizza…beer. Hell, this pub's even got a wet T-shirt competition going.'

'Really? I didn't think they existed any more.'

'They're as rare as hen's teeth,' David warned. 'We might never get the chance again.'

'I can't. Listen, Dave, Anne's mother has just been admitted with an MI.'

'Are you treating her?'

'No, but Anne's on her way in and I can't leave.'

'Of course not. How bad is it?'

'Looks like a biggie. The paramedics had to jump-start her three times on the way in.' Mike hesitated. 'God, Dave, what am I going to say to Anne? We haven't even spoken to each other for three months and that was a blazing row about…about—'

'It doesn't matter what it was about,' David broke in. 'That was then. This is now. You'll know what to say, mate. This is Anne we're talking about, remember? The woman you loved enough to marry.'

'Yeah… I guess.' Mike still sounded dubious.

'I'm on my way,' David told him. 'You sound like you could use a friend and, to tell you the truth, I'd grown out of wet T-shirt competitions by the time I was sixteen.'

The bed nearest the main doors of the coronary care

unit had a clear view of the corridor that linked the wards and gave access to the lifts and stairwells. The occupant of that bed had more entertainment during the day, watching the varied hospital traffic, so it was a bed saved, if possible, for people who might appreciate a greater distraction from their situation.

David recognised the face of the patient in bed one as soon as he stepped from the lift. Stephen Taylor—the teenager in desperate need of the heart transplant. Word on the hospital grapevine had been that the initial approach to the potential donor's family had been unsuccessful, and the husband was now keeping a twenty-four-hour-a-day vigil by her life support system to prevent anyone turning it off. Staff were allowing the situation to continue in the hope that the family might come to terms with the decision that the inevitable termination of life support might be able to give hope to others.

Namely, Stephen Taylor. And Lisa Kennedy. Somehow David wasn't surprised to see the senior registrar sitting on the end of Stephen's bed. What was surprising was seeing her in jeans and a sloppy sweatshirt. A pile of classic car magazines was spread out on the bed cover. Lisa was off duty and using the time to enjoy a shared passion with another devotee.

'Look at that!' he heard her exclaim. 'Nice little MGB roadster. It's a 1967 model.'

'What year is yours?' Stephen's head was also bent over the picture in the magazine.

'Nineteen seventy-eight. But it's a V8. Talk about grunt!'

'Yeah, but look at this. That's for me!'

'An Alfa Romeo? In your dreams, kid.'

They looked at each other—the young doctor and the

teenager—and David felt his own heart squeeze pain-fully as he walked slowly behind Lisa's back. The way the boy looked! There was more than friendship there. More than a teenage crush. He was looking at a lifeline. And Lisa barely missed a beat.

'Hell, why not?' He could hear the smile in her voice. 'Dreams are free. But you might only be able to afford a Ferrari.'

'Not if he becomes a surgeon.' David couldn't help pausing. Lisa's head swung around.

'Not even surgeons earn enough for an Alfa Romeo 8c 2900,' she told him with gleeful certainty. Her curls bounced against her shoulders as she turned her head again. 'Stevie, this is David James. I told you about him.'

The boy looked suddenly even younger. Vulnerable. 'You're the guy that can do transplants,' Stephen Taylor said quietly.

'Sure can.' David stepped forward and laid a hand on Stephen's shoulder. 'I hope we're going to get much better acquainted in the near future.' He gave Lisa a quick sideways glance. Sitting there, in her jeans and oversized top, she looked almost as vulnerable as Stephen. The same mixture of doubt and hope crowded her expression and David had the ridiculous urge to gather them both up, to offer protection and comfort. And further hope. Instead, he allowed his gaze to be distracted by the hurried arrival of a newcomer.

'Anne!' he called.

The woman paused at the sound of her name and looked confused. The baby in her arms was crying. David excused himself and moved towards Anne just as Mike emerged from the curtained-off bed at the other end of the unit. They both seemed unaware of David's presence and spoke at the same time.

'Anne, I'm so sorry—'

'Mike, how bad is it?'

They both paused. Mike's face was a picture of concern. 'She's holding her own but it's quite serious. Would you like to come and see her?'

'Yes…of course… But…' Anne jiggled the red-faced baby, who was still crying loudly. They both appeared to notice David for the first time and again spoke as one.

'David! How good to see you!'

'Dave, would you mind, mate?'

David smiled and shook his head, holding out his arms. The baby was heavier than he had expected. Heavier, and distinctly damp. The baby took one look at his dismayed face and protested vigorously at her abandonment to someone so clueless. David moved quickly. A shrieking rugrat was not going to be welcomed by any of the unit's inhabitants.

Lisa and Stephen both watched him approach. They were both grinning from ear to ear.

'Suits you.' Lisa nodded. 'Shame *she's* not impressed.'

'Seems like I have trouble impressing a lot of females around here,' David muttered. He paused indecisively. 'Say, Lisa?'

'Mmm?'

'You couldn't give me a hand here, could you? It seems to have sprung a leak.'

This time he actually made Lisa laugh but David got no satisfaction from the accomplishment. He had been quite serious.

'Plumbing's your specialty, isn't it?' Lisa was still laughing. 'Sorry, David. I don't *do* babies.'

It was all too much. David stumbled from the unit, feeling totally useless and increasingly alarmed. The baby was going to damage itself, putting this much effort into trying to avoid his assistance. He found himself walking into the adjacent cardiology ward. He looked desperately into the first doorway he passed, hoping to find someone in a nurse's uniform. He needed help. He needed...Mrs Judd.

Funny how comforting a sea of pink candlewick could look. 'Mrs Judd? Do you know anything about babies?'

'I should do, dear.' The voice was wheezy but immensely reassuring. 'I've had eight of my own.'

Saturday morning was a good time to catch up with paperwork. It was also a good time to launch an unforgiving glare at Lisa during a quick visit to the CCU. He and Mike had postponed their drinks session in favour of lunch. Mike had made the suggestion himself late last night, having thanked David for caring for his daughter.

'It was no trouble,' David had assured him. And it hadn't been after he had discovered Mrs Judd. Cushioned on the wonderfully accommodating pink bosom, the baby had instantly succumbed to overwhelming exhaustion despite the wet nappy. Even after being returned to David's tense arms some time later, she hadn't woken, and David had strolled triumphantly back into the unit.

Damn shame Lisa hadn't been there to witness his success. And she certainly hadn't been prepared to lend a hand in adversity. The jeans had gone. Power dressing was back, high heels and all. So David glared and was rewarded only by a serene smile. His card was marked. Incompetent with cars, worse with babies. Mike didn't make him feel any better.

'Sorry, mate. I can't make lunch. I promised to babysit Sophie so that Anne can come in and visit her mother. She responded really well to the drug therapy. I rang Anne to tell her this morning and she was thrilled.'

Mike sounded thrilled himself. David wished he could share the happiness but his day was going steadily downhill. He left the unit, thinking that at least things probably wouldn't slide any further, but then the lift doors opened and he knew that they just had.

'Davey! I was looking all over for you.'

His younger sister, Melanie, bounced out of the lift and David's heart sank. If she'd come all the way to Christchurch, hunting for him, then she had to be in even more trouble than usual.

'Mel! You look great!' David resigned himself to his fate and held out his arms. And she *did* look great. Melanie was nearly as tall as he was. She had the same corkscrew curls but on her they were no handicap. She wore them long and very blonde and they had been a major drawcard during her brief flirtation with a modelling career. Big hair, which went with the same wide smile and a much less restrained personality. Already Mel had twisted out of his arms and had grabbed his hand.

'Where's your office, Davey? I've got something *really* important to tell you.'

'I'll bet.' David was grinning as he allowed himself to be towed along. 'It's that way.' Seven years Mel's senior, he had always enjoyed the role of older brother.

A steadying influence and, God knew, Melanie had needed one often enough. He cast a disapproving eye at the black leather mini-skirt and knee-high boots she was wearing. As for the cropped top—God, she'd even had her belly button pierced.

'*Mel!*' he gasped. 'You are unbelievable!'

'I know.' The unrepentant grin flashed. 'I love you too, Davey.'

Mel's voice had never been particularly quiet. David registered with some consternation just what it might do to his as yet unsalvaged reputation to be seen being enthusiastically dragged away by this startling woman. It took a while to get used to Mel. The thought was enough to make him glance over his shoulder as they passed the doors of CCU.

Stephen's expression suggested it was the most entertaining scene he'd witnessed for some time. Unfortunately, the expression on Lisa's face suggested something quite different. A faint groan escaped David's lips. It was all part of some conspiracy to turn his life upside down. Whenever he felt he was regaining his footing someone jerked the rug out from under him. And that someone was standing there beside her patient with the absolute confirmation of what she thought of him written all over her beautifully expressive face.

David had managed to forget the incident by the time Monday's workload was well under way. By that evening he was quite confident that Lisa's mood had nothing to do with him. She was, however, definitely miffed.

Her tone was clipped and formal and had been ever since they had begun their meeting an hour ago. She was also avoiding any eye contact. Something had upset her but David had no clue what it was and he wasn't about to ask. He caught enough flak from Lisa as it was. He wasn't about to step into her firing line.

Their discussion had gone very well and their proposed joint research project was shaping up nicely. Already they had agreed on entry criteria for patients and had categorised and ranked all the appropriate risk factors, such as advanced age, previous stroke, high blood pressure and diabetes.

'How clearly do you want to define cerebral damage?' David was scribbling notes. 'Another ranking system?'

'No. I'd rather keep that simple, the way I outlined in my original protocol. Two types. Type one—fatal injury, stroke, stupor or coma and transient ischaemic attacks.'

'And type two?'

'New deterioration in intellectual function. Confusion, agitation, disorientation, memory deficit or seizure without evidence of focal injury.'

'A lot of that is a bit arbitrary,' David pointed out. 'Some patients will experience things like agitation and disorientation as a quite normal result of major surgery and being in an intensive care situation.'

'I know.' Lisa sounded defensive. 'I've worked out a neurological checklist and time frame which should be able to distinguish anything significant. The focus for assessment will obviously be on the results of the CT scans.'

'What schedule did you have planned for them?'

'One prior to surgery, one at three days post-surgery and again at two and six weeks post-surgery.'

'And you got the go-ahead for that? Whew!' David whistled, impressed.

'Drug company funding is generous. They see acceptance of Neuroshield for clinical use as a priority. I've got the budget figures here.' Lisa reached for another manila folder in the pile beside her.

'Could you leave it with me?' David glanced at his watch. 'It's eight o'clock. Time we called it quits for today.'

'Sure.' Lisa rose to her feet instantly, as though glad of an excuse to escape his office. 'I hope I haven't made you late for anything.'

'Not at all.' David was watching Lisa as she gathered her folders. She was really quite tense but it didn't come across as her usual confrontational style. There was an underlying uncertainty that piqued his curiosity. Was she nervous about spending time out of hours alone in his office? Yet the meeting had been at her suggestion.

'I'm planning a quiet night,' he said cheerfully. 'I need to recover from the weekend.'

'I can imagine.' Lisa still didn't meet his eyes but David knew instinctively that he had stumbled on the reason for her disquiet. He wanted to prod a little deeper.

'Melanie is rather exhausting company,' he added. 'I didn't get much sleep.' He hadn't either. Melanie had bombarded him with talk of the new love of her life. An Australian opal miner who was absolutely *it*. There could never be anyone else as important to his sister's happiness. She was going to marry him. She knew this because he had called to invite her to visit him, on site, at one of his opal mines.

'Mmm.' Lisa's attention seemed to be very firmly focused on the papers she was sorting as she stood beside him. 'Yes. She looked rather…*energetic*. Here's the neurological checklists. You might want to have a look at them as well.'

David ignored the sheaf of papers deposited on the desk in front of him. Her tone had given the game away. Lisa was disapproving, to say the least. Of Melanie. He almost had the absurd impression that she was jealous. Surely not!

'It was rather an expensive weekend, too,' he found himself adding. Melanie had needed money for her desired trip to Australia and David had finally given in. He knew he should tell Lisa that Melanie was his sister but the very idea that Lisa might be rattled by his supposed relationship to another woman was intriguing. Very intriguing.

'I'm sure you got value for money.' Finally, Lisa looked directly at David. He held the eye contact, still musing over the underlying motivation for Lisa's disapproval. He wanted to spin the conversation out to allow more time for assessment.

'And you? Did you have a good weekend, Lisa?'

'Great, thanks. Sean Findlay and I went skiing on Mt Hutt.'

'*What?*' David was appalled. Lisa looked startled.

'What's so wrong with that?'

David swallowed hard. What *was* so wrong with that? Was *he* jealous? No way! And what business was it of his, anyway? Perhaps that was the sort of relationship Lisa wanted. If so, David needed to find out.

'Just how well do you know Sean Findlay, Lisa?'

'Well enough. He's been my registrar for a couple of months. He's good at skiing. We often catch a day on the slopes together.'

Skiing wasn't all Sean Findlay was good at. Should he tell her? He'd only found out himself this morning. David had been much later going in to work. His plan to drive Melanie to the airport had been thwarted by his car's refusal to start again, despite an expensive mechanical overhaul in the last fortnight. A taxi had been hard to procure in the rush hour and David had been kept late enough to finally meet the occupant of the neighbouring room.

David had eyed Sean with a new respect at the time. Now the thought of him alone with Lisa Kennedy was nothing short of horrifying. No. That wasn't the sort of relationship Lisa wanted. Look at the way she had dealt with Lewis's shallow advances.

'It's just…ah…' David hesitated. 'Some men, as you know, are only after a…a more shallow type of relationship.' He cleared his throat. 'I just wouldn't have considered him your type, that's all.'

'And what *is* my type?' Lisa enunciated very clearly. 'Someone like *you* perhaps?'

David felt inexplicably nervous. He had brought this on himself, playing games with the conversation. Lisa had managed to turn it in a very unexpected direction. Now, how the hell was he going to extract himself? The nervousness stemmed from an irrational desire to answer in the affirmative. Fortunately, he didn't get the chance.

'What's the problem here, David? Did Melanie have to go back to the library?'

'Sorry?' David was genuinely perplexed by the reference. 'No, she went to Australia. She was only here for the weekend.'

'And you have the nerve to accuse me of shallow relationships?' Lisa's smile was smug. 'Perhaps what is sauce for the gander, David James, should also be considered sauce for the goose.'

'But that's different!' David exclaimed.

'Why?'

'Because...because you're a woman.' David was actually shocked. Equality was fine. This, however, was unacceptable. 'Women are supposed to want more meaningful relationships.' And if Lisa didn't want something more, why hadn't she just played along with Lewis—and kept the bloody ring?

'Is that right?' Lisa sounded as though it was news to her. 'You forget, David. I'm a cardiologist, not a woman.'

'I give up.' David grinned, handing her the victory. 'You win—as usual.' She might have won a battle, certainly, but the picture of the whole war had shifted somewhat. David's grin widened a little. Lisa was jealous. Of Melanie! And he liked the idea. He really liked it.

'Shall we meet again, say, Wednesday evening?' he added quickly. 'After I've had time to peruse the budget?'

'Fine by me.' Lisa seemed happy to step off personal ground. The wind had gone from her sails and she looked vaguely disappointed. 'I'd like to get this sorted as soon as possible so we can get approval and get started.'

'We could go over it now if you like—over some dinner?'

'No.' Lisa looked up at the wall clock. 'I'm just going to look in on Stephen. He hasn't had a good day. It looks like his renal function is going downhill rapidly now.'

'Any word from Intensive Care?'

'Yes.' Lisa bit her lip. 'The woman's husband has come to terms with the idea that the life support system has to be switched off. He just wants one more night.'

'And?'

Lisa's lip trembled. 'He won't consider what he thinks of as further mutilation. No organ donation.'

David caught the single tear with his own thumb. Lisa's arms were full of manila folders and he couldn't bear the sight of that tear trickling down the side of her nose. The extra moisture still caught in her eyes made them shine.

Her voice was a whisper. 'I guess we can't win every battle.'

David was startled by her choice of words. It echoed too closely his own thought regarding their personal relationship. Lisa had won that one. And David didn't want her to lose this one either.

'We haven't lost yet, Lisa.' His thumb was still tracing the path of that tear. 'Not yet.'

His thumb had reached her lip. God, it was so soft! He could feel a remaining tremor. He could also feel an overwhelming urge to stifle the tremor with more than his thumb. He wanted to cover her lips with his own—to explore that extraordinary softness and mobility. David found his head lowering. He was so close he could almost taste her. It was Lisa's robust sniff that broke the spell. That, and her hurried exit from his office. David found himself walking after her—as though Lisa was stretching something between them that he couldn't bear to have broken just yet. He stopped just outside his office door.

We? David stared after Lisa as she headed down the corridor. Did I say, 'We haven't lost yet?' It wasn't his battle, was it? He wasn't involved, not really.

Damned right he was. David grabbed his white coat off the back of his chair. He was in it right up to his neck. And he was damned if they were going to lose. Not if he could help it.

Enter, stage right, cardiac surgeon. The hero of the hour. But David didn't feel like a hero. He felt humbled. It was an unusual sensation and he knew he looked far more serious than usual as he faced his small audience.

Stephen was propped up on a pile of pillows. An oxygen mask covered much of his face but didn't disguise the unhealthy, dusky shade to his skin, and it didn't detract from the expression his eyes conveyed. An expression that was mirrored on the faces of his parents, sitting quietly beside him. On the faces of three young women, presumably his sisters, and especially in the eyes of Lisa, perched on the end of Stephen's bed. David had eased himself through the closed curtains which had heightened his impression of enacting a drama. Now his audience was waiting and the spotlight had never felt so fierce.

He held up a single sheet of paper. 'This is a consent form for cardiac surgery.' His voice was uncharacteristically tentative. David swallowed and then spoke more firmly. 'Cardiac transplant surgery. We have a donor heart available.'

The silence and lack of any change in the expressions of his audience were nerve-racking. The air within the curtained-off area around bed one crackled with tension. David defused it as his slow smile broadened into a grin. Suddenly everybody was talking at once. Talking, laughing, crying and hugging each other. Arms only left one body to be wrapped around another. The sisters hugged each other, their parents and Stephen. They hugged Lisa. Lisa hugged Stephen's parents. David stood watching it all, a stupid grin still on his face. There would be time enough to arrange all the preoperative details later. When it was Lisa's turn to hug Stephen it became too much. David felt the prickle of tears in his own eyes and moved to distance himself. He couldn't afford to become too emotionally involved at this point in time. Not when he was responsible for the surgery that Stephen and his family looked so eager to consent to. He mumbled some incoherent excuse and explanation that he'd be back shortly and ducked out from the scene. Out of CCU. David stood in the darkened corridor with his eyes shut, taking a few deep breaths. He felt someone's rapid approach but he was unprepared for the strength of the arms that wound themselves around his neck.

'David! Thank you. You're amazing!'

David smiled at the excited face so close to his own. 'About time you noticed, Lisa. You're not so bad yourself.' David's arms closed around her a little more firmly. He could feel the length of her spine, the softness of her breasts against his chest. He could feel the intense heat of the desire suddenly kindled at a much lower level. There was no way he could deny it now. He *wanted* this woman. He had to move. Now. Before she became aware of his body's reaction to her proximity.

Lisa unwrapped her arms the instant he moved. She hadn't noticed. She was still smiling happily.

'So, how on earth did you manage it? To get the husband's consent?'

'I'll tell you later. Right now we'd better get the ball rolling at this end. I need to go over the procedure with the family and get this consent signed.'

'Is Theatre booked?'

'Both of them.' David nodded. 'Seven-thirty a.m. tomorrow. Gerry's going to anaesthetise. Alan's going to assist me. Lewis was happy to delay his turn in Theatre.'

'*Was* he?'

David grinned. 'No. But I persuaded him.'

'You must be extremely persuasive.' Lisa was shaking her head in disbelief.

'Oh, I am. Just wait—you'll find out.'

David led the way back into CCU. He hoped she would find out. There had to be some way he could persuade Lisa into his life. God, into his bed at least.

There *had* to be!

CHAPTER SIX

'I THINK it's way past time we went to bed.'

'Exactly what I've been thinking.' David could feel the desire flickering. If Lisa looked up and caught his eye, he was sure it would explode into an unparalleled conflagration. Look up, Lisa, he urged silently. Never mind that it was nearly midnight and they'd both been sitting in a reflective silence as they'd finished yet another cup of coffee in the staffroom. He had never felt less tired in his life.

Lisa sighed wearily. 'You just can't help yourself, can you, David?'

'Sorry?'

'Flirting.' She did look up but her expression was a disappointment. No encouragement to fan the flames there. 'You just can't let any opportunity slip past. It's as automatic for you as breathing.'

'Some women appreciate it.'

'Oh, I know that.' Lisa's glance was as speculative as her tone. 'Don't think I haven't noticed the way nurses trip over themselves to be helpful. The right piece of equipment is always found, the patient's results are always available. *Your* patients are always in their beds and even the cleaner keeps the vacuum cleaner away while you're trying to examine someone.'

David grinned. He couldn't deny it. She'd left out his secretary, though.

'Even your secretary is a force to be reckoned with on your behalf,' Lisa continued acerbically. 'Do you know she pushed in front of me to get to the photocopier yesterday? Some reports that just *had* to be ready for you.'

'Did she?' David made a mental note to buy Sue a box of chocolates, while managing to look apologetic for Lisa's sake.

'*I'm* still waiting for discharge summaries which should have been typed up two weeks ago. And what about Mrs Judd?'

'What about her?'

'She wouldn't let me examine her this morning. She was hanging about, clogging up the corridor with her walking frame. It all became clear when she caught sight of you and had a chat. *Then* she was happy enough to relinquish her post.'

'I have *not* been flirting with Mrs Judd. We had a small bonding session, that's all—over a baby.'

'Well, it won't wash with me, David James, I'm warning you.'

'Why not?' David felt genuinely curious. 'This is a tough game, Lisa. It helps to lighten the atmosphere. You've got a sense of humour—I've heard you laughing often enough. What's so wrong with making people feel good about themselves, maybe feel attractive and appreciated.'

'Because you're playing on sexuality and you target women.'

'My inclinations *have* always been in that direction, I must confess.' David couldn't help smiling.

'It's chauvinistic and outdated,' Lisa growled. 'And it only makes it harder for women to succeed. How many female cardiology consultants do you know of, David?'

David thought hard. 'There's a brilliant woman at the Mayo Clinic and…ah…'

'Exactly. It's not an easy field for a woman. I intend to succeed, David. My career is my life. That's why I despise flirting.'

David had a flashback to their first meeting—to his husky comment about looking forward to working with her, to his crack about breaking her heart. He could write a manual on how to get off on the wrong foot with Lisa Kennedy. Yet she didn't seem to be berating him. It was more as if he was being pointed in the right direction. That was fine. He could modify more than his surgical technique. David was ready and more than willing to accommodate Lisa's preferences. Especially when they were explained so convincingly.

'Point taken. I hereby take the pledge to stop flirting.'

'Good luck.' Lisa was smiling. 'You might manage to cut down a bit where I'm concerned, anyway.'

'Being friendly never hurts. Look at the co-operation we've pulled together tonight on Stephen's behalf. I think we've got everything sorted now.'

Lisa nodded wearily but then her eyes widened with concern. 'Did you contact the blood bank?'

David nodded. 'Typed and cross-matched two units of whole blood and two units of packed cells, and we've got some platelets and fresh, frozen plasma on standby.'

'Did you get that last creatinine level through yet?'

He nodded again. 'His renal function isn't great, is it? We'll use a modified pre-transplant immunosuppressive regime with a reduced initial dose of cyclosporine.'

'Is Alan going to do the harvesting?'

'No, I'll do that while he gets Stephen onto bypass. Then I'll do the implantation. I can match things up better that way.'

Lisa was silent for a moment, then she sighed. 'It's wonderful for Stephen but it's a bit easy to lose sight of the other side of the coin. What's her name? The donor?'

'Stephanie Barry. Her husband's Greg. They've been married for three years, no children. She's twenty-five and worked in a pharmacy.'

'What happened?'

'A minor accident, really. They'd been out, celebrating Greg's promotion, and had had rather a lot to drink. Steph tripped over the front doormat·when they got home and knocked her head on the doorhandle. She insisted she was all right, took some aspirin and went to bed. Must have had a severe intracranial bleed during the night and Greg was unable to wake her the next morning. He feels responsible now, of course. If only he'd taken her to a doctor. If only they hadn't had so much to drink—you know how it is. She's rather lovely, Stephanie. Long, black hair, at least what's left of it after the surgery…' David's voice trailed off.

Lisa broke the reflective silence. 'How *did* you get him to agree to the organ donation, David?'

'I'm not sure. After our meeting I wandered up to Intensive Care. I wasn't sure that there was anything I *could* do but maybe I just put myself in the right place at the right time. Greg wanted to talk. When he finally stopped I offered to tell him another story. He wanted to listen.' David gave Lisa a crooked smile. 'I gave him a version of your Wednesday lunchtime presentation. Not as well delivered as yours, but it seemed to be enough.'

Lisa nodded. Her smile was warm. 'Thanks again, David. It was a pretty special thing to do.'

'Do I get another hug?'

The look became withering. 'So much for the pledge, David James.'

'Sorry, I forgot. Only a momentary lapse, I promise.'

'Just as well you're not an alcoholic.' Lisa got to her feet and stifled a yawn. 'Sleep well, David. It's going to be a big day tomorrow.'

'Big' wasn't really the word for it. From the moment David set foot in the hospital, a mere six hours later, it seemed as if nothing else was going to happen that day which would be of any interest to anyone. The entire hospital was humming with the news that the first heart transplant in Christchurch was planned, and David began what he anticipated would be an emotional day with uncharacteristic apprehension.

His visit to Stephen Taylor and his nervous but excited family contrasted sharply with his next stop in the intensive care unit. There was no hope amongst the relatives of Stephanie Barry. There was a calm acceptance that only thinly covered the beginnings of a grief process which had, so far, been held firmly in abeyance, particularly by Greg. The visit had been difficult but David felt that Stephanie and her family deserved the dignity of her being treated like any other pre-operative patient.

This dignity was automatically extended by the staff in the theatre to which Stephanie Barry was delivered a short time later, still connected to her life support system. As David scrubbed, he could see through the window into the adjacent theatre where Alan Bennett was already under way, getting Stephen onto bypass. Gerry Greene gave a thumbs-up signal that made David smile as he reached for the sterile towel. Had Stephen

Taylor been conscious, no doubt he would have made
an identical gesture.

Stephanie's theatre was crowded. A renal surgical
team stood by ready to harvest her kidneys—David
knew there were patients lined up to receive the organs
later that morning. Theatre schedules had been dis-
rupted hospital-wide but no one amongst the staff were
grumbling, apart from Lewis Tanner. The atmosphere
in this operating room was subdued but it didn't occur
to David to request any background music. It was a
grim task and one that they all wanted to complete successfully but as quickly as possible.

David made the initial long midline incision from the
jugular notch to the pubis. As he began opening the
chest, the renal team moved in to remove the kidneys.
He glanced up as the renal surgeon requested a clamp,
stating that he was about to clamp the renal pedicles.

'Start the heparin, thanks.' David nodded to the
anaesthetist. 'And I'll have the cardioplegia needle.' It
was placed in his hand and he inserted it into the ascending aorta and secured it. As soon as the blood-
thinning properties of the heparin had taken effect,
David signalled the anaesthetist to activate the pressure
bag that would infuse the heart with the chilled cardioplegic solution. It took two minutes for sufficient cardiac cooling to occur and only a matter of a few more
minutes for David to divide the main arteries and veins
and remove the heart. The organ was placed in ice-cold
saline solution and David led the way into the adjacent
theatre.

His registrar and a volunteer general surgeon were
going to close up and had assured David that the end
result would be as visually acceptable as they could
manage.

He couldn't afford to think about Stephanie Barry any more at this point. He had to concentrate on trimming and preparing the donor heart, a task that was carried out on a separate sterile table in Stephen Taylor's theatre. The marked change in atmosphere helped enormously. The positive side of the equation was paramount here.

When the preparations were complete, David moved rapidly towards the scrub room. He would have to re-scrub and re-gown, before starting the second part of the procedure—the removal of Stephen Taylor's heart.

He nodded at his assistant surgeon. 'That's great, Alan. You've cannulated the aorta in exactly the right place.'

'It was as high as I could make it. Are you ready for cross-clamping?'

David nodded again. 'Let's do it.' He concentrated fiercely on his excision, holding the memory of his trimming of the donor heart as closely as he could. The match needed to be as exact as possible.

'How are the haemodynamics looking, Gerry?'

'Great—pH is fine, arterial and venous saturation looking good. No problems at this end, Dave.'

David lifted Stephen's diseased heart clear of his chest cavity. It was carried away in a stainless-steel bowl that matched the one now on his trolley containing the healthy donor heart. David experienced a familiar jolt as he gazed briefly into the surgical field of Stephen's chest, devoid of the vital organ. This really was an extraordinary thing to do.

The atmosphere in Theatre changed again as David began the implantation.

'This is the easy part,' he told his team. 'Just a bit of fancy plumbing, really.' He broke the unusually tense silence he had been working in up till now and began a running commentary for the benefit of the large theatre team, none of whom had previously witnessed a cardiac transplant.

'We'll start at the level of Stephen's left superior pulmonary vein. Stay suture, thanks.' David placed the first temporary stitch. 'Now I'll have some double-armed 3.0 polypropolene and we'll use a whip stitch to join the left side of the atrial wall until we reach the septum.' He worked in silence for some minutes, tied the suture as he reached his starting point again, then held up the extra length of polypropolene.

'Cut, thanks,' he instructed the scrub nurse. 'Now we open up the donor right atrium,' he explained. 'I'm using a curvilinear incision up towards the appendage to avoid any later damage to the sinus node. Now we'll join up the right atrium. Suture, thanks.'

The whole team worked together brilliantly. David was very glad he had Gerry overseeing the haemodynamic status of his patient. It took a lot of the pressure off him and allowed him to concentrate totally on his careful suturing. The stitches were tiny and too numerous to consider counting. David was aware of his weariness as he worked to join the pulmonary arteries and the aortic openings. He straightened and pushed his shoulders back eventually, hearing a click in his neck which heralded some relief from the discomfort.

'Large-bore needle,' he ordered. 'Thirteen-gauge if you've got it.' He inserted the needle to evacuate air from the left ventricle of the heart. Turning his attention to extracting any air from the aorta, David ordered the removal of the cross-clamp as he applied strong suction to the needle vent. Air was taken from the right ventricle through the point at which the pulmonary arteries had been joined and the final suture was tied, with David confident that the danger of air embolism following the surgery had been minimised as much as possible.

Movement of Stephen's new heart had begun as David tied the final stitch, but it was uncontrolled and ineffective. A nurse stood by, holding the miniature paddles that were used for direct internal defibrillation, but David waited, watching the heart. It gave a more vigorous jerk of its own accord within thirty seconds and Gerry's voice was triumphant.

'We have sinus rhythm, folks!'

'We have lift-off.' David grinned. He raised a fist. *'Yes!'*

An excited buzz of conversation broke out. David nodded at the team of senior technicians who were responsible for the bypass technology.

'Start ventilation, Gerry. Let's get this lad off bypass. I'll have a wedge pressure, too, thanks. I want to assess cardiac function before we close up.'

At last it was over. Stephen had come through the major procedure with flying colours. He was well wired up for post-operative assessment but the care from now on would be routine, apart from the immunosuppressive drugs and reversed isolation nursing techniques.

David's stiff neck wasn't helped by the congratulatory back thump he received from Gerry and the vigorous handshaking from Alan Bennett and at least half a dozen others. With a pleasurable anticipation of a hot shower, David escaped the party atmosphere, noticing as he passed that the adjacent theatre was again in full swing as the first kidney transplant was being done. Still wearing his theatre gear, David went to the recovery room to check on Stephen. Lisa was already there.

'He looks great!' she told him excitedly. 'The family's all waiting outside. Could you talk to them?'

Of course he could. And did for some time. David still hadn't made it to the showers, however, as a small media contingent purposefully entered the waiting room.

'Could you give us a brief interview, please, Mr James?' The square end of a television camera moved in, the fluffy cover of a microphone hovering overhead. 'Tell us whatever you can about Christchurch's first cardiac transplant surgery.'

David hesitated. 'I doubt that the family wants any publicity. I must insist on the privacy of my patient being respected.'

'We don't mind.' It was Stephen's mother who spoke up. 'We feel like we're part of an historic occasion here. And it may be our only chance to thank the family of the donor.'

The camera changed direction.

'Could you repeat that, please, Mrs…?'

David couldn't escape it. Everybody wanted to offer congratulations. The bedside television sets of patients seemed to have his face on them every time he walked past. The flowers and cards that were pouring in for Stephen were causing problems for administrative staff, and even poor Greg Barry had been cornered by a television crew. David had felt very angry about that. Who had broken the rules of confidentiality? Too many people had been aware of the situation ever since Lisa had brought it to hospital-wide attention. Surprisingly, Greg had been as willing to talk as Stephen's family.

'It's actually helped me a lot, making that decision,' Greg explained to David when the surgeon had rung to apologise on behalf of the hospital. 'I don't mind other people knowing. Maybe it might help others to make the same decision themselves and let some good come out of tragedy.'

Certainly, hotlines had been set up and advertised on television for free phone calls to gain information about living wills, and a new debate began on whether an organ donation card system should be set up and incorporated into driving licences.

Stephen was doing brilliantly. His colour looked better than David had ever seen it and his renal function was already improving.

David escaped, late in the afternoon, to get some fresh air. The area of Hagley Park that bordered the other side of the river from the botanical gardens was a sea of daffodils at present. It was an inviting and relaxing environment which David shared with many other strollers, their children and numerous dogs. He was feeling much refreshed by the time he turned back to the hospital. Cutting through the staff car park, his eye was immediately drawn to the distinctive outline of Lisa's little red car. He ran an appreciative finger over the shiny paintwork and stooped to peer in at the low-slung seats. Only room for two people in that car.

'Fancy a ride, then?'

Lisa's breezy voice startled him. David stepped back a pace. 'Yeah, I would. But not right now, thanks. I've got rather a lot of paperwork. I want to write up my surgery report. Are you escaping?'

'Mmm. It's been a big day. I could do with a break. I might even get home in time to watch the news. I understand you're a media star as well now.'

David felt embarrassed. The cardiological side of Stephen's treatment until now had been ignored in favour of the drama of the surgery. The limelight had been all his. Again.

'Everybody's very impressed.' Lisa was selecting her car key from a full ring.

'Everybody except you.' David stepped closer again. Close enough to prevent her inserting her key into the door.

'Why should you want to impress me?' Lisa looked disconcerted.

'Damned if I know.' David stared at the face that had haunted his nights for weeks now. He'd better ignore the body, which had been even more of a sleep-killer. 'You're the most aggravating, opinionated and bolshy woman I've ever come across.' He took a deep breath. It was now or never. 'You're also the most sexually attractive, exciting and out-of-reach woman I've ever come across.'

Lisa's tone was matter-of-fact. 'You want to sleep with me.'

'Damned right I do.' But even as he rasped out the words David knew they came nowhere near expressing how he felt. Sleeping with her—that didn't cover it. Sex wasn't exactly it either. He wanted to be with her in a way he'd never been with any woman. And in a way she'd never been with any man.

'Why didn't you just ask?'

'Oh, sure.' David didn't like her cool appraisal of him. 'That would have gone down really well. Even better than flirting.'

'It would have been more honest. Who knows?' Something glinted in the brown depths to which David's gaze was locked. 'I might have said yes. Why don't you ask me now?'

'And become another notch on the old belt? No, thanks.'

'Isn't that what your sexual conquests have always been for you?' Lisa asked calmly. 'Chalk them up and get rid of them—in the nicest possible way, of course— if they get any ideas about something more. Sauce for the goose, David. Fair's fair.'

'This is different.'

'Why?'

'Because I feel different.' David put a hand on the door of her car. He wasn't going to let her make any attempt to escape just yet. 'I don't want to be a number. A slot on a time line between say…*ski* trips. I want it to be something special.'

'But you don't want something special.'

'How do you know?' David's voice rose. He was going out on a limb here in his admission. He felt torn by the desire to explain exactly how he felt, how important it seemed to be, but the fear of her reaction made it impossible. He was trying something that was costing him a lot of emotional effort right now. It was just typical of Lisa to want to argue about it.

'I overheard you talking to Mike the other day. He's rapt to be back with Anne and the baby. You listened to him rave on about the joys of marriage and the magic of kids with an expression like you were sucking on lemons.'

'I knew it was going to change things. I wouldn't get so much time with Mike.'

'So now you're looking for a new playmate. That's fine, but don't kid yourself that you want something special. You don't want marriage. You certainly don't want children.'

'Neither do you.'

'That's right. I don't.'

'So what's the problem, then? We're perfect for each other. I want you, Lisa Kennedy, and I think, maybe…' David leaned closer and noted her dilating pupils and quick intake of breath with satisfaction. 'I think, maybe, you want me, too.'

'Not on your terms.'

'What terms?'

'The "something special" terms. "Special" implies something worth keeping. A relationship that's allowed to develop and lead on into something more. Something more implies marriage…children.'

'Not necessarily.'

'In that case, "something special" implies a relationship that's going to cause a lot of pain when it's terminated.'

'Why should it be terminated?'

'Because there's no commitment. Why start something that's either going nowhere or going to end in disaster? It's something I've successfully avoided so far.'

David felt caught in a catch-22 situation. He couldn't win with Lisa if he offered any sort of commitment. He couldn't win with himself if he settled for anything less. 'And you intend to keep on avoiding it?'

'Yes.'

'Perhaps there's something else you should take into consideration.'

'Which is?'

'This.' David's hand snaked behind her neck, beneath the soft tumble of curls. The pressure he applied was gentle, but firm. At the same time he bent his head and his lips covered hers with a determination David had never before experienced.

He expected resistance—maybe a slap on the face or even a knee in the groin—but the fear of any consequences dissolved the instant his lips made contact with hers. They were softer that he had dreamed possible, the taste of her mouth sweeter. He had to taste more. David cupped her face in his hands, totally unable to prevent deepening the kiss. When her tongue flickered in response, David felt a wave of heat through his whole body. He was aware of her hands on his neck, her fingers in his hair. God, she wanted this as much as he did.

With a self-control David would never have believed he possessed, he broke off the kiss.

'Think about that, Lisa Kennedy.' His self-control even extended to making his tone nonchalant. 'If that's not something special then I don't know what is.'

If nothing else, the kiss had clearly given her food for thought. David did not seek out Lisa's company for the rest of the week. In fact, he was so busy that their planned meeting to discuss their research project on Wednesday night had to be postponed.

Media attention on Stephen Taylor had faded quickly and the teenager was doing extremely well. Mechanically ventilated in the immediate post-operative period, moved onto intermittent mandatory ventilation before transfer to the surgical intensive care unit, he had been weaned from assisted ventilation completely by the following morning. No bleeding problems had been experienced. Cardiac, respiratory and renal functions were more than satisfactory and Stephen was already talking hopefully about going home. Not that that would be a possibility for some weeks yet. Mike and Lisa had already done the first cardiac biopsy at three days post-surgery to check for any signs of rejection. The result had been excellent and the next of a series of biopsies was planned for the following week.

David's Wednesday morning theatre case was a patient from a different cardiology team, and he was under pressure from the respiratory side of his duties. A young patient with what should have been routine surgery for a minor lung lesion was experiencing complications that worried David. Already in the hospital well after hours, initiating a new course of treatment, David was kept even later when a major car accident sent him back to Theatre to attempt a repair on a badly crushed chest. They had to admit defeat at 4 a.m. and David returned briefly to his room without any hope of sleeping.

He felt dispirited. Another busy day was lined up tomorrow and even the weekend didn't promise any rest or relaxation. The conference in Queenstown was only a week away and David had still not prepared the paper he was expected to deliver. He was also lonely. He wanted someone to talk to about how he felt, losing the car accident victim.

He knew that the person who would understand best would be Lisa. Who else shared his passion and commitment to his career to the same degree? He knew nobody else who had avoided any distraction by a meaningful relationship in their private lives. Lisa would understand and that understanding would bring them closer together. Gerry was right. It was the bad times that really counted—that gave an opportunity for growth. The good times were the icing on the cake.

What good times? David snorted. One kiss? Lisa might be acting differently around him now, less confrontational, but there was a new wariness there as well. She hadn't given any indication that she might want to extend their professional relationship into something more personal and she'd made it sound as if that had been *his* decision when he'd been forced to cancel their planned meeting.

'Just let me know when you can fit it in,' she had said coolly. 'I'll make sure *I'm* available.'

Available. Ha! David sat on the edge of his bed, his shoulders slumped wearily. He rubbed his eyes, trying to remove the gritty sensation caused by lack of sleep. Available for sex, possibly. But that wasn't good enough for David. He wanted more. He wanted to be part of her life and for her to want his involvement in her life just as much. He wanted— God, *no*! David buried his face in his hands with a groan. He wanted to *marry* the woman!

'You're overtired,' he told himself, splashing liberal amounts of cold water on his face a few minutes later. Overtired and overwrought. It had been an extremely emotional week one way and another. But *marriage*! That was the last thing he wanted. The last thing Lisa wanted. He could just imagine her incredulous laughter if he voiced the suggestion. Or a caustic response along the lines of, 'Not in this lifetime, mate!'

David could feel angry, just imagining her response. He tried to turn the anger on himself. It had been his own bizarre idea after all. If he was stupid enough to even consider marriage before a first date had been agreed to then he deserved everything he got. No. He changed his mind and redirected his anger back at Lisa. Had this been the tack she had used to manipulate Lewis Tanner? Could that be why the infamous ring had appeared in the first place?

The solution was easy. Don't start anything, David warned himself. Men were supposed to be much better than women at letting their heads rule their hearts. He knew that the further the woman got under his skin the harder it would be to get over her. If her sexual promise lived up to that kiss then he would be a goner. And she had spelt out very clearly that she had no desire for 'something special'. It would be far preferable not to start anything than to get deeper in than he was already and then get dumped. David nodded with a resigned grimace as he reached to turn on the shower. That was it. He simply wouldn't let anything start.

But he knew, even as he let the needles of hot water erase his physical fatigue, that it was too late. The start had been made the instant he'd set eyes on Lisa, no matter how successfully he thought he'd denied it since. Now he was powerless to call a halt. The best he could hope for was a status quo and perhaps the natural death of an unnourished seedling. It was a technique he had used himself when he knew that a girlfriend had wanted more than he was capable of offering.

Now, for the first time, he could understand what they had gone through. He resolved, with a genuine determination this time, never to flirt again. The thought of past girlfriends was not cheering. Why couldn't he have fallen for one of *them*? Uniformly pleasant to be with, cheerful and eager to please. They had been ideal. *All* of them. Why, in God's name, did it have to happen with the most demanding, aggravating and challenging woman he'd ever come across?

One who didn't even want what he was capable of offering for the first time in his life. A commitment that would transcend a sexual liaison. A meeting of souls and not just bodies. Something that David knew, with a bitter realisation, that he would never have again to offer anyone else.

CHAPTER SEVEN

THE wariness was now mutual.

They were circling each other at a distance. When their orbits crossed there was a peculiar tension that seemed to David equally capable of exploding into a fracas or dissolving into wild, physical passion. Fortunately, the presence of other people prevented either outcome and David had been as careful as Lisa not to engineer any time alone together.

It had been quite easy to dictate the letter, outlining his approval of the budget for the research project, and send it on with the suggestion that Lisa organise the applications for clearance with the various authorities. Her response had been rapid, positive and also in writing. Perhaps they could conduct their entire collaboration by correspondence. It would take some time to get the go-ahead in any case and David had other things on his mind.

Like getting the medical illustrations department to make up the slides he needed for his presentation at next weekend's conference. He had almost reneged on his resolution to cut the flirting. The girl in medical illustrations had been ripe for a compliment on her ability to cope under pressure with maybe a special smile or appreciative glance. But David had held back. Instead, he sought out Alan Bennett as he came out of Theatre that afternoon and asked if he could throw his weight around as head of department to ensure the job was done on time.

'Of course.' Alan had nodded. He gave David a speculative glance as he ripped off his mask. 'I wouldn't have thought it would be any problem for you to have persuaded Ginette to cooperate. Are you feeling short on charm today?'

'Lisa has cured me.' David watched as Alan stripped off his gown and gloves, unaware of the despondent tone he had used. Lisa was right. Using sexuality as an advantage was chauvinistic and unacceptable. It was a potentially hurtful pastime and David had a new respect for the power of emotions. Unrequited lust was not to be recommended. It felt like a bad dose of flu—permeating every aspect of life. It helped to think of it as a viral illness. Maybe it was simply a matter of weathering it out. The symptoms would fade and with a bit of luck he would then be inoculated against a recurrence.

Alan was now regarding David with frank curiosity. 'Got time for a quick coffee?'

David followed his boss into the small theatre staffroom. They were alone as they helped themselves to coffee and biscuits. Alan broke the silence.

'What has Lisa cured you of, exactly?'

'Specifically—flirting.' David's grin was brief. 'Generally, I think I might be cured of believing myself to be more trustworthy than the average man is presumed to be.'

Alan's smile was thoughtful. 'Lisa's trust might be hard to win, but once you've got it, it's there for ever.'

David sighed. 'Why does she have to make it so bloody difficult, Alan? I know she's been let down but it's kind of insulting to be tarred by the same brush she used on Lewis Tanner.' He raised his eyebrows questioningly over the rim of his coffee-cup. 'How come you get to escape the mind set she has against men?'

Alan gave David a long, silent stare. Whatever he saw in David's expression seemed enough to end his indecision and he gave a slight nod. 'Lewis wasn't the first man to let her down.'

'Really?' His coffee forgotten, David leaned forward in his chair, eager to discover more. He knew so little of Lisa's background, and its importance suddenly seemed paramount. 'You know her pretty well, don't you, Alan?'

'I'm a father figure.' Alan smiled. 'Though she would be appalled if she heard me say that. She doesn't have much time for her own father.'

'Why not?' David prompted quickly.

'Lisa's mother died when she was quite young. Eleven or twelve. Her father wasted no time in replacing her, apparently. Lisa never got on with her stepmother.'

'Does she have any brothers or sisters?'

'Two brothers. They were quite a bit younger and had no trouble accepting a substitute mother. Lisa rebelled, her father supported her stepmother and Lisa gradually got pushed further out from the family. I doubt she'll ever forgive her father for what she sees as a complete betrayal—both of her mother and herself.'

'But that's well in the past. She's thirty-one—she must have been away from home for at least ten years.'

Alan nodded. 'She left home officially as soon as she started medical school but she'd been in boarding school for five years before that. There was an involvement at medical school. A much older student, I gather.'

'Another search for a father figure?'

'Maybe. It was very serious as far as Lisa was concerned. I don't know what happened but it was a disaster. He let her down so badly she told me once she had no intention of ever letting someone that close again.'

'And then there was Lewis.'

Alan nodded again but this time he smiled. 'Indeed. Though her methods of self-protection were well honed by then. He didn't hurt her as much as confirm her opinion of men in general. She's well armoured now.'

'You're telling me. Impenetrable barrier.'

Alan spoke carefully. 'She might like to think it is but I know differently. She's got a great deal to give the right person. If she gets hurt again she might be able to lock it away for ever.' He gave David a sharp glance. 'Don't hurt her, David. Lisa is a very special woman.'

'I'm aware of that.' David lowered his voice as several nurses entered the room. 'I have no intention of hurting her.' He rose slowly to his feet and picked up his cup of now cold coffee and an untouched biscuit. He shrugged. 'I don't think I'm going to get the chance, anyway.'

The woman from the administrative offices might also have responded to a bit of flattery but David knew he was cured when he didn't even think of trying. The month of temporary accommodation in the junior staff quarters had expired a week ago. Some overseas junior doctors were arriving within a fortnight and Administration was obliged to provide accommodation for them. Could he please make sure his room was available by then?

David had assured the woman he could—and would. What was one more hassle after all? Moving away from being Sean Findlay's neighbour would probably be beneficial. David had been astonished at the way he had shot across to his door and opened it last night, on hearing voices as Sean unlocked his door. He had peered around the edge, feeling ridiculously childish, but the relief of finding that Sean had not persuaded his senior registrar to experience the delights of his nocturnal company had made it worthwhile at the time.

The ecstatic postcard from Melanie which had arrived on his desk that morning had rubbed a little more salt into the wound. Her love was very far from unrequited, though no wedding arrangements were forthcoming quite yet. They were taking a trip to the Great Barrier Reef shortly—a much more conducive setting for a proposal.

Queenstown would be, too, David had thought suddenly. He'd had a vivid image of flying down a snowy slope on skis, Lisa keeping pace with him...just. He would stop with a spectacular flourish that would send a huge spray of sparkling snow against the brilliant clear blue of the sky, lift his goggles and shout, 'I can't possibly live without you, Lisa. Marry me!'

David shuddered. He certainly had a bad dose. Just as well he didn't know the first thing about skiing. And, according to Mike, Lisa was still undecided about whether she would even attend the conference.

'I imagine the recreational activities on Sunday morning will tempt her along,' he told David on Wednesday afternoon as they were both preparing to leave work.

'I haven't seen the programme for social events.' David leaned back against the corridor wall. 'What's on offer?'

'What isn't? Skiing, bungee jumping, a deer park and historic village tour, four-wheel-drive trip to the historic mining settlement at Macetown. The Shotover jet-boat ride or a trip out to the Skippers Canyon.'

'Wow. There's more on the social agenda than the clinical side.'

'Of course.' Mike grinned. 'Why else do we all go to these things?'

'I suppose Lisa will go skiing.' David damped down the replay of his fantasy.

'More likely bungee jumping. She's a great one for picking something risky.'

'Really?' She wasn't prepared to take a risk on *him*. After his conversation with Alan Bennett, David could understand that the possibility of serious physical injury was less offputting than an emotional equivalent. Right now, David felt inclined to share the preference.

The sight of Lisa, following a new arrival through the coronary care doors, caused a now familiar sinking sensation mingled with the pain of a very frustrated desire.

'Not for me, though,' Mike was saying. 'I know exactly where I plan to spend Sunday morning.'

'The deer park?'

'No way, mate. I'll be in the same place I'll spend Saturday night after the conference dinner. In bed.'

'Sounds restful.'

'Don't you believe it. Anne's coming too.'

'Is she?'

'You bet. Things are better than they've ever been, Dave. Her mum's doing really well at home now and Anne's sister is coming down for the weekend and will look after Sophie as well. It'll be the first time we've had to ourselves in a very long time. It's going to work out—I know it is. We both know it.'

'That's great.' David smiled at Mike's obvious delight. 'Hey, I've just thought of something. That flat you've been in while you were separated—can I take it over? I've got to move out of the staff quarters next week.'

'Sorry, mate. The landlord had someone lined up the day I handed in my notice.'

'Oh.' David's face registered his disappointment. Then his expression changed. The corridor outside the doors of CCU had suddenly filled with a small group of people, including a woman in a wedding dress. David's jaw dropped. First he spotted Lisa and now he was faced with the sight of a bride looking like a giant meringue, full-length dress, veil, bouquet and all. There was just far too much of it around. Why couldn't people get on with their lives, without messing them up with archaic concepts like marriage?

And why did he seem totally unable to avoid his own preoccupation with it? He knew why, of course, and the thought of Lisa wearing a fluffy white creation like that was ludicrous enough to make David laugh aloud and ease the tension he felt. Mike turned his head at the sound in time to see the numbers in the group increase. The volume of their agitated conversation also increased. There was more than one argument in progress.

'Come on. I can't wait to find out what this is all about.' Mike strode down the corridor. 'Could I ask you all to move into the relatives' room, please, folks? We need to keep the noise level down a bit. We've got some rather unwell people nearby.'

The bride burst into tears. 'You mean Daddy, don't you? He's going to die!'

The young man in the grey morning suit glared at her. 'Well, don't blame *me* if he does.'

'He didn't want me to marry you in the first place.'

'We're not married yet—thanks to your father's histrionics.'

'Are you suggesting my husband pretended to have a heart attack just to interrupt your wedding?' An older

woman in a beige suit with a matching hat leaned forward and poked the young man in the chest. 'How *dare*
you! George was right about you all along.'

'Please!' Mike said loudly. '*This* way. All of you.'

The group shuffled sideways reluctantly. David was
watching it all in total amazement. His eyes focused on
the man who put an arm around the groom's shoulder.

'Don't I know you?' David queried.

'No,' the man answered quickly. 'I don't believe
we've ever met.'

Another young man in the same attire as the groom
looked at David curiously. 'Have you bought a car recently?'

'I wouldn't call it a car exactly.' David grinned.
'More of a conversation piece. It doesn't go.'

'That'd be right. And you probably paid five times
as much as it's worth.'

'The man's a crook!' someone called.

The woman in the beige suit nodded emphatically.
'Talk to my husband, George,' she advised. 'If he re-
covers.' She sighed heavily. '*He* could sell you something decent—at an honest price.'

Mike had stopped trying to move the group. He was
barely able to suppress a smile. Lisa strode out of the
CCU doors at that moment.

'Just *what* is going on out here?' she demanded.

'Ah, Dr Kennedy.' The beige suit moved away from
David. 'It was so lucky you were on duty today. So
nice for George to have someone he knows from the
Classic Car Club. Can I see him now, please? Is he
going to be all right? It's all the stress, you know. It's
just been too much for all of us.'

'He's going to be fine, Mrs Hammond. It looks like
it's a severe attack of angina. We can't find any evi-

dence of a heart attack. It's a shame he forgot to take his medication to the wedding.'

'I told you!' the groom snarled. 'He was just trying to foul things up yet again.'

'And he was right!' the bride sobbed. 'You only want to marry me so you can work in a decent business. It was all your father's idea.'

'Well, I never!' Another middle-aged woman, in a pink dress, clutched her matching handbag to her chest. 'I told you she wasn't good enough for you, Dwayne. Selling BMWs has made the whole family into unbearable snobs.'

'That's what you need.' The best man nodded at David thoughtfully. 'A BMW. Dad's probably got just the thing. You can get rid of the bucket of rust Clive here has ripped you off with.'

'I don't rip anyone off. And I don't put ridiculous mark-ups on cars that decent folk can't afford anyway.'

'Cheap rubbish, that's all you sell. Only fit for the scrap yard.'

Lisa was looking stunned. Mike was now grinning openly. The bride was sobbing uncontrollably and David watched her with some interest. He couldn't see any indication of vital orthodontic work needed.

'I guarantee satisfaction,' Clive stated loudly. He put his hand on David's shoulder. 'If you want your money back on your car, young man, you can have it. Every penny.'

'Well...I...' David caught Lisa's eye. She was now standing between the hysterical bride and Mrs Hammond. She was trying hard not to laugh.

'Take it quick. You've got witnesses,' a new voice broke in loudly.

'Shut up, Doreen. This has got nothing to do with you.'

'Don't you tell me to shut up. You know perfectly well your brother's as crooked as they come. And you're not much better—falsifying your tax return.'

'Doreen, shut *up*!'

'And I'll bet your nephew got that girl pregnant on purpose. It's all about money, isn't it? It's all your whole family cares about.'

'I'm *not* pregnant!' the bride wailed. 'I only *thought* I was.'

'That wasn't why we're getting married,' the groom added. 'I love Charlene. She loves me.'

'No, I don't. Not any more. I don't want to marry you.' The bride wiped her nose on her sleeve. 'I want to see Daddy.'

'So do I.' Mrs Hammond's arm was firmly around her daughter. 'He's going to be so happy about this, darling. You'll see, it's all for the best. And don't you worry about the cost of the reception. It doesn't matter a bit.'

David's gaze hadn't left Lisa's throughout the last rapid-fire exchange between the acrimonious group. They were both smiling but now it had nothing to do with the farce being enacted around them. They were smiling at each other, enjoying each other's amusement. David felt a wash of emotion much deeper than amusement. A feeling of caring about how someone else felt which was entirely selfless. A warm, melting sensation that went right through him.

Instinctively, he recognised the unfamiliar sensation. He wanted to throw his own voice into the babble of arguments they had been caught up in. He wanted to shout, 'I love you.' Or at least mouth the words now that he had made what seemed to be the most exciting discovery ever. The whole situation was so ridiculous it was almost appropriate, but even as David opened his mouth Mrs Hammond used her free hand to grip Lisa's arm.

'Take us to George, Dr Kennedy. He needs us.'

The white veil floated behind the women. Clive, the car dealer, looked at the groom.

'I guess that's that. Let's go and have a drink, son.' He didn't look back at David. 'You wouldn't want to hock off BMWs anyway. Where's the challenge in that?'

Mike ushered the remaining Hammond relatives into the waiting room. He nodded at David as he closed the door behind him.

'I'd better go and make sure George is coping with the excitement of the news.' He smiled. 'Want me to put in a word for you?'

'About what?' For an insane second he thought Mike was offering to let Lisa know what he had discovered.

'A BMW.' Mike laughed. 'Doesn't pay to pass up a good opportunity. You could have got your money back there.'

'I'm not bothered,' David assured him. And he wasn't. At least not about missing that opportunity. He wasn't going to carry on avoiding Lisa's company, however. Any opportunity that presented itself in that direction he was going to grab with open hands. Somehow he was going to persuade Lisa that he deserved her trust. And when that happened he was going to make damned sure he never let her down.

The conference in the Central Otago tourist destination of Queenstown should have provided any number of such opportunities, but by Sunday morning David was despairing of finding any at all.

He had flown in early on the Saturday morning on the chartered flight, catering for a large number of the conference delegates, disappointed that his searching hadn't revealed Lisa to be one of the passengers. Perhaps she had decided against coming after all. They had all been ferried directly to the conference venue and the pace had been relentless for the rest of the day. Presentations, satellite meeting and panel discussions had run back to back. The cardiology side had run parallel to the surgical interests, but David's presentation had been part of a combined session that had run for the first half of the afternoon.

David was between Mike Foster, presenting a physicians' perspective of diagnosis and treatment, and another cardiologist, looking at the haemodynamic and angiocardiographic considerations of the congenital heart condition of tetralogy of Fallot. David was well prepared to update delegates on the advances in surgical treatment. The three speakers would then form a panel to answer any questions from their audience. The discussion at the conclusion was lively and it was only then that David spotted Lisa in the packed auditorium, sitting near the back, beside Alan.

The drug companies funding the conference outdid themselves in preparing the Saturday evening entertainment. Black tie had been requested and David was still fumbling with a cufflink as he arrived, having had to rush to shower and change following the final satellite group he had attended.

The hotel venue was lavishly decorated with hundreds of red, heart-shaped balloons. The numbers of people had nearly doubled as partners had joined the delegates and David was disappointed to find the seating pre-arranged to mix the representatives from the various centres. David was at a table with an Australian surgeon and his wife, an Auckland cardiologist, who was accompanied by his wife and daughter, and a registrar from Dunedin who was, like David, without a partner.

Mike and Anne were at a nearby table and David was aware of a distinctly unpleasant wave of jealousy when he saw that Alan and Lisa were also sitting together as partners. Lisa looked stunning. Her hair was piled up in some kind of a loose knot arrangement that allowed a few curls to escape and, in David's opinion, rather too much of a beautifully tanned skin was revealed by the shoestring straps and high hemline of the elegant black dress she wore. David poked at the heart-shaped terrine they had received as an entrée and wondered if he was going to enjoy the evening after all.

He had little choice. A popular street theatre group had been engaged for entertainment and they had unearthed or invented a whole new field of hilarious jokes and stories about doctors in general and cardiac specialties in particular. Many of them were acted out and audience participation was demanded and became more enthusiastically offered as the evening wore on and the waiters tirelessly refilled champagne glasses.

The dessert of strawberries, ice cream and tiny heart-shaped biscuits had barely been cleared away when each table was presented with a bag of objects. They had to devise a new or improved version of a heart operation and then demonstrate it to the rest of the gathering.

David was soon caught up in playing with the balloons, straws, paper clips and string they had been provided with. He thought his group had done a creditable job of revising a mitral valve replacement and it was amusingly presented by the Australian surgeon, but it was Alan's group that got by far the biggest laughs. They had added one of the red, heart-shaped balloons to their booty, which Lisa held clutched to her chest. She lay on their table as Alan seriously explained the highly unlikely theory behind their new method of balloon angioplasty.

Even David was convulsed with laughter as the red balloon popped unexpectedly and the street theatre group joined in as a voluntary transplant team.

It was after midnight as the gathering broke up. David saw Mike and Anne hurry away, hand in hand. He hadn't even had a chance to speak to Lisa but she and Alan were now surrounded by a laughing group, congratulating them on their impromptu presentation. Frustrated and suddenly weary of the whole event, David slipped away to his room.

The foyer was beginning to fill up with people when he came down again the next morning. David scanned the lists for the recreational events on offer. He wanted to know what Lisa was planning. Groups were already on the move to board the line of buses parked outside the main entrance to the hotel. Bungee jumping was surprisingly popular and the Shotover jet-boat excursion was fully booked. He was too late for the four-wheel-drive trip to Macetown and there was no point in going up Coronet Peak for the skiing. David spotted the names of both Alan and Lisa on the trip for the Skippers Canyon. Hurriedly, he added his own name, taking the only slot still vacant for the six-seater minibus. He would be playing gooseberry but that was preferable to having no time with Lisa at all.

The driver, a man in his forties with a cheerful smile and a cowboy hat, was leaning against the minibus, smoking a cigarette. David thought he would be the first passenger to board the vehicle but the driver grinned at him.

'Good-oh, another customer. I was beginning to think you'd all chickened out.'

It would be Lisa who had beaten him to it. Typical! Not only that, she had taken the seat with the best view, alongside but slightly behind the driver's seat. It gave a clear view through the front windscreen.

'Hi.' David greeted her casually. 'I thought you'd be hitting the slopes with your penchant for skiing.' He hadn't intended any innuendo but Lisa's expression tightened noticeably.

'I can ski anytime. Besides, it gets very boring, repeating the same activity endlessly.'

'Does it?' David's query was polite but he wasn't inclined to agree. He could think of one activity he wouldn't mind repeating for the rest of his life—as long as his partner was the woman he was now seated next to. 'Oh, sorry,' he added quickly. 'Were you saving this seat for Alan?'

Her glance was curious, her voice a little unsure. Was she as aware as him of the contact their thighs were forced into by the width of the seat?

'Alan's not coming after all,' Lisa told him. 'He's got a bit of a hangover after last night.' She looked away and seemed to take a deep breath. 'Sit wherever you like.'

'I like it here,' David said mischievously. He settled himself a little more comfortably. Lisa looked studiously out of the window but didn't try and edge away from the now firmer contact of their legs.

David's Auckland cardiology companion from last night's dinner strode towards the minibus driver. His voice carried through the open door.

'Look, I'm sorry about this but someone's just warned my wife off from doing this trip. She has a fear of heights and we had no idea that the road was so primitive. She and my daughter have decided to go for the deer park trip. I'll have to go with them.'

'No worries,' the driver said. 'It's all paid for, anyway.' He leapt aboard the bus and smiled broadly at his only passengers. 'We'll be able to go a lot faster with fewer people on board. Either of you two want to chicken out and give me a morning off?'

David and Lisa both shook their heads. Their driver sighed theatrically and flopped into the driver's seat. 'Spread yourselves around, then,' he invited. 'There's stacks of room.'

David and Lisa both stared out through the windscreen as the bus lurched and then picked up speed. Neither of them moved.

'My name's Harry.' The driver seemed to take his eyes off the road for a considerable length of time as he tugged his hat in his passengers' direction. 'Had to give up being a ski instructor when I broke my legs. Boy, I miss those ski bunnies, but, hey! This is much more exciting.'

Lisa's eyebrows had been rising steadily. She caught David's eye and he grinned.

'Is there something about this trip I haven't been told?'

'I believe it's rather spectacular. Somebody did mention hair-raising.'

'You can always hold my hand,' David invited. He

expected a rebuff—an exasperated look at the very least—but Lisa's mouth curved just a little.

'I'll keep that in mind.'

David stared at her profile. He was rather tempted to take the hand lying in her lap anyway but Harry's enthusiastic wave towards the side window distracted him.

'Look at those suckers!' Harry crashed down through the gears and slowed the minibus.

David and Lisa looked. The ancient bridge spanned a deep, narrow gully and was crowded with people. As they watched, a figure fell from the bridge and they could hear a scream of pure terror. The bungee line attachment curved behind the rapidly descending body until the slack was taken up, but the body kept falling until almost at water level as the line stretched. They heard another scream as the person was jerked back up on his first bounce. Harry pulled away again.

'Beats me why they line up to do it,' he announced cheerfully. 'Bloody dangerous.'

Within minutes, David began to wonder whether he and Lisa had, in fact, chosen a safer option. With only room for one vehicle, the winding, unsealed road was carved into the edge of the Skippers Canyon. He couldn't see the edge of the road from his vantage point but he could see the spectacular drop of what seemed thousands of feet to where the Shotover river snaked through the depths of the canyon.

Harry had gone into tour-guide mode. 'If you put the Shotover together with the Arrow River and Skippers Creek, you've got one of the highest densities of gold-bearing gravel in the whole world. The original road was made in 1863. You can still see a bit of it over there.' He waved towards the side window again but David was relieved that he kept his own eyes on the road. Perhaps he wasn't quite as casual about his responsibilities as he seemed.

'How much traffic does this road get?'

'Heaps. 'Specially over summer.'

'What happens when you meet something coming the other way?' David asked cautiously.

'One of you has to back up. There's the odd place you can pass.' Harry laughed. 'It's good fun. We have to watch out for rock falls as well and slips can be a problem when it rains.' He leaned forward and looked up. 'Looks like rain, now,' he remarked happily. 'Or snow, maybe. But don't worry. I've got enough shovels for all of us in the back.'

They stopped briefly to admire some of the old gold-working sluices and a little longer at a small museum. The weather was, indeed, beginning to look a little threatening with black clouds edging out the huge fluffy mounds of cumulus. Then it was on to the main tourist attraction of the ride, the astonishing Skippers suspension bridge.

'The original bridge was built in 1868 and was replaced by this one in 1901. It hangs ninety metres above the river, which makes it the highest suspension bridge in the country.'

David and Lisa had climbed out of the bus again and were following Harry along the bridge on foot.

'The span is ninety-six metres and the towers are eleven point five metres high and made of concrete, which was an unusual building material here at the time.'

It was incongruous, the magnificent bridge at the end of a tortuous road to nowhere.

'Why did they build it?' Lisa queried, echoing David's thought.

'The Bullendale Mine was the big industry—up at the head of Skippers Creek. Site of New Zealand's first hydroelectric plant in 1885, but it was already in decline by the time they built this bridge and it closed only six years later.' Harry laughed with genuine pleasure. 'Typical political miscalculation, I guess. The ratepayers are probably still footing the bill.' Harry checked his watch. 'We'd better head back. We're going to get dumped on pretty soon, and don't you guys have a plane to catch at one?'

David nodded but Lisa shook her head. 'Not me,' she said. 'I prefer to do my own driving.'

'Cool.' Harry flicked a cigarette butt over the side of the bridge. 'You can drive back if you like. How's your insurance?'

Lisa laughed. 'Not that good. I'll pass, thanks.'

They sat together in the bus again. It seemed silly to take different seats on the return trip. David was thoroughly enjoying the rough surface of the road and he allowed his leg to rest a little more heavily against Lisa's. The trip wasn't quite as nerve-racking, going in the opposite direction, as the sheer drop was now on Harry's side of the road. Harry put the windscreen wipers on as the first heavy drops of rain hit the windshield. He changed into a lower gear as they began to move up a sharper incline. Whistling 'She'll be Coming Round the Mountain', he seemed perfectly happy until the thunderstorm broke.

The fork of lightning was more spectacular than anything a tourist company could have laid on. It seemed to be pointing into the canyon right beside them and the instantaneous clap of thunder demonstrated how close it was. Lisa jumped and her face paled. David was

equally startled but the effect it had on Harry was cat-
astrophic.

'Bloody *hell*!' he exploded. Then his face lost any
vestige of colour and he collapsed forward onto the
steering-wheel in an apparent dead faint. His foot fell
off the accelerator, the bus gave a jolt, stalled and began
a backward drift down the incline.

David's expletive was just as forceful as Harry's had
been. He was out of his seat and hauling Harry back
from the wheel before he had time to draw another
breath. Lisa's face was now white. She was terrified.
The bus was picking up speed in its backward slide and
was heading towards the edge of the precipice.

David held the unconscious driver back with one arm
and made a grab for the handbrake. The bus slowed but
continued to slide. His face set with grim determination,
David took hold of the steering-wheel and pulled. The
bus turned only a fraction then it leaned to one side—
the side with the drop into the canyon. Lisa gave a
stifled scream but David was again pulling forcefully
on the hand brake. Finally the backward movement
ceased. The van teetered for a second and a horrified,
still silence fell.

David pulled the lever that opened the door. He put
his hands under Harry's armpits and began to drag him
clear. The van seemed to lean sideways as the internal
weight shifted and Lisa sat, frozen, her knuckles white
where she gripped the bar in front of the seat.

David was back within seconds. He came only halfway up the steps, leaning forward so that he was only
inches from Lisa's pale face. He laid his hand gently
on her cheek.

'Come on, love,' he said calmly. 'I need you.'

The bus teetered again as Lisa stood up. It was a

small movement but her eyes widened with renewed fear. David reached out and took her in his arms, lifting her clear of the bus.

'It's not going to fall,' he told her. 'We've got one wheel that's a bit off the road, that's all.'

'That's all?' Lisa's voice was a squeak. David allowed her to cling to him for just a second longer.

'Harry needs some help,' he whispered in her ear. 'He may have had a heart attack. He needs a *real* doctor.'

Somehow Lisa managed to laugh and fight off her shocked paralysis. David was proud of the way she turned her attention to Harry's plight. It seemed far too long since the emergency had begun but Harry's face was only now changing colour to indicate a dangerous lack of oxygen. It had been little more than a minute since he had collapsed.

Lisa launched into vigorous CPR, having checked Harry's airway. She directed David's chest compressions as she breathed for their patient. After several minutes Lisa told David to pause as she laid a hand on Harry's neck.

'We've got a pulse,' she said excitedly. She put her ear close to Harry's face. 'And he's breathing.' She sighed in frustration. 'I wish I had an ECG going on him right now.'

'Do you think he has had a heart attack?'

Lisa shook her head thoughtfully. 'It was an extremely sudden collapse. No hint of chest pain or sweating or nausea.'

'Maybe he's got hypertrophic obstructive cardiomyopathy—like Wayne Drummond.'

'Could be. Or possibly something like long QT syndrome with an arrhythmic reaction to a sudden shock. That lightning gave him a hell of a fright.'

'He wasn't the only one,' David muttered.

Harry was still unconscious but David smiled at Lisa's triumphant expression as she rechecked his vital signs. Then his smile faded abruptly. He could hear the sound of an approaching vehicle that would not be able to see them around the tight bend. Springing to his feet, David began to run uphill, signalling frantically as he began the turn.

The driver of the other minibus was a mate of Harry's. He looked shocked. His expression was mirrored by the full busload of Japanese tourists staring from the windows of his bus.

'Is he going to be OK? Has he had a heart attack? I've been telling him to quit smoking for years!'

'We need to get him to hospital as fast as possible,' Lisa stated. 'We're not sure what happened yet.' Lisa was watching over a now conscious but very subdued Harry.

'I've already called for help.' The second driver patted the mobile phone clipped to his belt. 'Search and Rescue are on their way with a Jeep.' He walked a few steps and stared yet again at the wheel of their bus which was, in Lisa's opinion, a lot more than a little way off the road. Words failed him and he simply shook his head and whistled silently.

'Do you guys have any idea of just how lucky you are?'

David and Lisa stared at each other. It was Lisa who spoke quietly.

'I think we do, don't we, David?'

'Oh, yes.' David agreed wholeheartedly. 'I think we know exactly how lucky we are.'

*   *   *

'Next time, we'll go bungee jumping.'

'Absolutely. Much safer.'

'You saved my life, David.' Lisa's eyes darkened at the memory of horror but her face was now quite calm. They were standing outside the doors of Queenstown's small hospital.

'And you saved Harry's. I would have picked a heart attack as first choice but you were right. Long QT syndrome. Prone to arrhythmias and cardiac arrest under emotional stress. I wonder whether he'll be transferred to Dunedin or up to us in Christchurch for further tests and treatment.'

'I wonder.' Lisa was watching a small plane begin its ascent, having taken off from the airport close to the hospital. 'You've missed your flight,' she commented.

David grinned. 'I was going to ask you for a lift, anyway. I fancy a ride in a fast, red car.'

Lisa returned the grin. 'I was going to offer you one, anyway. You didn't have to save my life in order to get it.'

'Oh, yes, I did.' David's hand cupped Lisa's chin.

'Why is that?' She was still smiling.

'I was saving my own life as well, Lisa. Without saving you, that would have been a little pointless.'

Lisa's eyes were locked with his. 'You were right, David. You *are* something special.'

David's lips were nearing their target and he didn't reply. His kiss was tender. It wasn't the time or place to unleash the passion that Lisa's response confirmed was reciprocated. He could wait. But not for too long.

'Let's go, Dr Kennedy. Take me home.'

CHAPTER EIGHT

NOTHING had ever felt so good.

David dared not move, even to ease the cramp in his left leg. Lisa lay curled against him, her head buried in the hollow of his shoulder, her arm flung across his chest. He could feel the tiny puffs of her breath, stirring the hair on his chest, and he was aware of his nipple tightening in response. That wasn't all that was tightening but surely he couldn't expect her to want any more just yet?

They hadn't even stopped to eat when they'd arrived at Lisa's small town house early last evening. She had led him straight into her bedroom without saying a word. David hadn't dared break the silence for fear of breaking the spell that had allowed this miracle to happen.

It had been a revelation. He had guessed at Lisa's passionate nature and had known how good it would be, but David had had no idea of the difference in his own response. For the first time he'd realised what it was to really make *love*. More concerned with Lisa's satisfaction than his own, it had had the unexpected effect of making his own overwhelmingly more intense. The memory only raked the embers of the desire he had woken with and he stirred slightly, trying to distract himself.

Lisa moved but didn't open her eyes. The hand that lay on his chest also moved, with a slow, downward stroke that made David's breath catch in his throat.

'Mmm.' The hand stopped only briefly. The invitation was irresistible.

David bent his head to her breast with a happy groan. The hours of joyous discovery last night had given him the confidence to know that whatever either of them did, it was perfect. It just didn't get any better than this. And Lisa seemed to be in agreement. When the alarm clock sounded, some time later, she ignored it.

'What have you done to me, David James? I'm usually up long before the alarm goes off.'

'Exactly what I've wanted to do to you since the first moment I saw you,' David murmured. 'I still can't believe you've changed your mind.'

'I haven't.'

David's eyes flew open. He propped himself up on one elbow so he could try and gauge Lisa's expression. She was grinning at him.

'I fancied you something rotten as soon as you walked into my office. *Your* office, I mean.'

'You hid it very well.'

'Of course. I've had a lot of practice.'

'You mean, you fancy lots of men something rotten?'

'No!' Lisa gave him a shove. 'I mean I've had a lot of practice not letting personal feelings interfere with my career. Besides, your reputation had preceded you, thanks to Jane and Mike. I was determined to dislike you on sight.'

'That was certainly the impression I got.'

'And then you turned up with that rose just after I'd readmitted Desmond Knight and got myself really steamed up about cardiac surgeons in general and Lewis Tanner in particular.'

'You let me have it with both barrels,' David agreed solemnly. 'You were scary—but I still fancied you.'

'And then...*then* you made that crack about library books and I knew you were just the same as all the rest.'

'It was a joke,' David protested. 'Not one that I'd have mentioned if I'd known a woman was present. And I don't personally subscribe to the philosophy.' Not any more, anyway, he added silently. God, he wanted to tell her that he loved her and could never want anyone else ever again. A warning bell rang loudly. Lisa didn't want to hear something that heavy with all its long-term implications.

'What about your famous reputation?' Lisa demanded. 'Listening to Jane Maddon and Mike, it sounded like you'd been on *very* friendly terms with every female in the hospital.'

'I hope so,' David said thoughtfully. 'I might have missed one or two, I guess.'

Lisa gasped and shoved him again.

'I didn't sleep with them all.' David caught Lisa's hand and pinned it to the bed. 'I'm very particular. And what about you? What about Alan Bennett *and* Sean Findlay? Hmm?'

Lisa's jaw dropped. 'They're *friends*. That's *all*!'

'Touché.' David still held Lisa's hand trapped. He bent and kissed her lips. 'Now, where were we?'

'No! We've got to get up. It's Monday.' Lisa wriggled away decisively. 'We have careers waiting for us. Mike and I are on take today.'

'Guess who got admitted this morning?' Lisa bit hungrily into a ham salad bagel at lunchtime.

'Not Harry?'

Lisa nodded and swallowed. 'He asked to be transferred here rather than Dunedin. We've lined him up to have a defibrillator implanted tomorrow morning.'

'I'm not sure I can fit it in.' David frowned. 'You could have asked first.'

'Why should we?' Lisa looked bemused. 'We do it ourselves.'

'It's always been the job of a surgeon where I've been.'

'What's always been the job of a surgeon?' Mike deposited his tray on the table beside them and sat down. 'Being a hero?' He began unloading his tray. 'Did you guys know there's a picture of your bus in this morning's newspaper? Do you have any idea of how close you came to falling off that cliff?' Mike shook his head. 'You should have followed my example and stayed in bed. Both of you.'

David caught Lisa's eye. Mike glanced up from his sandwich in time to catch the lingering look they exchanged. A wide grin spread over his face.

'Like that, is it?' He nodded with evident self-satisfaction. 'I told you you were perfect for each other. Another problem solved, mate.'

'You could say that.' David winked at Lisa. 'Frustration's not a pleasant symptom.'

'I mean about your accommodation.' Mike reached for his coffee.

'What are you talking about, Mike?'

'Dave's getting kicked out of the staff quarters this week. He needs somewhere to live.'

'So?' David winced at Lisa's measured tone.

'So he can move in with you.'

'Hey, wait a minute, mate,' David said forcefully. He wanted to erase the look of alarm he saw in Lisa's face. 'We're not talking walking up the aisle here.'

'Course not. I wouldn't dream of suggesting it to either of you career freaks. But think about it.' Mike picked up his last sandwich. 'With the hours you two work it's the only way you'd get to see each other, let alone— Ouch!' Mike glared at Lisa. 'Kicking your boss under the table is no way to get promotion, Dr Kennedy. And I know you're after my job.'

'She's after my job as well.' David eagerly latched onto the change of subject. 'She wants to put in an implantable defibrillator. That's surgeon stuff in my book.'

'We like to pretend sometimes.' Mike grinned. 'I was actually planning to wield the scalpel myself.' He leaned back in his chair. 'No reason why we can't all come to the party. You can put it in, Dave, and Lisa and I will run the electrophysiology side and do the follow-up testing.'

David looked at Lisa. 'Is that OK with you?'

'Sure. Harry will probably be very reassured.' Lisa's mouth twitched but David leaned forward.

'Any more remarks about *real* doctors and it'll be you that gets kicked under the table. I do happen to have a personal interest in this particular case.'

Mike stood up and collected his empty plate and cup. 'I've got to run. Got an angioplasty due. I'll leave you two to play under the table by yourselves. Have fun.'

'I've got to go too,' David told Lisa reluctantly. 'My outpatient clinic starts in five minutes. Will I see you later?' He lowered his voice. 'I would *really* like to see you later.'

Lisa's colour heightened. 'I'm on take. I don't know when I'll get away.' She hesitated and dropped her gaze. 'I'd like to see you, too.'

There was a longer pause and David knew they were

both thinking of what Mike had suggested. Lisa finally glanced up and smiled tentatively.

'Maybe I'll get lucky. I'll give you a ring if I'm not too busy.'

The call did not eventuate and Lisa looked weary enough the next day for David to believe she hadn't had the chance to make any personal calls. Lisa gave no indication of regret, however.

'Harry's signed the consent form but I think he's having second thoughts. Could you have a word with him and then beep me when, or if, you get up to Theatre? I'm a bit caught up in the unit. We've got a temporary pacing wire to put in one of our overnight customers.'

Harry, the bus driver, was understandably nervous.

'Do you mean you're going to knock me off and then see if you can revive me? I think I might give it a miss after all, Dave. Sounds dicey to me.'

'The risk is one that you're walking around with all the time, Harry. Any sudden shock, or stress, or pain might cause your heart to go into an abnormal rhythm and simply stop. Could be something as simple as a thunderstorm.' David paused and let the memory of Harry's brush with death resurface a little more clearly.

'The device we're planning to put in is this.' David held up a small silver object like an undersized cigarette case.

'Can't fit my smokes in that.' Harry grinned.

'What smokes? You told me you'd given up.'

'I have, I have. Isn't that enough to cure me?'

'It will certainly help, but not with your rhythm abnormality.' David tapped the silver case. 'This has a little wire attached to it that will sit inside your heart. If your heart stops it will deliver a very small electrical charge which will restart it. You might not be lucky enough to have a cardiologist to jump on your chest next time.'

'That's what Lisa said. Boy, I wish I'd been awake when she was giving me the kiss of life.' Harry looked wistful but then saw David's frown and grinned. 'How do you know it's going to work?'

'We test it.' David patiently went back to repeat the beginning of the interview. 'We use a stronger electrical current to put you heart into its abnormal rhythm and then we wait to see if this implantable defibrillator does its job and starts your heart up again.'

Harry swallowed hard. 'And if it doesn't?'

'Then we have all the equipment necessary to do it ourselves. Certainly there's a small risk but it isn't nearly as big as the risk you're living with all the time.'

'I'll be asleep, right?'

'Right. You won't know about any of it.'

'Well, that's OK, then.'

It was a relatively minor surgical procedure. David made the incision just below Harry's collarbone, opening up a pouch beneath the skin for the defibrillator. He located the subclavian vein and inserted the wire.

'Let's light him up,' he suggested.

Lisa pulled the handle on the overhead X-ray equipment and eased it over Harry's chest. David depressed the foot pedal to start imaging and they all stared at the screen. Lisa manoeuvred the machine into a better position.

'It's in the liver,' she announced.

David gently pulled the wire back, still watching the screen. 'That looks pretty good.' He placed a stay suture on the end of the wire and Mike clipped it onto the dummy defibrillator unit.

'Let's induce ventricular fibrillation. Give him fifty hertz, Lisa.'

'We'll try two shocks,' David added. 'If the second one doesn't revert then rescue us with the external paddles, please, Lisa.'

'OK.' Lisa adjusted a knob on the machine beside her. 'Delivering fifty hertz now. We've got VF. Cardiac arrest!'

Mike was holding the tiny defibrillator. 'Device sensing… Charging…' There was a click like a light switch being flicked off. Harry's hands jerked once. 'Successful reversion with twenty-four joules,' Mike announced.

David got Harry's defibrillator off the sterile trolley and slipped it into the pouch he'd created. They tested again and got a successful result with a minimal sixteen-joule charge. Satisfied, David closed the wound. 'When are you going to do the retest?'

'Friday morning. We'll just use the treatment room on the ward. IV sedation rather than a full anaesthetic. Feel free to join us if you've got the time.'

David caught Lisa's eye as she was leaving the theatre. 'Are you free tonight?'

'I'm going to have to crash after last night. I wouldn't be great company. How about tomorrow?'

'*I'm* on call.' David smiled ruefully. 'But maybe we'll get lucky.'

They didn't. David dialed 1 for an outside line at 8 p.m.

'Lisa, I'm sorry, I can't get away. We've got a three-year-old boy who's inhaled a piece of balloon. We're about to take him up to Theatre. I'll be too late by the time we've finished.'

By Thursday David was seriously frustrated. His

night with Lisa was beginning to take on a dreamlike quality. A taste of nirvana that might never be repeated. For the first time in his working life he began to wonder at the wisdom of a career choice that interfered so blatantly with a personal life. Lisa seemed to be taking the delay calmly. By Friday David was not only frustrated, he was worried. The more time went by the more opportunity Lisa had to change her mind about seeing him again. Dropping some papers into his office midafternoon, David saw Lisa disappearing into her own office. He strode after her, shut the door of her office behind him and stood with his back firmly against it, glowering.

'This is driving me crazy, Lisa. Why can't we find any time to be together?' The treadmill started up in the adjacent exercise testing laboratory and David groaned. 'Now we can't even have a conversation without a 747 taking off next door.'

Lisa stepped closer to David and any worries he might have had concerning her possible reluctance to see him again evaporated as he saw his own frustration mirrored in her intense gaze. He reached out and touched her lips, astonished at Lisa's instant response as she closed her eyes. Her faint moan undid him completely. If he had to beg then so be it.

'Tonight,' he urged. 'Please!'

Lisa jerked her head unhappily. 'I can't. Mike and I are going down to Timaru. There's a dinner meeting of local doctors and GPs. We're showing them some angiography and angioplasty films. We agreed to it months ago.' She bit her lip and looked away from David. 'And I'm on call again this weekend.'

David's groan was almost loud enough to be heard over the roar of the treadmill. Whoever was being tested didn't seem to be suffering from overly severe exertional angina. As though in response to his thought, the treadmill came to a sudden halt.

Lisa was still chewing her lip as she raised her eyes tentatively to meet David's.

'Have you found somewhere else to live yet, David?'

David shook his head and snorted with unamused laughter. 'If I can't find time to see you, why on earth would I make time to do something I don't even want to do?'

'Maybe Mike had a point,' Lisa said quietly. 'Living together might be the only way to see each other. I've got a spare bedroom at my place.'

David couldn't suppress his incredulous chuckle. 'Do you really expect me to live in the same house as you and occupy a separate bedroom, Lisa?'

Her eyes dropped as the colour flooded her cheeks. 'No. It's just that…it's not something I've ever done before. I…I wouldn't want you to get the wrong idea, David.'

'I'm not.' David touched a finger gently under Lisa's chin which had the desired effect of bringing her gaze back up to his. He knew what this was about. Lisa was taking a step towards trusting him. A big step. 'I know what you want, Lisa. And I know what you *don't* want. I feel the same.' His voice caught. 'Trust me.'

She was still struggling. 'What about…the others?'

'The others?'

'Yes. Like the echo technician, Jenny. And what's-her-name—Melanie.'

David would have laughed except that the horrifying implications of his deception flashed through his mind. He could have told her of his relationship to Melanie when the subject had first arisen. But he hadn't. He hadn't forgotten the wave of pleasure it had given him to discover that Lisa was jealous of another woman in his life. The deception had been deliberate.

And now he was begging her to trust him. The moment was too crucial to jeopardise. Lisa's gaze was searching and there was a hint of desperation in their dark depths. She wanted to trust him but she had been let down by too many men in her life. This was a huge risk she was considering. If he let her down now, even in a small way, he would lose. And David had no intention of losing.

'There's no one else in my life, Lisa. Only you.'

She couldn't doubt his sincerity. He was telling the truth after all.

'That's all right, then.' Lisa's gaze relaxed and she broke the intense eye contact. 'We may as well give it a go, I guess. I wouldn't like to see you put out onto the streets.' She glanced back, her confidence returning. 'Can you cook?'

'Of course.' David grinned and straightened as his beeper sounded. 'Can you?'

Lisa's eyes narrowed speculatively. 'We'll see. I'll organise a key for you, then. If I'm home you can cook tomorrow night.'

It was Lisa's turn to visit David's office after her ward round on Saturday morning. 'I've brought you a key. I'm not sure when I'll get home.'

'Are you sure about this, Lisa?' David asked gently. 'I'll understand if you've changed your mind.'

'You mean about it being your turn to cook?' Lisa's gaze was wary. 'Of course I haven't changed my mind. You won't get off that easily.'

'That wasn't quite what I meant,' David muttered.

'Here's your key.' Lisa produced the item from her

white coat pocket. Her fingers shook a little as she held it out and David knew she was nervous about the risk she was taking.

The thought aroused a protective instinct in him that he found strangely satisfying. He closed his hand around hers to steady it. 'Don't worry.' He smiled reassuringly. 'I'm a great cook...really!'

The Wednesday morning coronary artery bypass case was a marathon. Five grafts and three attempts to wean off bypass meant that it was well past lunchtime when they finished, but David felt great.

The last few nights had been just as good as the first they'd had together. Better, even, because now his shirts hung in the wardrobe beside Lisa's clothes. His toothbrush stood beside hers on the bathroom shelf.

'Make sure you put the top back on the tube,' Lisa had told him sternly that morning. 'I can't stand oozy toothpaste.'

'Come in the shower with me, Lisa.' David poked his head around the curtain and grinned. 'I fancy rubbing soapy hands all over that glorious body of yours.'

Lisa hesitated. 'You're on call tonight, aren't you?'

'Sure am,' David called. He could see Lisa's outline through the curtain as she slowly untied the knot on her dressing-gown cord. 'Don't know when—or if—I'll make it home.' He reached for the soap as the curtain twitched back. He hadn't expected Lisa to disrupt her getting-ready-for-work routine and respond to his invitation, but her unpredictability was one of the things he loved about her. Awkward when she wanted to pick a fight but incredibly arousing when she chose to respond physically. He was never quite sure which way she would jump. Life was an exciting business these days.

David's feeling of well-being carried him through a heavy week of duties, including a gruelling respiratory outpatient clinic on Thursday afternoon. A downturn in his mood only occurred when his last patient came through the door. The man was seventy-four, his breathing sounded laboured and his wife looked frightened. David knew that neither of them would leave the appointment feeling reassured.

'I have all the reports that came from your GP, Mr Parkinson, and the test results from your appointments with the respiratory physicians. Did Dr Wallace discuss the results of your bronchoscopy with you?' David had been caught in Theatre but his senior registrar had coped well with the procedure.

His patient nodded. 'Kind of.'

David returned the nod. The shock of the initial confirmation of a malignancy often rendered patients incapable of retaining much of the information they received. 'You have a cancerous growth on the left side of the main part of the airway to your left lung.' David indicated the area on the X-ray illuminated on the wall viewing screen. 'Are you a smoker, Mr Parkinson?'

'Yes.'

'How long for?'

'About sixty years. My father was a heavy smoker,' he added, as though excusing himself.

'And what happened to him?'

'Lung cancer.'

Mrs Parkinson clicked open her handbag and removed a handkerchief, which she pressed against her eyes. David's spirits sank a little further.

'Your lung-function tests show us that your respiratory system isn't in great shape.' David took a deep breath. 'That makes surgery a significant risk, especially if we remove the whole lung. What we need to do now is weigh up the risks so that you can make a decision.'

Mr Parkinson nodded slowly.

'The long-term risk is obviously the cancer. The short-term risk is the surgery. You have maybe a one to two per cent chance of not making it through the operation or getting out of hospital.'

'Lewis wouldn't touch him.'

'I don't suppose he would. His statistics must be wonderful.'

'The best.' Lisa nestled her head against David's shoulder and curled her feet up on the couch. The television was just a background mumble, a late night news broadcast neither of them were following.

'He doesn't have the right to refuse treatment because of his judgement of people,' David said angrily.

'He thinks he does. Of course, he finds good medical reasons for refusal.'

'God complex,' David muttered. 'I hate that.'

'Me too.'

'Addiction is an illness in itself,' David continued quietly. 'We can try to treat it but if we can't then we need to try and treat the consequences. Just as we would if the patient were hypertensive or diabetic.'

'That reminds me. We readmitted Serafina Judd today. Her angina's worse and she's come in under Lewis's name. Next week's meeting should be fun.'

David's jaw had sagged. 'I don't *believe* it!'

'Just wait.' Lisa's head popped up. 'He thinks obesity is just as much of a personal failing as smoking. He'll wriggle out of any—'

David was grinning broadly as he interrupted Lisa. '*What* did you say her name was?'

'Serafina.'

David laughed. 'I love it! Makes you think of cherubs...or fairies.'

Lisa laughed too. 'She has lost ten kilos in the last three weeks but she's nowhere near flying yet.'

David stared down into Lisa's laughing brown eyes. His own smile faded as his emotions focused. The sound of her laughter and the sparkle in the depths of her eyes captured his heart. Her happiness was more important than his own. Far more important. Lisa's face stilled as she registered his intensity. The look they held wasn't broken by any words and its ending was inevitable. David could convey what he felt with his lips and hands far more eloquently than he could phrase it verbally. And Lisa seemed willing to accept the physical expression.

No mention was made out loud of any emotional depth. It seemed to David to have been a ground rule right from the start, and it had been confirmed as the days sped past. He had no desire to break any rules that made this possible. If this was as good as it was going to get then that was more than enough for him.

Mike *had* been right. Their time together was precious. On Sunday they had the rare treat of an entire day without any medical commitments. The spring weather was perfect and Lisa suggested a ride in her car with the roof down. They roared off out of town, taking the road to the Bank's Peninsula, and Lisa whooped with joy when they reached the twisting hillside road after a long stretch of straight driving.

'Now you'll see what she can *really* do!' Lisa yelled.

David's fingers tightened on the leather upholstery but by the time they reached the bottom of the enormous hill he, too, was shouting gleefully as they accelerated out of each corner.

The exhilaration faded into a contented companionship when they reached the small and originally French settlement of Akaroa. They walked through the township, admiring the quaint cottages and French road signs. They sipped cappuccinos at an outdoor café and watched the activity of yachts on the picture-postcard harbour.

'Let's stay the night,' David said suddenly.

'We haven't brought any clothes!'

'So? Who needs clothes?' David hooded his eyes and was gratified to hear Lisa's sharp intake of breath.

'I was thinking about work. It's Monday tomorrow.'

'We can leave early enough to get home and change. Forget work. Some things are more important. Like us.'

It had been a perfect evening. Even leaving at 5.30 a.m. to make it back to Christchurch in time to change and get to the hospital by 7.30 a.m. had been worth it. It was a treat unlikely to be repeated in the near future. More often than not during the week, any time together was interrupted. As it was on Tuesday evening.

'I'm sorry I'm so late. We had an emergency. A woman was stabbed by her de facto husband.'

'I thought Lewis was on call.'

'He was. He was also halfway through surgery on someone at Greenpark. Someone had to fill in or the woman would have died.'

'Is she OK?'

'She will be. We'll be keeping her in Intensive Care for a few days, though. I may have to go back in later tonight. Have you eaten?'

'I had the leftover pizza.' Lisa screwed up her nose in distaste. 'I thought you said you could cook.'

'I can,' David insisted. 'When I have the time.' Luckily he was unlikely to have to prove it, the way things were going.

'That remains to be seen,' Lisa pronounced. 'All you've provided so far have been take-aways. You must have the number of every restaurant in town that delivers.'

'Yeah.' David's grin was unrepentant. 'I hope so.'

'You're not on tomorrow, are you?'

'No.'

'Neither am I.'

'Let's toss a coin. See who gets to do the honours.'

'It's your turn.'

'Why?' David tried to look offended. 'I haven't experienced the delights of your culinary skills yet.'

'What? I made an omelette. Last week.'

'Was that what it was?' David checked that Lisa's hands were empty of any potential missiles. 'I thought it was an edible paper plate. Aren't omelettes supposed to be, you know...fluffy?'

'I never said *I* could cook. You said *you* could cook. Why do you think I invited you to move in?'

'I know exactly why.' David moved closer. 'You fancied me something rotten. You only wanted my body.'

'Mmm.' Lisa also stepped closer. 'That's right. How could I have forgotten?'

The touch of their lips was enough to dispel any other thoughts. It could even dispel David's alarming impression that Lisa wasn't joking. That all she wanted from him was their physical relationship. They shared an addiction to each other's bodies. Was that all that was holding them together?

David arrived early at the hospital the following morning, thanks to a lift in Lisa's little red car.

'You'd better get rid of that heap of rust,' she advised David. 'It doesn't do anything for my image, being parked in front of my town house.'

Her image. *Her* town house. David felt shut out. 'I can't afford a new car just yet. Why do you think I moved in? I need a resident mechanic.' He watched Lisa's face closely, hoping for a reaction, but Lisa just smiled.

'Oh, sure!' Her glance reminded him of last night's session. They had been almost naked by the time they were halfway to the bedroom. And that had only been the beginning! Her expression was thoughtful as she swiped her pass card through the slot that controlled the barrier arm into the staff car park. 'Why don't you have any money, David?'

'I give it away,' David said ruefully. He thought of the cheque he had posted to Melanie yesterday. It was going to be the last one. It was more than time his sister learned to cope by herself. Perhaps she'd better marry the opal miner—and soon—but the tone of her letter had been worrying. She was planning to head home again, it seemed. Alone. David shook off the worry that trouble was looming. 'Would you rather I were rich, Lisa? Maybe I can go into hock on a BMW or something.'

Lisa switched off her car's engine. 'No.' She gave David a rather shy smile. 'I like the fact that you don't seem to care about money. It was when I found you with that broken-down heap, holding up the traffic, that I thought maybe I'd been wrong about you after all. You *weren't* like all the others.'

'I won't be poor for ever.' David reached into the

back seat to collect his briefcase. 'I had some debts to repay, but I've done that now.'

'Debts?' Lisa raised her eyebrows. 'Is this where I get to hear about the ex-wife or the gambling addiction?'

David laughed. 'My parents went through a lot, paying for my education. I bought them a house last year.'

'Really?' Lisa's eyes widened. 'Not many people would do that.'

'Not many people have such great parents.' David hesitated. 'I'd love you to meet them, Lisa. Why don't you come up to Auckland with me for a weekend?' David knew he'd said the wrong thing as soon as the words left his lips. Lisa's eyes looked like shutters had gone up.

'Pass,' she said lightly. She opened her door and David followed suit.

'Why not?' He had been encouraged by her comments about his finances. Now he was being shut out again and he didn't like it.

'What would your parents think? About us living together, I mean?'

'They'd think that I'd finally found the perfect woman. They'd be thrilled.'

'Exactly. And then what would they think?'

David strode out to keep pace with Lisa. He stayed silent. He couldn't admit that, of course, they would expect news of an engagement or marriage plans. The silence continued and deepened. David struggled with an urge to tell Lisa that he loved her. What was so wrong with the idea of marriage anyway? He was getting quite used to the idea. Maybe Lisa might, too. Perhaps it just needed the right words to sow the seed. But David had no idea what those words might be.

'Let's just leave our families out of this,' Lisa suggested firmly as they reached the main entrance. 'We don't need the complications.'

'Kiss,' David murmured.

'In the main foyer? In your dreams, mate!'

'No.' David grinned. 'Kiss as in, ''Keep it simple, stupid''. Our relationship,' he added. 'No complications.'

Lisa nodded, but her eyes were on her watch. 'Kiss, it is, then. Have a good day, David.'

David detoured into the cardiology ward on his way to his office. He checked the names on the doors and entered Room 4 as the breakfast trolley was being loaded for removal.

'Mrs Judd?'

'Hello, dear. How nice to see you. How's your baby?' Mrs Judd was in bed, attached to the IV infusion that was controlling her angina.

'It wasn't my baby,' David reminded her. He pulled out a chair and sat down. 'But I do need some more advice. What do you know about making omelettes, Mrs Judd?'

'Call me Serafina, dear. Everybody does. Omelettes, you said?'

'Mmm.' David leaned closer. 'Really fluffy ones.'

CHAPTER NINE

LEWIS TANNER'S abrupt resignation from the cardiothoracic surgical team at Christchurch Hospital the following week was a shock but no great surprise.

'It was all your doing, you know,' Lisa admonished David. They were in bed, a now-familiar haven. Passion had been sated, at least temporarily, but neither of them felt inclined to sleep.

'What was? Seems to me you were quite an active partner.' David stroked his hand down Lisa's arm, brushed suggestively over her breast and finally caught hold of her hand.

'I'm talking about Lewis resigning. You were the straw that broke the camel's back.'

'Was I?' David sounded pleased. 'How do you make that out?'

'Well, there he was in the meeting last week, offering every reason he could think of why he couldn't operate on Mrs Judd, and you look up with that innocent expression and say, "But, Lewis—she doesn't *smoke*!" ' Lisa gurgled with laughter. 'I thought he was going to walk out then and there.'

'I think the resignation had more to do with Alan laying down the law and saying that refusal to operate due to personal preferences was unacceptable.'

'And the fact that he'd been operating at Greenpark the night he was on call here and that stabbing victim came in. Even management was disgusted over that one.'

'All's well that ends well, I guess. Apart from the extra workload that Alan and I will have to shoulder until we get a replacement.' It was David's turn to chuckle. 'Who would have guessed that Serafina Judd would end up being patient number one in our trial?'

'How's she doing tonight?'

'Great. We had a long talk—about omelettes.'

'What?' Lisa propped herself up on her elbow.

'I have to confess. You remember that omelette I made that night?'

'The one night you actually did some genuine cooking? How could I forget? It was great.'

'It was, wasn't it? Really fluffy.' David sighed. 'It was Mrs Judd who told me how to do it.' His voice rose in a fair imitation of their shared patient. 'Beat the yolks and whites separately, dear. Half a tablespoon of water to each yolk and make sure you beat the whites till you've got firm peaks. Then fold them together— very gently. Don't let the air escape—'

Lisa was laughing helplessly. 'You fraud! And I thought you could really cook.'

'I can. Omelettes!'

'You'd better expand your repertoire. I've invited Mike and Anne to dinner next week. I found a night when none of us are on call.'

'Oh, no! Can't we have pizza?'

'No way. I'm bored stiff with take-aways.'

'You cook, then.'

'Pass.' Lisa was grinning wickedly. 'I fix cars. I don't *do* dinners.'

'Why on earth did you invite dinner guests, then? This is *your* problem, Lisa. Don't expect me to bail you out. Omelettes are it.'

'I invited them for you, David. Mike was making

forlorn noises about never seeing you any more. He suggested that I was monopolising your company.'

'I'm not complaining.' David bent his head to kiss her. 'Monopolise me some more.'

'Mmm.' Lisa's arms came up willingly to allow David to move in closer. 'But I can't cancel Mike. He said he can't wait to taste your cooking.'

'I'll bet,' David said grimly. 'He knows I can't cook.' He began raining small kisses over Lisa's face.

'Let's compromise,' he suggested persuasively. 'I'll do the main course. You do dessert. Think of it as a research project. A collaboration—as equal partners.' He raised his head. 'We're good at that, aren't we?'

'Oh, yes.' Lisa pulled David's head down, her lips parted expectantly. 'We're very good at collaborating.'

It was nearly a month now since David had moved in with Lisa. What had seemed perfect to begin with was now seeming more and more like a shell. Something was missing and David knew exactly what it was. It was what Lisa didn't want. Commitment. Something more. It was easy to let it slide. Their arguments were minor and even when they weren't they both enjoyed the making up that followed swiftly. It was their physical relationship that was the glue holding them together and it increasingly bothered David that this was the case.

He hadn't pushed—yet. He hadn't even told Lisa that he loved her, although on several occasions he had almost bitten his tongue to prevent the words escaping. Instead, he tried to convey how he felt in bed and her response was always all he could ask for. Except that now it wasn't. He wanted to ask for more. And he was afraid she would refuse.

They had enrolled their fourth patient in their Neuroshield trial now. Lisa was talking about setting up a statistical programme to start entering the data for later analysis. She was right. They were good at collaborating. They spent a lot of time discussing the overlap of their caseload.

Serafina Judd was due for discharge by the end of the week. They had both been delighted by her uneventful recovery from surgery. If anyone had noticed David sitting beside her bed, making rapid notes, they wouldn't have thought it particularly unusual. Had they come close enough to hear the conversation they might well have changed their minds.

'Sear the meat at a high temperature first, dear. Then turn it down to cook slowly. Put your vegetables in the pan an hour and a half before you plan to serve dinner. I always like a roast for a dinner party. It gives you plenty of time to talk to your guests.'

'And I get to carve.' David grinned. 'I should be good at that at least.'

Desmond Knight had been seen in David's outpatient clinic but he provided the basis for his conversation with Lisa over supper that night.

'He's complaining of sternal pain. It's enough to make sleeping difficult and he's frustrated because it's interfering with his rehabilitation programme.'

'Non-union of the sternum, do you think?' Lisa looked concerned.

'I've booked a CT scan but I don't think so. It's quite stable clinically. I couldn't find any evidence of a click. The upper part of the sternal wound is very tender, though.'

'It's a bit early for new bone formation to show up on CT, isn't it?'

David nodded. 'And the edges are often distorted by the chest retractors so they won't line up perfectly anyway. It can give a false impression of non-union.'

'Maybe he's sensitive to the sternal wires.'

'Could be. I've started him on a non-steroidal anti-inflammatory.'

'Can you take the wires out?'

'Yes, but not until there's been enough time for a good union. I'd leave it a few months yet. I'm going to see him again next week, after the scan.'

Harry, the bus driver, had been seen by Lisa in Mike's outpatient clinic. David was pleased to hear about his clearance to return home.

'He's a bit disappointed to have to give up the driving,' Lisa reported, 'but he's happy he has less chance of dropping dead unexpectedly.'

'What's he going to do?'

'Apparently he's lined up a job with the bungee jumping outfit. He said something like, "I can't wait to push those suckers off the bridge."'

'Sounds like Harry. Let's hope he doesn't try it himself. I'm not sure his defibrillator would cope with that.'

Stephen Taylor was very much a shared patient. He would be in hospital for at least two months before they could be confident he was fit for release. He was now in his sixth week following the surgery and so far he had been doing brilliantly. The day before Mike and Anne were due to come for dinner, however, Lisa beeped David.

They met outside Stephen's private room. Lisa was still wearing the gown, hat and mask she had worn to enter the room due to the reverse isolation protection that Stephen still needed. The mask was pushed down to hang around Lisa's neck and she was holding a sheet of biochemical test requisition forms.

'It's nothing I can put my finger on,' she told David anxiously. 'I just know something's not right. He hasn't been doing any schoolwork all day or even listening to music. I brought him in the latest copy of *Classic Car* and he wasn't really interested. Said he might read it tomorrow.'

'Signs?'

'Temperature's up but only slightly. BP's fine. Heart rate's 105 but 95 to 100 is normal for a denervated heart. He says he feels a bit "blah".'

David smiled. 'I know about "blah". We had a special lecture at medical school.'

'It could be anything from the start of a cold to rejection.' Lisa waved the forms she held. 'I may be over-reacting.'

'What have you lined up?'

'Blood count, chest X-ray, echo, blood and urine cultures and a throat swab.'

'Biopsy?'

'Of course—first thing tomorrow, but I'm wondering if I should try and call the cath lab staff in and get it done tonight. I thought I'd talk to you and then we could both talk to Mike.'

'Have you checked the cyclosporine levels?'

'It's on the list. Stephen's not going to be too impressed by the amount of blood I'm going to take off.'

'I'll come in and distract him.' David pulled a hat and mask from the dispensing boxes attached to the wall. 'Grab me some of those cute little bootees, could you, please, Lisa?'

The biopsy was done later that evening. Stephen's temperature and heart rate had increased by the time Mike joined them, and he was complaining of chest pain. Nobody wanted to take any chances on a possible episode of rejection. Mike did the biopsy, feeding a catheter through the subclavian vein to bite tiny samples of tissue from the ventricle of Stephen's new heart. Microscopic examination would confirm any inflammatory reaction that indicated an attempt by Stephen's immune system to destroy the foreign tissue.

The results would be some hours away, however, and David and Lisa decided to go ahead with their planned shopping expedition for dinner-party supplies as the supermarket was one that stayed open until midnight. Lisa rang the hospital as soon as they got home but no results were available yet, apart from the white cell count which was normal.

'Probably not an infection, then.' David nodded. 'And there's no evidence of heart failure so even it if is rejection it's not severe. We'll get on top of it.'

'You bet.' Lisa eyed the items David was unpacking from the carrier bags. 'Do you really know how to cook a leg of lamb?'

'It'll be even better than the omelette,' David promised. 'And *I'm* not going to cheat. You agreed to make dessert, remember?'

'I am. See?'

David glanced at the large cardboard box. 'Buying a ready-made pavlova doesn't count.'

'But I'm going to whip the cream and do something pretty with kiwifruit. We can pretend I made it.'

'Pretending doesn't work.' David put down the pumpkin he was holding, suddenly serious. 'You tend to get found out and someone winds up hurt—or em-

barrassed.' Now that he had started, David was unable
to stop his next words. 'Like pretending we're living
together.'

'We *are* living together.'

'In your house. You won't even let me pay rent, Lisa.
I feel like a guest.'

'You bought all these groceries...and you've spent a
fortune on take-aways in the last month.'

'OK. I feel like a caterer, then. Like an extra. Like
I'm not really a part of your life.' David knew he was
stepping onto dangerous ground. He didn't need to see
the wariness in Lisa's face to know that he was breaking
the rules.

'You're more a part of my life than anyone else has
been.' Lisa seemed fascinated by the kiwifruit she was
holding. 'We're living together. Isn't that enough for
you?'

'Depends on your definition of living, doesn't it,
Lisa? Are you trying to make sure I don't get too far
in? Does it make you feel more in control of the situation if I'm just a visitor?'

'If I had been in control you wouldn't be here at all.'
The admission seemed ripped from her.

There was a moment of shocked silence before David
spoke very quietly. 'Do you want me to leave? Is that
what you want?'

'What do *you* want, David?'

'I want...' David felt his face contort with the effort
of trying to formulate the right words. Or, rather, trying
not to say what sprang instantly to mind. He wanted to
say, I love you, Lisa. I want to hear you say that *you*
love me. What then? She might say, ''But I don't love
you. There's no room in my life for that kind of com-

mitment. You *know* that.'" He did know it. And he wasn't prepared to precipitate a final showdown.

'I want what you want, Lisa,' he said heavily. '*Do* you want me to leave?'

She seemed to be having the same struggle he had just had. The silence seemed interminable. David's future was hanging in the balance. He felt like he was playing Russian roulette. Was the bullet coming in this shot?

'No,' she whispered finally, unable to meet David's eyes. 'I don't want you to leave.'

'Good.' David's voice was raw. 'Because I sure as hell don't *want* to leave.'

The space was still there between them. The tension still high. David recognised the opportunity to step into that empty space, to reveal even a little of how he felt— of how much he wanted to stay. The shrill call of the telephone was so intrusive it was painful.

'OK, so it looks like a mild rejection?' He listened wearily as Lisa spoke. 'Can you put me through to the lab? I want to know what the cyclosporine levels are like.'

It was safe ground to retreat to, discussing the plan to deal with Stephen's rejection of his donor heart. It was only mild. They could adjust the immune suppression therapy. Bump up the steroid dose and maybe start a high-dose IV steroid if control proved difficult.

The knowledge of their shared admission of wanting to stay together hung between them but nothing more was said. David could sense the new dimension in their love-making that night. It was a confirmation of their need to be together. A recognition that while the future might be too complicated to consider, their need to be together was too great to contemplate a termination.

Next day Stephen still showed no signs of any heart failure, which would have indicated a worsening of his condition and necessitate intensive monitoring. Both David and Lisa left work earlier than usual and David took over the kitchen the moment they got home.

'Go away,' he ordered Lisa. 'I've got a serious operation to perform in here. I need to concentrate.'

'But I need to make dessert.'

'Ha!' David scoffed. 'Five minutes to whip some cream, that's all you need. I'm the one making the real effort here.' He ushered her back towards the door. 'You go and find some wine. Get some beer as well. I forgot.'

He shook his head as he opened the notebook in which he had scribbled down Mrs Judd's pearls of culinary wisdom. Not so long ago the beer would have been at the top of his list for entertainment requirements. Hell, it would probably have been the only thing on the list. Times had changed.

Lisa took so long to return that David thought their guests might arrive first. She tried in vain to find a clear space to set the bottles down in the kitchen.

'My God, David. It looks like a bomb's gone off.'

'Ah!' David followed her stunned appraisal of the room. 'You should have stayed after all, Lisa. I think I needed a scrub nurse.'

'You sure need one now. What's that all over the walls?'

'Potato peelings. Haven't you seen any before?'

'Not stuck to the walls.' Lisa's smile was disbelieving. 'You must have been rather enthusiastic.' She sniffed cautiously. 'Doesn't smell too bad, though.'

'It's going to be perfect. You can do your dessert now.' David offered. 'I'm going to get changed.'

Lisa gazed around again. 'Just where am I supposed to do that? In the bathroom?'

'You can if you like but I'm planning to have a shower. Your pav might get a bit soggy.'

The doorbell rang as David emerged ten minutes later. Mike was carrying a six pack. Anne was carrying the baby. Lisa's eyes met David's with dismay. Mike caught the glance.

'Sorry, we had to bring Sophie. Our babysitter got sick and Anne's mum isn't up to doing the honours again just yet.'

'She won't be any trouble,' promised Anne.

Sophie took one look at David and burst into tears.

'He has this way with women,' Lisa said, laughing.

Anne looked worried. She jiggled the baby reassuringly and then smiled brightly. 'Something smells wonderful! What is it?'

'That's David's department.' Lisa was glaring at Sophie as though a stern look would be enough to turn off the tears. David's heart sank. She really wasn't into kids at all. But, then, neither was he so why should the confirmation make him feel disappointed?

Mike handed David the beer. 'This I've got to see. When did you learn to cook, mate?' He began to follow David into the kitchen.

'It's a fairly recent accomplishment,' David said modestly. Mike appeared not to have heard.

'Good grief, man! What have you been *doing* in here?'

'Cooking,' David said firmly. He began to steer Mike out of the door again. 'Come through here. I'll get you a beer.'

Mike had caught sight of the dessert, perched precariously between a spilled bag of flour and the debris

from the dismembered pumpkin. He whistled appreciatively. '*Mate!* I take it all back. You must be some kind
of genius!'

'Lisa made the dessert.' David caught Lisa's eye and
grinned as she blushed. She opened her mouth, obviously on the point of confessing, then she snapped it
shut and returned David's grin. He winked, enjoying the
collusion.

Sophie was now sitting on a rug on the floor, banging
two wooden blocks together.

'We brought the port-a-cot,' Mike announced. 'She'll
crash soon.'

David handed Mike a beer and put a bowl of crisps
on the coffee-table. Sophie dropped her blocks and held
out a small hand commandingly. David smiled at Anne.

'A lady who knows what she wants. I like that. Is
she allowed one?'

Anne nodded indulgently and David selected a large
crisp and offered it to Sophie. She accepted and examined the offering with rapt attention, before putting
it into her mouth. Then she withdrew it and offered it
back to David, bestowing a beaming smile on him.

'That's OK,' David said hurriedly. 'You keep it,
Soph.' He bit back a smile. 'Quite cute, isn't she?'

'Uh-oh!' Mike's tone was ominous. 'He's getting
clucky. Watch out, Lisa.'

There was a moment's awkward silence which David
broke with a laugh, just a fraction too late.

'No chance. Kids aren't on the agenda, are they,
Lisa?' He glanced away from Sophie who was now
moving towards him at a fast crawl.

She was staring at him with a peculiar look of dismay
on her face. David groaned inwardly. He'd put his foot
in it again somehow and he'd only been trying to re-

assure her. Sophie reached the coffee-table. She put her hand on the rim of the crisp bowl as she heaved herself to her feet. The decisive tipping movement of the bowl sent the crisps flying in an arc to cover a wide area of carpet.

'Oh, no!' Anne leapt to her feet. 'Sophie!' She started to pick up the crisps. 'We shouldn't have brought her, Mike. Look at this mess!'

'Don't worry.' Mike popped the tab on his beer can. 'You should see the kitchen!'

'Hadn't you better check on the roast, David?' Lisa's query sent David moving at a fast pace. He had managed to forget his responsibility for the meal since their guests had arrived. God, it might have burnt by now.

He needn't have worried. The meat was cooked to perfection, the roast vegetables crispy, the boiled ones just tender. David was not going to confess that the gravy had come out of a packet and Lisa wouldn't dare say anything, with that pavlova lurking in the kitchen. David's surgical skills were the butt of more than a few jokes as he carved the roast.

'It's not as easy as it looks,' he complained.

'Watch out,' Mike hooted. 'You just severed the pulmonary artery there, mate.'

There were no complaints as they ate. Even Lisa made impressed noises and David basked in the glow of a new achievement. Sophie occupied herself happily, finding crisp fragments in the carpet and eating them, periodically crowing with delight as she found a larger piece. David found his gaze straying to the child more than once.

What would it be like, having a child of your own? What would it be like to have one that was his and Lisa's? David tried to concentrate on his minted peas.

It would probably be a monster. Stubborn, argumentative, challenging, passionate and more often than not—a sheer joy.

'Sorry?' David realised he had missed Mike's comment.

'I just asked how Melanie was these days.'

'Running full tilt towards her next crisis, I expect. As usual.'

Lisa's fork stopped halfway to her mouth. David watched her toy with the contents of her plate for a few seconds before the cause of her sudden loss of appetite occurred to him. Thanks to her rule about not involving their families, he had never got around to explaining that Melanie was his sister. Not that it excused his earlier avoidance of the subject but surely it had been reasonable to want to establish a basis of trust so that the deception could then be seen as an amusing tactic. David tried to look amused now. He made a good attempt at a casual laugh.

'I keep hoping Mel will get married and become someone else's problem.'

'No chance, mate. You'll never get rid of Melanie that easily.' Mike was helping himself to another roasted potato.

David cringed inwardly, desperate to change the subject. If he couldn't catch Lisa alone in the kitchen for a second or two then he'd have to make sure he cleared up her misunderstanding the moment their guests headed home.

'Where is she at the moment?'

'Australia.' David ground out the word and glared at Mike, trying to signal an end to the topic. 'More vegetables, Anne?'

'Thanks. They're wonderful. I must say I've never

thought of you as a domesticated type, David. I'm really impressed.'

Lisa had started eating again and David allowed himself to relax. 'I do a great omelette, too,' he informed Anne. 'And I clean.'

Lisa was inspired to rejoin the conversation. 'He does, too.' She nodded at Anne. 'He cleaned the toilet last week.'

Anne pointed her fork at Mike. 'That's one thing you've never done, Michael Foster. Take note!'

Lisa laughed. 'Be careful. David used the dishwashing brush.'

David didn't join in the explosion of mirth. 'How was I to know?' he protested. 'It was in the cupboard with all the cleaning stuff.'

Mike was still laughing. 'Thank God for that. I was beginning to think you were setting some standard that no husband could ever live up to.'

'I'm not a husband,' David protested. 'Lisa and I are collaborators. Equal partners.'

Lisa nodded. 'Marriage isn't on the agenda. Is it, David?'

David was unsure whether it had been a statement or a question. He met her glance and smiled, he hoped, reassuringly. 'We operate on the Kiss principle,' he explained to Mike.

Mike's eyebrows wriggled. 'I'll just bet you do.'

Lisa blushed. 'He means keeping it simple.'

'Stupid,' added David with a grin.

'No complications,' continued Lisa. 'Like titles or roles. Or expectations. From us—or anyone else. Isn't that right, David?'

'You're the boss,' he said lightly. He met her gaze squarely. It had sounded disturbingly like a warning.

'I thought you were equal partners.' Mike didn't seem to have any idea of the nuances he had precipitated.

'It's time for dessert. It's Lisa's turn to be in charge.'

Anne helped Lisa clear the plates. Mike and David began discussing an upcoming rugby match. As Lisa carried the masterpiece of the dessert into the room, the phone rang. She hastily put the plate down on the coffee-table. She listened in silence for a minute and then held the phone out.

'Mike? You'd better take this.' Lisa didn't return to the table. She looked worried. 'It's Stephen. His blood pressure's down and he's short of breath. The registrar on says he sounds pretty congested.'

Mike put the phone down within a minute. 'I'll have to go in,' he said calmly. 'Thank goodness I only had the one beer. We're going to have to get an arterial line and Swan-Ganz catheter in. Looks like Stephen's gone into heart failure.'

Lisa stood up. 'I'm coming, too.'

'So am I.' David jumped to his feet. 'He's my patient as well.'

They all looked at Anne. Mike sighed. 'I guess you'll just have to eat all that pavlova by yourself, love.'

'I don't think so.' Anne's face was a picture of dismay. 'Look!'

Sophie held up fistfuls of the flattened pavlova. Her face was entirely covered with whipped cream.

'I'm so sorry, Lisa,' Anne apologised. 'Your beautiful dessert! I'll clean it up.'

'No worries.' Lisa was reaching for her car keys. 'It was David who made the real effort here. I was just pretending.'

David held the door open for Mike and Lisa who

hurried past. She didn't even look at him. The comment rang in his ears. Had she been referring simply to the dinner party?

Or did she mean their entire relationship?

CHAPTER TEN

THEY had all scrubbed up.

If the nurse who had prepared the treatment room had been surprised at the overkill of skilled staff available for the procedure of inserting a Swan-Ganz catheter, she didn't show it. The atmosphere was tense. Everybody wanted Stephen to be a success story, and those who had come to know the teenager in recent weeks were giving no consideration to the hospital's reputation or the media's reaction to an unsuccessful outcome. The determination to see him through this episode of rejection had everything to do with who Stephen was and nothing at all to do with *what* he was.

The nurse quietly finished draping the top half of Stephen's body with sterile green cloths and then handed Mike the syringe of local anaesthetic.

'This'll sting for a second, mate,' Mike told the boy. 'Grit your teeth.'

Stephen was lying with his head tipped slightly down. Lisa checked his oxygen supply and touched the automatic blood-pressure cuff to get an extra reading.

'I took the MG for a run out to Akaroa last weekend,' Lisa told Stephen. 'You should have seen the way she held those hill corners. It was awesome!'

David's eyebrow quirked. It wasn't the car that had been responsible for the breathtaking ride.

'As soon as you're allowed out of this joint for a day or two I'll take you,' Lisa promised. 'We'll really burn some rubber.'

Mike was unclipping the syringe attached to his introducing needle as Lisa talked. He exchanged it for the guide wire David had ready, then swapped the needle for a plastic sheath which slipped into the vein over the top of the wire. He screwed it gently into place.

Lisa was now laughing at something Stephen had said. 'Yeah, right!' She chuckled dubiously. 'And when did you get your driver's licence, then?'

Mike nodded at the radiographer who switched on the fluoroscopy unit. David nodded with satisfaction as Mike skilfully threaded the tip of the catheter through Stephen's heart and into the pulmonary artery.

'Take a deep breath for me, Stephen. Good, now cough!' Mike carefully removed the sheath. 'We're all set to rock and roll,' he announced. 'Stitch that end for me, Dave. Then you won't feel entirely superfluous.'

Lisa kept chatting to Stephen as Mike and the technician set up the pressure transducers and took the initial recordings of the intricate measurements of heart function the catheter was able to provide. Then Lisa was left with the nurse and a new sterile trolley to insert an arterial line in Stephen's arm. Mike and David moved away to launch into a detailed discussion of the heavy drug therapy they needed to balance.

'We'll have to increase the calcium antagonist…'

'Dopamine for the blood pressure…'

'What diuretic do you favour?'

'We'll start the IV steroid treatment, stat…'

'What's the current cyclosporine level?'

Lisa elected to stay in the hospital overnight and gave David her car keys to drive home. Arriving at the town house at 3 a.m. David was confronted by the devastated kitchen. Anne had cleared up the mess Sophie had made with the pavlova. Her note said she was sorry she couldn't do more but Sophie wouldn't settle so she'd had to take her home. She also wished David luck and advised him to find a fresh dishwashing brush.

It took David well over an hour to clean up and he spent most of it wondering whether domesticity was really what he wanted. Being with Lisa, it had a curious effect of throwing him into role reversal situations. Here she was, following the demanding dictates of her chosen profession, and here he was—washing the dishes!

What would happen if their arrangement did become anything more permanent? A series of cooks, house-keepers or even nannies? It wasn't David's idea of an ideal marriage. He might consider himself new age but the prospect of being a househusband was one even Lisa couldn't tempt him into. If they were equal partners, how come he'd cooked the dinner and was now left to clear up as well? Lisa's comment came back to haunt him. He was the one making the real effort. She was just pretending.

The consideration of the potential truth in the state-ment provoked a sense of dissatisfaction that grew over the next few days. Lisa was preoccupied with Stephen and spent another night at the hospital. Even as he be-gan to show definite signs of recovery Lisa spent her time at home reading every textbook and journal article she could lay her hands on that dealt with the manage-ment of organ rejection.

David felt that Stephen's new heart was not the only thing in danger of being rejected. David knew what he wanted. He also knew what Lisa wanted. It seemed like a case of never the twain should meet, and David was left wondering whether he would have to settle for a second-rate compromise if he didn't want to lose Lisa.

He found himself very distracted, searching for some sort of resolution.

'You're very restless.' Lisa looked up from her journal.

'I've got things on my mind.'

'Such as?'

David looked around him. 'Let's buy a house, Lisa.'

'What?' The journal slipped from her fingers. 'Why? What's wrong with this place?'

'Nothing's wrong.' David shrugged helplessly. He couldn't say it didn't feel like a home. Modern, compact and full of textbooks, journals and the overflow of paperwork from the hospital. It felt like a comfortable office extension. 'It's just…yours.'

'Why should that bother you? It's very handy to the hospital. It's not as though we even spend that much time here.'

'Maybe that's the problem.' David drummed his fingers on the arm of the couch. 'Don't you ever feel you'd like more out of life, Lisa? More than just a career?'

Lisa stared at him, her expression disturbingly neutral.

'You told me you get bored, doing the same thing all the time. Don't you get bored, shuttling between here and the hospital? Doesn't it bother you how much time we spend talking to each other about work?'

'Are *you* bored?'

'No… I'm…' David stood up and paced across the room. 'I don't know what I am.' He rubbed wearily at his face. 'I'm tired, I guess. Let's go to bed.' They hadn't made love since the night of Stephen's crisis. Perhaps that was the main cause of his restlessness.

'You go ahead. I just want to finish this article.' Lisa picked up her journal and appeared to be reading again, but David stood still for a moment, staring at her. The vibes weren't great. Perhaps a showdown didn't need to be engineered. Maybe his prevarication was simply postponing the inevitable. If that was the case, he wasn't sure he had any desire to speed the process up.

The showdown was much closer than David had suspected. He was delivering a CT scan result to Lisa on the latest Neuroshield trial patient the next morning when his beeper sounded.

'Mind if I use your phone?'

'Not at all.' Lisa was reading the scan report as she stepped aside. 'Be my guest.'

David cast her a sharp glance but she didn't look up from the report. He hadn't been asleep when she'd finally come to bed last night, but he had pretended to be, wondering whether Lisa would make any attempt to rouse him. Or, hopefully, arouse him. She hadn't. Perhaps that, too, had become an activity repeated endlessly enough to bore her. Her early morning politeness was obviously set to continue. It had the effect of making her appear distant but at the same time antagonistic.

David sighed audibly as he pushed zero to contact the switchboard operator. Perhaps he didn't have the stamina to cope with Lisa long term after all. He knew she coped with stress by becoming bolshy and unapproachable. He also knew he was causing the present level of stress they were experiencing. It wasn't a happy situation.

'We have an outside call for you, Mr James. A collect toll call from Australia. Will you pay the charges?'

'Yeah. Put it through, thanks.' David tried, unsuccessfully, not to let his spirits slide any further.

'Davey? Oh, God!' The sobs on the other end of the

line were clearly audible to Lisa, who looked up questioningly.

'Melanie? What on earth's the matter?' David gave Lisa a dismayed expression and held the phone closer to his ear to try and muffle the other end of the conversation. Lisa turned her back, holding a CT plate up to the light of the window.

'Oh, no!' David groaned. 'Not *again*.' He raised his voice. 'Calm down. Stop *crying*, Melanie.' David waited for the hiccuping to stop and then lowered his voice. 'Just how far overdue are you?' He wished he'd taken this call in his own office. Lisa didn't want to know about his family. If anything was likely to be a complication then Melanie's problems, landing on their doorstep, would surely take first prize.

'Have you had a test? Why not?' David listened in silence for a while. Glancing over his shoulder, he could see the ramrod- like stance of Lisa's back. He had one woman who didn't want what he wanted to offer. Now he had another who wanted more than he wanted to offer. Quite suddenly, David reached the end of his emotional tether. They were an alien species. He'd be better off without any of them.

'For God's sake, Melanie,' he exploded. 'You can't always assume the man is going to take responsibility for birth control. I've told you how I feel about that before. Take the damned test. Ring me later and we'll go from there.' David slammed the phone down with an exasperated growl.

Lisa dropped the CT results envelope on her desk. 'I take it this isn't the first time this has happened?' she enquired calmly.

David was still furious. 'No. And it probably won't be the last. I don't know. *Women!*'

'And you don't want to take any responsibility?'

'Why the hell should I?' David glared at Lisa. 'It's not *my* problem.'

Sean Findlay, bursting into the office as David spoke, stopped in his tracks. 'Oh, sorry. Am I interrupting? I've got a bit of a problem.'

'Don't tell me about it, mate,' David snarled. 'I've got more than enough of my own.'

Lisa failed to put in an appearance at the departmental referral meeting that afternoon. David's relief at Melanie's follow-up phone call evaporated. He waited impatiently to corner Mike when the discussion finally wrapped up.

'Where's Lisa?'

'I'm not sure. She was looking a bit pale. I told her go home if she wasn't well. I haven't seen her since. Hey, did you know we took out Stephen's Swan-Ganz catheter this morning? He's looking great.'

David tried to smile at the good news but his mind was racing. Lisa unwell? Why hadn't she told him? His concern all but obliterated the sound of Mike's voice.

'So we'll do another biopsy on Thursday but we're confident that we've got the rejection under control.' Mike paused. 'You don't look so great yourself, mate. Is there some bug going around?' He peered anxiously into David's face. 'You haven't been using the dish-washing brush to clean the toilet again, have you?'

'I've got to go, Mike. It's urgent.'

Mike clucked sympathetically. 'Hope you get over it soon, mate. It's not like you to get sick.'

David did feel sick. Sick with worry. He tried beep-

ing Lisa to no avail. Going outside, he scanned the staff
car park. It was all too easy to see that the little red
roadster had gone. David walked around the building to
the main entrance and waved tersely to the first taxi in
line at the stand. Within minutes he was flinging open
the door of the town house.

'Lisa? Are you all right?' She wasn't in the kitchen.
The sitting room and bathroom were both empty. David
stopped his frantic search with a painful jolt when he
reached the bedroom door. Lisa was in the bedroom. A
suitcase lay opened on the bed. David stared, stunned.

'What are you doing?'

'Packing.' Lisa didn't look at him but David could
see she had been crying. Her eyes were red, her face
puffy and she sounded like she had a badly blocked
nose.

'God, Lisa!' David took two long strides into the
room and caught her arm. 'What the hell has happened?'

'You. That's what's happened.' Lisa angrily shook
his hand off her arm. 'I was right all along. I should
never have trusted you.'

'Bloody hell, Lisa. What have I *done*?' David
watched as Lisa scooped up the entire contents of her
underwear drawer and dumped them into the suitcase.

'How *could* you, David? The only other time I really
loved someone.' Lisa sniffed loudly. 'He got someone
else pregnant, too, and went off and married her.'

David felt a wave of confusion. 'Lewis?'

'*No!*' Lisa was pulling hangers out of the wardrobe.
She threw the clothes, hangers and all, into a crumpled
heap on top of the underwear. 'The man I was prepared
to…almost did…give up medical school for.' Lisa's
red-rimmed eyes grazed David's. 'I ruined my grades

for a year, thinking I wanted him more than a career. I almost ruined them the next year, getting over it.' Lisa swooped down and grabbed several pairs of shoes, stacking them on one arm. 'It was failing a term paper that cured me. Nobody was going to ruin *my* life.' Lisa jerked to her feet, dropping several shoes. 'That goes for you too, David James. I'm leaving!'

'But this is your house.' David couldn't quite fight off the confusion. It was only now that her words were beginning to sink in. The only other time she had really loved someone. Did that mean she loved *him*?

'Oh, God!' Lisa turned the suitcase upside down, spilling its contents onto the floor. 'Fine. *You* leave, then.'

'I still don't understand, Lisa. Why do either of us have to leave?'

'How can you even ask? Melanie's pregnant and you won't even take any responsibility for it. You're a bastard, David. Or your child will be at any rate.'

'What? Lisa, you *know* Melanie's my sister.'

'Like hell I do.'

'But I told you—that night after Mike and Anne had gone home.'

'I stayed at the hospital remember?'

David groaned. 'And you stayed the next night too. And then I was so worried about what was happening with us that I forgot I hadn't told you after all. Anyway, she rang me. She's not pregnant, after all.'

'Bully for her,' Lisa snapped. 'I don't care any more, David. I've had enough. I *trusted* you. You let me believe Melanie was something special. You could have told me she was your sister a very long time ago.'

'I know.' David's grin was shamefaced. 'I was too

excited about the idea that you might be jealous. I didn't say anything that wasn't true.'

'You implied it,' Lisa snapped. 'And I asked—*specifically*, about her before I asked you to move in. And you *still* didn't say anything.'

'No.' David couldn't deny the accusation. A sensation of impending doom began to close around him. 'I knew how hard it was for you to trust me, Lisa,' he offered quietly. 'I couldn't let myself blow it.'

'Well, you've blown it now, mate.' Lisa stepped angrily over the pile of clothing. 'If you're not going to leave then I am.'

David stepped back and put his arm out to block the door.

'Don't you dare walk out on me.'

'Why not?' Lisa's face radiated pure misery.

'Because you can't.'

'Why *not*?'

David took a deep breath. 'Because I'm going to marry you.'

'Like hell you are.' Lisa's hands were bunched into fists. David wanted nothing more than to take her in his arms, but he couldn't. Not yet.

'Why not?' he echoed gently.

'Because you don't buy books, remember? You've got a whole library to choose from.'

David gave just the ghost of a grin. The aggression meant that Lisa was rattled. She could only be *this* rattled if it was something she cared about passionately. And this was about *him*. 'That's right,' he agreed happily. 'And I've made my choice. The hardest one to read I've ever come across, and I have no intention of ever putting it down.'

Lisa's fists had uncurled but she was still glaring angrily at David. 'I'm still not going to marry you.'

'Why not?' Something loosened in David's chest. A warmth he recognised as having been missing for days now flickered back into life.

'For one thing, you haven't asked me.'

'OK.' David's grin was now half-strength. 'Will you marry me, Lisa?'

'No.'

'Why not?'

'Because you don't want children.'

'Neither do you. You looked appalled when Sophie turned up at our dinner.'

'Only because I knew how much you didn't like kids. You said they weren't on the agenda, remember?'

'I only said that to reassure you. I knew *you* didn't want kids.'

Lisa was staring at his feet. 'Maybe I've changed my mind.

'Maybe I have, too.' David dropped his arm from the doorway. 'I want the place crawling with rugrats. I want a really big house and a smelly dog and carpets full of crisps and pavlova.'

The corner of Lisa's mouth twitched. 'And who's supposed to look after this big house and clean up the carpets and look after the dog and smelly children?'

'Melanie needs a job. It might keep her out of trouble for a while. And the dog can clean up the carpets. Especially the crisps and pavlova.'

'I'm not going to have children and then let someone else bring them up.' Lisa was still trying to sound confrontational but the heat of her argument had been all but extinguished.

'We could collaborate.' David took a step forward so

that he was standing within touching distance of Lisa. 'I think we'd make a great team, Lisa.'

She met his gaze, her face solemn. 'Maybe. But I still can't marry you.'

'Why? Because you want to stand here and argue the toss for ever?'

'No.' Lisa's eyes darkened to an impossibly velvet hue. 'Because I can't marry someone who doesn't love me.'

'Who said I don't love you?'

'You've never said you did.'

They stared at each other in the sudden silence that fell. In her stockinged feet Lisa had to look up to meet David's gaze. Her eyes told him everything he needed to know. Her feelings were written plainly over every adored feature. David's mouth curled in a gentle smile and Lisa's lips trembled as they mimicked the movement.

'Hey, Lisa?'

'What?'

'I love you.' David caught hold of both her hands. 'You drive me crazy and I can't possibly live without you.'

'Good.'

'Is that it? I tell you I love you and that you drive me crazy and all you can say is ''good''? Aren't you even going to argue about it?'

'Not this time.' Lisa reached up to touch David's cheek softly. 'I meant it's good that you can't possibly live without me.' Her fingers traced the outline of his lips. 'I love you, too, David. You're not going to get the chance to live without me.'

'Does this mean we actually agree with each other?

We can share our careers and still have the kids…and the house…and the dog…and the pavlova?'

'I'll *make* the pavlova,' Lisa promised. 'Even if it turns out as flat as my omelettes. But, David?'

'Mmm?' His lips were hovering close enough to feel the movement of her words. He thought he didn't need to hear anything else Lisa might want to say just then but her lips were moving again and David knew he had been wrong.

'Do you think we could get married first?'

Modern Romance™
...seduction and
passion guaranteed

Tender Romance™
...love affairs that
last a lifetime

Medical Romance™
...medical drama
on the pulse

Historical Romance™
...rich, vivid and
passionate

Sensual Romance™
...sassy, sexy and
seductive

Blaze Romance™
...the temperature's
rising

27 new titles every month.

Live the emotion

MILLS & BOON®

MB3

Next month don't miss –

HOT LATIN LOVERS

These Latin men are impossible to resist, sexy as sin and sensational in bed; they can have anyone they desire! Then three beautiful women present them with the challenge of a lifetime – marriage!

On sale 3rd October 2003

Available at most branches of WHSmith, Tesco, Martins, Borders, Eason, Sainsbury's and all good paperback bookshops.

0903/05

1003/24/MB81

MILLS & BOON

The
Pregnancy
Surprise

Emma Darcy

Caroline Anderson

Gayle Wilson

when
passion
leads to
pregnancy!

On sale 3rd October 2003

*Available at most branches of WHSmith, Tesco, Martins, Borders,
Eason, Sainsbury's and all good paperback bookshops.*

MILLS & BOON®

Live the emotion

PENNINGTON

BOOK FOUR

Available from 3rd October 2003

Available at most branches of WHSmith, Tesco, Martins, Borders,
Eason, Sainsbury's and most good paperback bookshops.

PENN/RTL/4

MILLS & BOON®

Live the emotion

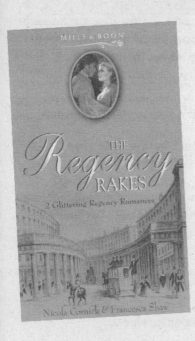

Another wonderful 6-book Regency collection

2 Glittering Romances in each volume

Volume 2 on sale from 3rd October 2003

Available at most branches of WHSmith, Tesco, Martins, Borders, Eason, Sainsbury's and all good paperback bookshops.

books | authors | online reads | magazine | membership

Visit millsandboon.co.uk and discover your one-stop shop for romance!

Find out everything you want to know about romance novels in one place. Read about and buy our novels online anytime you want.

* Choose and buy books from an extensive selection of Mills & Boon® titles.

* Enjoy top authors and *New York Times* best-selling authors – from Penny Jordan and Miranda Lee to Sandra Marton and Nicola Cornick!

* Take advantage of our amazing **FREE** book offers.

* In our Authors' area find titles currently available from all your favourite authors.

* Get hooked on one of our fabulous online reads, with new chapters updated weekly.

* Check out the fascinating articles in our magazine section.

Visit us online at
www.millsandboon.co.uk

…you'll want to come back again and again!!

WEB/MB

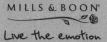

MILLS & BOON®

Live the emotion

Modern Romance™

MISTRESS FOR A MONTH by *Miranda Lee*

Rico Mandretti knows Renée Selensky despises him, and her history makes her as potent as poison. Then Fate delivers Rico an unbeatable hand: he wins a game of cards – and Renée into the bargain!

IN SEPARATE BEDROOMS by *Carole Mortimer*

Jack Beauchamp can have any woman he wants – so Mattie Crawford can't understand why he's so determined to take *her* to Paris. Maybe a weekend in the French capital with the best-looking, most charming man she's ever met is his idea of a punishment…

THE ITALIAN'S LOVE-CHILD by *Sharon Kendrick*

Millionaire Luca Cardelli broke Eve's heart years ago, and now he's back. Eve is soon entrapped in the whirlwind of their love affair but her shock is only equalled by Luca's outrageous reaction to some surprising news…

THE GREEK'S VIRGIN BRIDE by *Julia James*

When Andrea Fraser is unexpectedly summoned to Greece she is shocked at the news that awaits her. Her grandfather has found her a husband! Nikos Vassilis may be the most sophisticated man she's ever encountered, but she'll be leaving at the first opportunity – won't she…?

On sale 3rd October 2003

Available at most branches of WHSmith, Tesco, Martins, Borders, Eason, Sainsbury's and all good paperback bookshops.

0903/01a

MILLS & BOON®

Live the emotion

Modern Romance™

THE BILLIONAIRE'S CONTRACT BRIDE by *Carol Marinelli*

Zavier Chambers is one of Australia's most powerful playboys, and to him Tabitha appears to be the worst kind of woman. Tabitha isn't a gold-digger – but she does need to marry for money. When Zavier blackmails her into marriage she has no choice...

THE TYCOON'S TROPHY MISTRESS by *Lee Wilkinson*

Daniel Wolfe is not a man to be messed with – and he already has an agenda of his own. Charlotte Michaels soon finds herself being offered an unexpected career move – as her boss's mistress!

THE MARRIAGE RENEWAL by *Maggie Cox*

When Tara's husband returns after five years, she is willing to give him his divorce – but not until she has told Mac about what happened after he left. Mac is stunned, but he's as consumed with desire for her as he ever was. Is their passion a strong enough basis on which to renew their marriage vows?

MARRIED TO A MARINE by *Cathie Linz*

Justice Wilder was badly injured while saving a child's life – and now may be facing the end of his military career. Kelly Hart tracks him down in order to convince him to accept help for the first time in his life. But what happens when he discovers she used to love him...?

On sale 3rd October 2003

Available at most branches of WHSmith, Tesco, Martins, Borders, Eason, Sainsbury's and all good paperback bookshops.

0903/01b

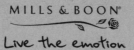

MILLS & BOON®

Live the emotion

Sensual Romance™

ROUGHING IT WITH RYAN by Jill Shalvis
South Village Singles

Gorgeous Ryan Alondo's life is overcrowded with responsibility, but he knows just how to alleviate some of the stress – an affair with fun-loving Suzanne. But she has vowed to forget about men and is determined not to fall for his charms. Good thing he can be very, very persuasive…

EVERYBODY'S HERO by Tracy Kelleher

When photographer Claire Marsden photographs hockey star Jason Doyle, it's not long before she persuades him into becoming a fake fiancé for her friend – but it's Claire he can't keep his hands off! Can he keep up the charade or will his secret desire be discovered…?

SOME LIKE IT SIZZLING by Jamie Sobrato

A half-naked man asleep in her bed isn't what Lucy Connors expected for her birthday. But soon she's shedding her conservative ways and letting Judd lead her to a sexy adults-only resort. When Judd Walker agreed to be Lucy's escort, he had no idea just how seductive she would be – and he's determined to prove to her that he's one gift she should keep!

HOT OFF THE PRESS by Nancy Warren *Sizzling*™

Reporter Tess Elliot is desperate for the chance to prove herself, but when the chance arrives she goes head to head with rival reporter and resident bad boy Mike Grundel, who's also out to get the scoop! Mike's sole interest doesn't lie in the job – getting under Tess's skin is just as fun – but it's getting her under the covers that's going to take some work!

On sale 3rd October 2003

Available at most branches of WHSmith, Tesco, Martins, Borders, Eason, Sainsbury's and all good paperback bookshops.

0903/21

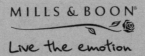

MILLS & BOON®

Live the emotion

Blaze Romance™

ABOUT THAT NIGHT *by Jeanie London*

Good girl Julienne Blake has decided she's going to be *bad*! With a bit of self-hypnosis, she'll unleash the passionate, sexy woman inside and experience the thrill of seducing a man with no strings attached. Her target is confirmed bachelor Nick Fairfax and he's instantly hooked. But is there more than just that one night between them?

THE ULTIMATE SEDUCTION

by Janelle Denison
HOT PURSUIT
Natalie Hastings won't give in to her attraction to private investigator Noah Sommers, even if it is mutual. Then an accident leaves her with short-term amnesia – and in danger – and the only way Noah can protect her is to convince her she's his fiancée. He's determined to keep his hands off until she can remember – only now *she's* determined to make him surrender! Can Noah resist the ultimate seduction?

On sale 3rd October 2003

Available at most branches of WHSmith, Tesco, Martins, Borders, Eason, Sainsbury's and all good paperback bookshops.

0903/14

MILLS & BOON®

Live the emotion

Tender Romance™

OUTBACK BRIDEGROOM by Margaret Way

Christine is on her way back to Koomera Crossing – home
to the only man she has ever loved...Mitch Claydon.
Outback born and bred, Mitch is angry whenever he thinks
of Christine. He'd loved her – even offered marriage – but
she chose a life far away. And now, despite his best
intentions, Mitch finds her as desirable as ever...

THE FORBIDDEN MARRIAGE by Rebecca Winters

When Michelle Howard finds herself agreeing to nurse Zak
Sadler for the next month she's not sure what she's let
herself in for. She is reluctant to get close to this sexy new
Zak, whom she hasn't seen for two years – surely *any*
relationship with him is strictly off-limits?

THE BOSS'S CONVENIENT PROPOSAL by Barbara McMahon

Ginny Morgan is desperately looking for the father of her
child when she meets intriguing Mitch Holden. He's not
the man she's looking for, but that doesn't stop him making
a proposal. If she is willing to be his secretary, Mitch will
pay for her son's operation...

THEIR ACCIDENTAL BABY by Hannah Bernard

When Laura discovers a break-in her gorgeous neighbour
Justin Bane comes running to help her. But the intruder is a
baby – left without explanation! As Laura and Justin are
forced to learn the art of baby care – fast! – will Laura be
able to stop herself giving her heart to both members of her
unexpected family...?

On sale 3rd October 2003

*Available at most branches of WHSmith, Tesco, Martins, Borders,
Eason, Sainsbury's and all good paperback bookshops.*

0903/02

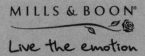

MILLS & BOON®

Live the emotion

Medical Romance™

THE BABY BONDING *by Caroline Anderson*

Surgeon Sam Gregory is the last person midwife Molly
Hammond expects to see. She once carried a child
for him and it led to a special and unspoken bond
between Molly and Sam. Now a single father, Sam
gives her the chance to get to know his son, but
Molly's bond with Jack leads to an even greater bond
with his father. If Molly enters into a relationship with
Sam now and it all goes wrong she may never see
either of them again…

IN-FLIGHT EMERGENCY *by Abigail Gordon*

Airport nurse Fabia Ferguson has kept her love for
handsome pilot Bryce Hollister close to her heart for
years. When he walks back into her life Bryce is
attracted to Fabia; it's an attraction he feels he can't
pursue because she reminds him of too many painful
memories – memories that made him give up his
medical career!

THE DOCTOR'S SECRET BABY *by Judy Campbell*

When Dr Lucy Cunningham hires a new doctor for
her practice in the Scottish Highlands she's not sure
about Callum Tate's laid-back lifestyle. But, forced to
live and work together, their passion quickly fires –
and then a baby is left on the doorstep, with a note
claiming that Callum is the father!

On sale 3rd October 2003

*Available at most branches of WHSmith, Tesco, Martins, Borders,
Eason, Sainsbury's and all good paperback bookshops.*

0903/03a

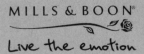

MILLS & BOON®

Live the emotion

Medical Romance™

THE ITALIAN DOCTOR'S PROPOSAL
by Kate Hardy

Lucy Williams was hoping to get the new consultant post at the maternity unit where she worked – but it went to drop-dead gorgeous, half-Italian Nic Alberici. Immediately sparks flew between them – until Lucy's former fiancé started pestering her and Nic came up with an outrageous proposal: that they pretended to be an item…

A CONSULTANT'S SPECIAL CARE *by Joanna Neil*

Dr Abby Curtis starts her new job in A&E with trepidation. Consultant Jordan Blakesley is notorious for his cutting criticism, and she's had enough of overbearing men! But he's so attractive that she cannot keep her eyes off him! And then dramatic events in Abby's life result in Jordan paying her very personal attention…

A CHILD TO CALL HIS OWN *by Sheila Danton*

Dr Ben Davey longed for a family, and meeting beautiful single mum Dr Tamsin Penrose was his dream come true. Until Ben discovers that Tamsin's child is the son of Ben's cousin – a man who disappeared mysteriously from his family's midst, several years ago. It unleashes a conflict and a tension that Tamsin believes makes a relationship with Ben clearly out of bounds…

On sale 3rd October 2003

Available at most branches of WHSmith, Tesco, Martins, Borders, Eason, Sainsbury's and all good paperback bookshops.

0903/03b

MILLS & BOON®

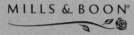

Live the emotion

Historical Romance™

ONE NIGHT WITH A RAKE
by Louise Allen

Beautiful widow Amanda Clare woke in a strange bed, next to a tall, dark and very handsome stranger. Knocked out in a stagecoach accident, they'd been rescued and it had been assumed they were married! Amanda had no idea who the man was – and, intriguingly, neither did he.
The gentleman had lost his memory…

Regency

COLONEL ANCROFT'S LOVE
by Sylvia Andrew

When Colonel John Ancroft is persuaded to escort an elderly widow to Yorkshire, he has no idea that the lady in question is heiress Caroline Duval. Her disguise is revealed when he happens upon her swimming naked in a pool, and his self-control is severely tested as he confronts this bewitching flame-haired beauty…

Regency

THE ELUSIVE BRIDE by Deborah Hale

12th century England

To protect her home and people, Cecily Tyrell would marry the devil himself – and if rumour held any truth, she might just have to! Lord Rowan DeCourtenay was a knight of some renown – but a widower of some repute. Still, he was the warrior she needed – but was he the man she wanted?

On sale 3rd October 2003

Available at most branches of WHSmith, Tesco, Martins, Borders, Eason, Sainsbury's and all good paperback bookshops.

0903/04